ADVENTURES OF THE MIND

ADVENTURES
OF
THE MIND

FROM

The Saturday Evening Post

Edited by Richard Thruelsen and John Kobler

INTRODUCTION BY

Mark Van Doren

1959

ALFRED·A·KNOPF   *New York*

For permission to quote the poetry in "The Poet's Vision" by
Dame Edith Sitwell, the editors wish to thank:

Harold Ober Associates ("A Refusal to Mourn the
Death by Fire of a Child in London" by Dylan Thomas;
Copyright 1946 by New Directions)

Random House, Inc. ("For the Time Being" by W. H.
Auden)

The Macmillan Company ("Melancthon" by Marianne
Moore; Copyright 1951 by Macmillan)

Harcourt, Brace & Company, Inc. ("Sweeney Among
the Nightingales" by T. S. Eliot)

Sacheverell Sitwell ("Such Are the Clouds")

L. C. Catalog card number: 59–11691
© The Curtis Publishing Company, 1958, 1959

THIS IS A BORZOI BOOK,
PUBLISHED BY ALFRED A. KNOPF, INC.

Introduction

BY

MARK VAN DOREN

The mind adventures, and the mind stays home. If this book both terrifies and reassures its readers, the reason will be that it shows man doing both of those extremely difficult, courageous things. And it shows man doing them now. The mind of man has always lived a double life, or had a double function: to go forth and return. Or perhaps one should say, to discover and remember. Either activity takes genius to perform it well, and genius gleams in many of these pages, where the mind of our time, true to the tradition of intellect at its best, alternates between exploring the unknown and reminding us of the known. If either function went by default, then we might be really terrified. We shall be disturbed in any case, yet it is just as clear that ground is made firm here for our reassurance. A philosopher I know once remarked, when he heard that a list was being drawn up of books that had shaken the world: "Very well, but I should also like to see a list of books that have left it solider than ever: books that were mountains, not whirlwinds or tidal waves." Both mountains and waves are present in this most impressive volume.

And they are present in all of its departments. Indeed I am not certain that it has departments. To be sure, the several authors go by several names: scientist, theologian, moralist, historian, artist. Yet in some deep sense they all seem to have the same concern. This concern is variously phrased, and at no point is it put into words convenient for my purpose. But I should call

v

it a concern lest man in our time go mad through the misuse or the disuse of the mind he has inherited from innumerable men before him. It is a concern felt now by the many as well as the few. In this age of science, this age that worships knowledge, can we nevertheless be said to know what we are doing? Are we preserving the world or destroying it? Are we controlling nature or is nature controlling us? And the many ask, not without fear in their voices: "Who knows how to answer such questions? Who is even supposed or expected to? Is there any center to our world, and if so, is there anybody who knows where it is, let alone knows what is going on there?" Well, there may be comfort for those many in the fact that these few share their anxiety. The first thing to do about a problem is to recognize it; the second thing is to state it; the third thing is to solve it. Perhaps man has never solved any of his true problems, but his glory is that he can recognize and state them. My own happy impression is that twenty-one living writers have posed our current riddle fairly and squarely: Do we know what we are doing?

And "we" here means all of us, for if we have forgotten our humanity it is everybody's fault. Paul Tillich tells us that nobody any more asks ultimate questions. Father D'Arcy says that "human beings without belief are subject to bad dreams," and appears to suspect that nightmare now is well-nigh universal. But those are theologians, and as such they might be expected to speak thus. It is noticeable, however, and so far it is good, that certain scientists speak likewise. Fred Hoyle, asking how deep the laws of physics are, ponders the probability that "no end will be found to the intricacy" of those laws. He intimates, in other words, that man will never wholly comprehend the natural world. Robert Oppenheimer, at the end of his marvelous essay on "The Mystery of Matter," says quietly enough: "We will not lightly concede such a defeat." Yet he seems to consider it possible. And if so, where are we in a world we thought to master? Loren Eiseley wonders whether man has not become that world's most sinister possession: in his search for the tools of mastery he has lost contact with himself. So as to the scientists; though some of them are less uneasy than others. As for the historians, there is Arthur M. Schlesinger, Jr., who accuses us of having surrendered the capacity to believe in great men. Perhaps this is what Edith Hamilton suggests, too, when she doubts that we know any longer how to conceive freedom as the Greeks conceived it, or to enjoy the intellect as they did. Sir Herbert Read thinks we have put it to inferior uses; we no longer, he says, live in a partnership with things, and learn about ourselves by handling them; in our rage to know matter in the abstract we have forgotten as artists that the world, just as it looks and feels, is the very material of our existence. Yet Clement Greenberg, defending abstract art, insists that contemplation of it will soothe our crazy nerves. And Jacques Barzun reminds us that the humanities are a mirror in which we can continue to view the more or less meaningful disorder of man's desires.

To discover and remember. It is a vast assignment, and it has been met here face to face. That is why any serious reader of this volume—one, I mean, who is not desperate for easy answers, but rather is willing to consider with some of the finest spirits of his age the toughest problem man is ever called upon to tackle —will be content with what he finds. "What is Man?" The question is immemorial, and no clear answer has ever been given. But the best men are those who, knowing this, still listen for the truth. It is as old as Creation, and as new as the infant who first saw light this morning.

Contents

Contents

ADVENTURES OF THE MIND

An Evolutionist Looks at Modern Man

BY

LOREN EISELEY

A *native Nebraskan, later a teacher at the University of Kansas and at Oberlin, in Ohio, Loren Eiseley is now chairman of the Department of Anthropology at the University of Pennsylvania and curator of Early Man in the University Museum. Following publication of his book* The Immense Journey (1957) *Dr. Eiseley was hailed for the imagination and lyricism with which he evoked the images of man in nature and the nature of man. In* Darwin's Century (1958), *Dr. Eiseley traces the history of the evolutionary concept.*

I n the age of technology which now surrounds us, and which boasts of its triumphs over nature, one thing is ever more apparent to the anthropologist—the student of man. We have not really conquered nature because we have not conquered ourselves. It is modern man, *Homo sapiens*, "the wise" as he styles himself, who is now the secret nightmare of man. It is his own long shadow that falls across his restless nights and that follows soundlessly after the pacing feet of statesmen.

Not long ago I chanced to walk through the Hall of Man in

one of the country's large museums. Persons of great learning had been instrumental in erecting those exhibits, and I hoped to find there some clue as to human destiny, some key that might unlock in a few succinct sentences the nature of man. The exhibit ended in a question mark before an atomic machine and a graph showing the almost incredible energy that now lay open to the hand of man. Needless to say, I agreed with the question mark which ended the history of humanity within that hall.

But as I turned and went in the other direction, step by step, eon by eon, back into the past, I came to a scarcely human thing crouched over a little fire of sticks and peering up at me under shaggy brows. The caption read: "Man begins his technological climb up the energy ladder. He discovers fire." I walked a short way backward and forward. I read the captions. I looked again at the creatures huddled over a fire of sticks— at the woman clutching a child to her breast. Again I searched the hall. This was the sum total of all that science had here seen fit to emphasize graphically as important to the human story. The hunters' tools were there, the economic revolution effected by agriculture was ably presented. Summarized before my eyes, populations grew, cities and empires rose and fell, and still man's energy accumulated.

One saw another thing. One saw the armored legions grow and grow until at last continent confronted continent and the powers of death to a world lay in the hands of the descendants of that maned woman and her consort by the fire of sticks.

I hesitated again before those forgotten engines of the past, for it seemed to me that there was lacking here some clue, some vital essence of the creature man, and that I was looking upon stone and polished sword and catapult from some place just a little remote and distorted. "This is the history of man," the caption ran through my head, and at that moment, finally, I knew I was looking at the past through the eyes of a modern twentieth-century American, or for that matter, a Russian. There was no basic difference.

In that whole exhibit were ranged the energies of wheat and fire and oil, but of what man had dreamed in his relations with

4

other men, there was little trace. Yet it is only on paper, or, in human heads, we might say in paraphrase of Shaw, that man has sought successfully to transcend himself, his appetites and his desires. In that great room was scarcely a hint of the most remarkable story of all, the rise of a value-creating animal and the way in which his intangible dreams had been modified and transformed to bring him to the world he faces today.

The educated public has come to accept the verdict of science that man, along with the plant and animal world about us, is the product of endless evolutionary divergence and change. In accepting this verdict of science, however, men have frequently failed to inquire in what way human evolution may differ from that of other animals, or by what extra dangers and responsibilities the human brain may be haunted. In the revolt from the fanatical religiosity of past centuries we have too often welcomed with open arms a dogmatic scientific naturalism which, like the devil with Faust, seemed to offer unlimited material power over nature while, at the same time, assuring us that our moral responsibilities were limited and excusable since we were, after all, only the natural evolutionary culmination of a line of apes that chanced to descend upon the ground.

Darwin and his compatriots, struggling to establish for their day a new and quite amazing interpretation of human history, placed great emphasis upon man's relationship to the animal world about him. Indeed, at times they overemphasized man's kinship with the existing apes, partly because of their anxiety to prove the reality of man's descent from lower forms of life, partly because in their lifetime the course of human evolution was very imperfectly known from fossils. The result was that Darwin's own interpretation of the early stages of human evolution wavered between a theory involving an early and Edenlike seclusion on some oceanic island, to a later more ferocious and competitive existence on one of the major continents.

These extremes of interpretation need not concern us now except to illustrate the hesitancy with which Darwin attempted to account for some of the peculiar qualities of man. Today we are well convinced of the general course of man's rise from some ancient anthropoid line. Each year new fossil evidence of this fact is brought to our attention. Each year the public grows more accustomed to this history, feels more at home in the natural world which it casually assumes to be dominated by struggle, by a dog-eat-dog interpretation of existence which descends to us from the Darwinian period.

Some time ago I had a letter from a professional friend of mine commenting upon the education his daughter was receiving at a polite finishing school. "She has been taught," he wrote to me a little sadly, "that there are two kinds of people, the tough- and the tender-minded. Her professor, whose science I will not name, informed her that the tough-minded would survive."

This archaic remark shook me. I knew it was not the product of the great selfless masters of the field, but it betrayed an attitude which demanded an answer. In that answer is contained the whole uniqueness of man. Man has not really survived by toughness in a major sense—even the great evolutionists Darwin and Wallace had had trouble with that aspect of man—instead, he has survived through tenderness. Man in his arrogance may boast that the battle is to the strong, that pity and affection are signs of weakness. Nevertheless, in spite of the widespread popularity of such ideas, the truth is that if man at heart were not a tender creature toward his kind, a loving creature in a peculiarly special way, he would long since have left his bones to the wild dogs that roved the African grasslands where he first essayed the great adventure of becoming human.

The professor who growled to his class of future mothers about being tough-minded spent a childhood which is among the most helpless and prolonged of any living creature. If our parents had actually practiced certain of the philosophies that now flourish among us, or if our remote ancestors had achieved that degree of sophistication which would have enabled them to discount their social responsibilities for the day's pleasure, we—you and I and all of us—would never have enjoyed the experience of living.

Man, in the achievement of a unique gift—a thinking brain capable of weighing stars or atoms—cannot grow that brain in the nine months before birth. It is, moreover, a peculiarly plastic

6

brain, intended to receive impressions from the social world around it. Instinct, unlike the case in the world of animals, is here reduced to a minimum. This brain must grow and learn, be able to profit by experience. In man much of that growth and learning comes after birth. The result is that the human infant enters the world in a peculiarly helpless and undeveloped condition. His childhood is lengthy because his developing brain must receive a large store of information and ways of behavior from the social group into which it is born. It must acquire the complicated tool of speech.

The demands of learning thus placed upon the human off-spring are greater than in any other animal. They have made necessary the existence of a continued family, rather than the casual sex life of many of the lower animals. Although the family differs in many of its minor features in distinct societies, it is always and everywhere marked by its tender and continuing care of the human offspring through the lengthened period of childhood.

The social regulations of all human groups promote the welfare of the young. Man's first normal experience of life involves maternal and paternal care and affection. It continues over the years of childhood. Thus the creature who strives at times to deny the love within himself, to reject the responsibilities to which he owes his own existence, who grows vocal about "tough-mindedness" and "the struggle for existence," is striving to reject his own human heritage. For without the mysteriously increased growth rate of the brain and the correlated willingness of fallible, loving adults to spend years in nursing the helpless offspring they have produced, man would long since have vanished from the earth.

We take the simple facts of human life too much for granted. To the student of human evolution this remarkable and unique adjustment of our peculiar infancy to a lengthened family relationship between adults is one of the more mysterious episodes in the history of life. It is so strange, in fact, that only in one group of creatures—that giving rise to man—has it been successfully developed in the three billion years or so that life has existed on the planet. Family life is a fact that underlies everything

7

else about man—his capacity for absorbing culture, his ability to learn—everything, in short, that enables us to call him human. He is born of love and he exists by reason of a love more continuous than in any other form of life. Yet this, in all irony, is the creature who professes to pierce the shams of life and to live by tough-mindedness!

Let us see how this nascent and once-aspiring creature now lives in great danger of re-entering the specialized trap that his ancestors escaped from ages ago when they evolved a brain capable of abstract thought. "Man is the dwarf of himself," Emerson once wrote, and never, perhaps, has he been more than dwarf than in this age where he appears to wield so much power. The only sign of health remaining to him is the fact that he is still capable of creeping out of the interior of his thickening crust of technological accomplishment to gaze around him with a sense of dissatisfaction and unease.

He has every reason to feel this way. For man has never lived before in so great an age of exterior accomplishment, so tremendous a projection of himself into his machines, nor yet so disheartening a period in all that stands for the nobler aspects of the human dream. His spiritual yearnings to transcend his own evil qualities are dimming as he is constantly reminded of his animal past. His desire to fly away to Mars, still warring, still haunted by his own black shadow, is the adolescent escape mechanism of a creature who would prefer to infect the outer planets with his problems than to master them at home.

Even now in the enthusiasm for new discoveries, reported public interviews with scientists tend to run increasingly toward a future replete with more inventions, stores of energy, babies in bottles, deadlier weapons. Relatively few have spoken of values, ethics, art, religion—all those intangible aspects of life which set the tone of a civilization and determine, in the end, whether it will be cruel or humane; whether, in other words, the modern world, so far as its interior spiritual life is concerned, will be stainless steel like its exterior, or display the rich fabric of genuine human experience. The very indifference of many scientists to such matters reveals how far man has already gone

8

toward the world of the "outside," of no memory, of contempt toward all that makes up the human tradition.

"Wars will be fought in space," prophesied a high military authority recently. "Teach children the hard things first." "Ah, but what hard things?" the teacher asks, because youth is shaped in the teaching and becomes what he is taught. Without spiritual insight and generosity, without the ability to rise beyond power and mechanical extensions, man will encounter in place of the nature which gave him birth only that vast, expanding genie rising from his own brain—himself. Nothing more terrible threatens to confront him in his final hour.

It is increasingly plain that if we read the past as a justification for a kind of moral complacency, an animal limit which justifies military remarks such as "man will always fight," we have not read it well. Until man came, it is true, the evolution of life had been an evolution of parts. It had been hook and clutching bur and fang, struggling upward in an agelong effort. Life had been shaped by the blind forces of the inanimate world. All it had that was different was the will to crawl, the will to find the crevice, the niche, the foothold on this mountain of inanimate matter, and to hold its place against the forces which ever seek to disperse and destroy the substance of life. In all that prehuman world there had been no animal capable of looking back or forward. No living creature had wept above another's grave. There had been nothing to comprehend the whole.

For three billion years that rule remained unbroken. At the end of that time there occurred a small soundless concussion. In a sense it was the most terrible explosion in the world, because it forecast and contained all the rest. The coruscating heat of atomic fission, the red depths of the hydrogen bomb—all were potentially contained in a little packet of gray matter that, somewhere between about a million and 600,000 years ago, quite suddenly appears to have begun to multiply itself in the thick-walled cranium of a ground-dwelling ape.

The event itself took place in silence, the silence of cells multiplying at an enormous pace under a small bone roof, the silence of some great fungus coming up at night in a forest glade.

The eruption had about it the utter unpredictability of nature when she chooses to bypass her accepted laws and to hurtle headlong into some new and unguessed experiment. Even the solar system has now felt the impact of that tiny, soundless explosion. The fact that it was the product of evolutionary forces does not lessen its remarkable quality.

For three billion years, until an ageless watcher might have turned away in weariness, nothing had moved but the slime and its creations. Toward the end of that time a small, unprepossessing animal sat on his haunches by a rock pile on a waste of open ground. He clutched a stick and chewed the end of it meditatively. He was setting the fuse of the great explosion. In his head was the first twinkle of that tenuous rainbow bridge which stretches between earth and the city of the gods.

At that moment the ancestor of man had become the molder of things, rather than their victim, but he had, at the same time, suffered a major loss of instinctive adjustments to life. As the psychologist Jung very aptly remarks: "The forlornness of consciousness in our world is due primarily to the loss of instinct, and the reason for this lies in the development of the human mind over the past eon."

In a recent paper given before the Research Conference on Growth and Aging, my colleague, Dr. W. M. Krogman, remarked that "The mind of man, the learning potential of an evolved cerebral cortex, enabled him to focus upon the *quality* of things rather than mere quantity." Man has become, in other words, a value-creating animal. He sets his own goals and more and more exerts his own will upon recalcitrant matter and the natural forces of the universe. In this activity he has passed from the specialized evolution of the parts of the body to a projection of such "part" evolution upon his machines and implements. In this respect man is a unique being. Having achieved high intellectual ability, he may remain comparatively unchanged in structure while all around him other animals are still subjected to the old laws of specialized selection. His brain evolves parts and replaces them, but only upon man's mechanical inventions: his tools. This fact gives man a kind of freedom which none of the crawlers-up-the-mountain ever had. He is, as the philosopher Henri Bergson once remarked, a reservoir of indetermination; his power of choice for good or evil is enormous.

It is here that we come upon what I choose to call the "unnatural" aspect of man; unnatural, that is, in the sense that there is nothing else like it on the planet. Even Darwin confessed that his principle of limited perfection—that is, the conception that life would evolve only sufficiently to maintain itself in competition with other life or to adjust to changes in its environment—had been upset in the case of man. A part, such as a tooth or an eye, could reach perfection only for a given purpose in a particular environment. With man, however, Darwin professed to observe no foreseeable limit to the development of the mental faculties.

Psychology had once regarded human nature as something consisting of separate abilities given to man at the time of creation. Mind was a fixed, unchanging thing that molded history. Now it was to be seen as malleable and moving, subject like the body, though in a different and more mysterious way, to change. Perhaps, indeed, there was no such thing as human nature in the old fixed sense, except the human ability to become what it most desired in terms of the social world in which it existed. As we have seen, the mind's power of choice has opened to man a tremendous freedom, but it is a freedom whose moral implications only a few great spiritual leaders have fully grasped.

Increasingly, at the very height of the human achievement, there loom two obstacles which threaten to cast man back into the world of parts, tools and processes, in a way he has scarcely imagined. In fact there are times when it appears man is so occupied with the world he is now creating that he has already lost a sense for what may be missing in his society. He is deeply influenced by his knowledge of the past and the animal limitations which it seems to place upon his earlier spiritual aspirations. Equally, he confuses "progress" with his mechanical extensions which represent his triumph over the caprices of biological selection. Man, in a new way, shows formidable signs of taking the road of the dinosaurs, though by quite another track.

On a night during the period of the Korean War I sat with an old hunter at a campfire in the wilds of Wyoming. Around us in the mountain dark were geological strata that contained the remains of dinosaurs. My companion threw a log upon the fire. As the flames rose upward, I could see the bronzed old American face looking at me across the fire. It could have been a face from any period out of the frontier past. And it was the frontier that spoke to me from the man who had two sons in Korea.

"America," he said, "needs a strong enemy. It will keep her from getting fat and make her strong."

I nodded dubiously. It was a philosophy of the frontier, of the woods. But I saw in my mind's eye the fate of the colossi that lay about us in the stone. They had warred and thundered, shaken the earth with their tread, grown larger, armored themselves with great shields of bone, and teeth like bear traps. Spikes had glistened on their tails and foreheads. In the end they had vanished with their monstrous tumult, and some small, ratlike mammals and a few birds had come hesitantly into the arena they had vacated. It had been a war of parts, won, not by the participants, but by some small, relatively intelligent creatures that had hidden in the trees.

"We need a strong enemy," my friend repeated. I did not doubt it was being said also in the Siberian forests and on the Manchurian plains. Faster and faster labor the technicians, the scientists of parts. They labor so today. The pace grows ever swifter. Already, and I quote from one recent industrial report, "scientists and engineers can be utilized more effectively by confining their work almost entirely to the field of their specialization." This remark indicates the re-emergence of the war of parts, and if continued, it forecasts the death of all we claim as human. Such statements convey a failure to grasp that it is the creative thinker capable of using his brain out of the immediate context of his surroundings who is the innovator, the religious leader, the artist, the man who in all ages has been, in the words of Lancelot Whyte, "the very creator of humanity."

"Man," John Burroughs once remarked, "is like the trainer of wild beasts who, at his peril, for one instant relaxes his mastery over them. Gravity, electricity, fire, flood, hurricane, will crush or consume him if his hands are unsteady or his wits tardy." It is true that man has been badly knocked about by raw nature, but that nature has never organized her powers for the deliberate purpose of destroying man. He has even benefited and had his wits sharpened by her vagaries. Man has survived the long inexorable marchings of the glacial ice that pressed him back upon the Mediterranean and threatened his annihilation in Europe. He has left his bones under the boiling mud of volcanic upheavals. He has known drought and famine—the careless buffets of the storm that blows unceasingly through nature. He has seen cities go down, cities full of adept artisans and clever technicians, cities fallen to the sands when an old enemy cut off the water supply.

Who was that enemy? It was man. He is the other face of that nature man has feared. Now, in an age when man lays his hands upon the lightning, and heat in millions of degrees shudders in his confining mechanisms, an old shadow, a monstrous growing shadow, falls across the doorway of all the world's laboratories. It is merely man, merely the creature by the fire of sticks, merely the museum wielder of the sling and spear, but now grown large enough to shadow the sun. This creature thinks with all the malignant concentration that man has so far escaped in nature, and it thinks toward just one purpose—the creation of the ultimate weapon. Ultimate, ultimate, and still more ultimate, as if there were a growing secret zero in its mind.

So terrible is the fascination of that zero, so much does it appeal to some ancient power-loving streak in our still primitive natures, that whether men plan aggression or defense from it, they are, in degree, corrupted. At heart they know the word "neutral" has lost its meaning; that the blow, if it falls, will mean what the ultimate weapon means—death to green grass and singing bird, death to a world.

Nevertheless, as I have said, no creature in the world demands more love than man; no creature is less adapted to survive without it. Man is a paradox. Individually most men hate and fear war in spite of much of the talk of professional militarists about instinct. Men have to be drummed to war, propagandized to war, assured their cause is righteous. Even dictators have to render lip service to humanitarian principles. None of this sounds particularly as though an "instinct" for war existed. There are, instead, things from the old dark midnight of the past that suffice as well for evil purposes. Fear of the stranger, when the stranger was two eyes in the dark beyond the fire at a cave mouth; aggressive hungers that were stoked to a high pitch by nature in the million years of man's wandering across the wastes of an open world. Man is not completed—that is the secret of his paradoxical behavior. He is not made. He is, perhaps, about to be. Once long ago in the Middle Ages he was called *Homo duplex*—a thing half of dust and half of spirit. The term well expresses his predicament.

Today we know a great deal about human evolution, but as scientists we have failed, I sometimes think, to convey successfully to the public the marvel of the human transformation. We have shown man the anthropoidal skulls of his ancestors. We have convinced him that the human brain is an instrument of ancient origin which has not sprung full blown into being, but rather partakes of both the old and the new; that it includes the imperfections which are written into the substance of all moving and growing life. The vestigial organs that are concealed here and there in our bodies and which tell tales of the long past—of trees and waters in our lost ancestral world—have their corollary in the mind of man. His flashes of unreasoning temper, his frustrations, his occasional irrationalities are, some of them, echoes out of an older, more primitive machine. Yet signs of affection and mutual co-operation, love of beauty, dreams of a future life, can be traced into forms of man physically more primitive than ourselves.

Now, however, it is the present which concerns us—the present that creates tomorrow. Who contends for it—the rocket century with its vast zero looming over the future? The now is *our* responsibility, not that of the hoarse-voiced animal that came from the wood in a dream and made our today. Nor can we call to those pleasant, wide-browed people whom we strive to conjure up as inhabiting the comfortable future of our novels and dreams. They are lost in the unfathomable, formless future which we are engaged in shaping. Do we want them deeply? Do we want them enough, in the heavy-handed violence of this day, to live toward them at all cost, to struggle once more against the destructive forces of nature? To stand up and face, as every man must face, that ancient lurking shadow of himself? Is the price of acquiring brains, brains to look before and after in the universe, only to mean subservience to man after escaping subservience to nature that has lasted for a million years? Is it to mean acquiescence in the plans of those clever intellects who talk glibly of psychological "break-throughs" and the subliminal control of nations? Is it for this that men have labored up the dark pathway behind us and died often and blindly for some vision they could scarcely see?

A society has an image of itself, its way of life. This image is a wavering, composite picture reflected from millions of minds. If the image is largely compounded of the events of the present; if tradition is weak, the past forgotten, that image can alter by subtle degrees. A "cold war" such as we are fighting demands great tenacity in democratic institutions. Secrecy grows, technicians multiply, two great societies shoulder each other down a road that may look increasingly alike to both. The humane tradition—arts, letters, philosophy, the social sciences—threatens to be ignored as unrealistic in what has become a technological race for survival.

Man was a social animal long before he was man. But when he created huge societies and elaborated the world of culture that surrounds him today, he was acting, in some degree, consciously. Man, unlike the animal, is aware of the nature of his society. His conscious image of it is tremendously important in shaping what it will become. It is this that helps to build the human future, and why the future must be fought for day by day in the lives of innumerable and humble men.

Man, whether he engages in war or not, is in a pyramiding technological society whose values are largely directed outward upon things. The important fact in such a material age is that we do not abandon or forget that man has always sought to

transcend himself spiritually, and that this is part of his strange
heritage. It is a heritage which must be preserved in our schools
and churches, for in a society without deep historical memory,
the future ceases to exist and the present becomes a meaningless
cacophony. A future worth contemplating will not be achieved
solely by flights to the far side of the moon. It will not be found
in space. It will be achieved, if it is achieved at all, only in our
individual hearts. This is the choice that has been presented
man, as a free agent, as one who can look before and after in
the cosmos.

And if indeed men do achieve that victory, they will know,
with the greater insight they will then possess, that it is not a
human victory, but nature's new and final triumph in the human heart—perhaps that nature which is also God. "The rationality of man," a great theologian once wrote, "is the little tell-
tale rift in Nature which shows there is something beyond or
behind her." It remains for man, in his moral freedom, to prove
that statement true.

Further reading:
> Eiseley, Loren: DARWIN'S CENTURY. New York: Doubleday
> and Company; 1958.
> ——: THE IMMENSE JOURNEY. New York: Random House;
> 1957.
> de Chardin, Pierre Teilhard: THE PHENOMENON OF MAN. New
> York: Harper and Brothers; 1959.
> Clark, W. E. Le Gros: THE FOSSIL EVIDENCE FOR HUMAN
> EVOLUTION. Chicago: University of Chicago Press; 1955.
> Frankel, Charles: THE CASE FOR MODERN MAN. New York:
> Harper and Brothers; 1956.

The Misbehavioral Sciences

A Truce to the Nonsense on Both Sides

BY

JACQUES BARZUN

"The test and the use of a man's education," says Jacques Barzun, "is that he finds pleasure in the exercise of his mind." Dean of Faculties and Provost of Columbia University, author of numerous books and essays on human freedom, music, and literature, Dean Barzun calls himself "a student of cultural history." He was born in France, the son of a distinguished writer and scholar, Henri Barzun. He accompanied his father to this country in 1919, attended Columbia University, and later taught history there. Jacques Barzun's writings have been distinguished, in the words of the critic Charles J. Rolo, for "monumental scholarship; elegant and eloquent writing; the pervasive imprint of a deeply civilized mind; and a wealth of insight into the life of art."

During the past year events at home and abroad have made Americans question some of their oldest intellectual institutions. One of these institutions is the school, and the question that has been put is: "Does it properly train the men we need in the present expansion of technology and competition in science?" The answer has generally been "No," and advice for immediate changes in our schooling has poured out, mixed with complaints and denunciations.

At times the note of panic has been heard; some have wanted to convert our entire educational apparatus to the mass production of scientists and engineers, evidently believing that this not only should but could be done. Others argue that disaster awaits us if we do not also cultivate the humanities.

This debate is not new, nor is it limited to the United States. It is going strong throughout the western world and particularly in England. The well-known diplomat and writer, Sir Harold Nicolson, testified to this when he told a B.B.C. audience a few months ago, "Everybody, in Great Britain at least, is now considering whether we have not in the past fifty years devoted too much of our time and money to what is loosely called 'the humanities'—namely, the teaching of classics, history, languages and the arts. . . ." And he concluded, "So I suppose that all the little boys and girls in this island will henceforward be taken away from the history books and the literature primers and set down to sums. This prospect fills me with gloom." At once and from all sides Sir Harold was set right, put in his place, taken apart.

In this country during the last two decades, arguments for the humanities have been no less emphatic than Sir Harold's, but a good deal more long-winded. They form the staple of commencement addresses and give businessmen the opportunity of proving in public that they are not Philistines. And yet all those good reasons why science is not enough, why the humanities are indispensable, do not seem to stick. Everybody applauds the speeches—the liberal arts are liberally praised—but the moment a satellite appears in the sky or a rocket fails to go off, the fair words are forgotten. Nothing but science and engineering seems to matter. Could it be that in our so-called better moments we are only hypocrites? Who is supposed to be fooled by the rhetoric which the businessman echoes from the commencement speech—is it the speaker or the audience? Or are they both being fooled by a set of ideas and phrases that do not breed conviction because they have never been seriously meant?

To get out of the rut and forget the clichés, let us for a moment give the humanities a new name. I suggest the "Misbehavioral Sciences." What I mean by it will, I hope, become clear as I go along. The sciences, three cheers! The humanities, what's that? Well, the humanities have existed in an unbroken tradition for 3000 years; there should be nothing left about them to define, advocate or challenge. But if there is nothing, why do we keep asking what the humanities are for and what their place is—as if it lay in our power to choose whether to save or kill them?

The cause of the unending discussion about the humanities is, I suspect, that most of those concerned do not quite know what to believe and do not quite believe what they know. Whether from fatigue or confusion, to which we are all increasingly liable, many distrust their ancient convictions and suppose that some new arguments have been found, some clinching formula, which will restore their faith in the humanities and make it secure in a world of technologists, businessmen and foundation officials.

It is the search for this formula which produces on this subject the great "and" literature—the humanities *and* the democratic way of life; the humanities *and* the well-rounded man; the humanities *and* a creative culture; the humanities *and* the understanding of the self; the humanities *and* leisure in a welfare state; the humanities *and* world peace. The hope implied is that the link between the humanities and things desirable will suggest the relation of cause and effect. The humanities will then be valued, justified, supported as essential to democracy, self-knowledge, world peace, and the rest. This is a deplorable hope. These well-meant attempts at raising price and prestige are not only tedious and vague but contradictory and unconvincing.

No set of subject matters can by itself secure these desired ends. If they could do so by influencing individual minds, why have they done so little in so long a time? The claim of the humanities to be a remedy is, in fact, absurd. The humanities will not rout the world's evils and were never meant to cure individual troubles; they are entirely compatible with those evils and troubles. Nor are the humanities a substitute for medicine or psychiatry; they will not heal diseased minds or broken hearts, any more than they will foster political democracy or settle international disputes. All the evidence goes the other way. The so-called humanities have meaning chiefly because of the *inhu*manity of life; what they depict and discuss is strife and disaster. The Iliad is not about world peace; King Lear is not about a well-rounded man; Madame Bovary is not about the judicious employment of leisure time.

If it is argued that the contemplation of disaster through art or history serves as a warning and teaches morality by inverse example, I ask what evidence there is that a good book has ever prevented a bad action, or a fine sonata a foolish deed. The addiction to books and music begins in early life, before passion and society pose their problems of conduct; and it is also true that in modern as in ancient times the persons reared in the humanities have been exemplars of individual and social unrest. It is men brought up on art, literature, languages, history and philosophy who have been the ambitious and the intriguers, the rebels and the tyrants, the libertines and the agitators, as well as the great tragic figures of discontent in the biographical history of art.

To this catalogue of misrule you may object that, as the term is used today, the servants of the humanities are found rather among another group of people who seldom riot or transgress, and that it is this group, the students and scholars of the humanities, who require prestige and support for the sake of their law-abiding example and harmless teachings.

True, and this double use of the word humanities confuses the argument; we need some definitions. We use the term at times in the loose sense of "the arts," or culture at large; and at other times in the academic sense of the study and teaching of the arts. To the scholar, the humanities are a group of subjects set off from the natural and the social sciences—simply open a college catalogue and you will find that chemistry, sociology and

English literature are under different headings, taught by different persons, usually in different buildings, and often in what seems like different languages. The pure sciences teach the behavior of nature; the social sciences, the behavior of men in large groups; the humanities deal with the individual—hence my notion of *mis*behavioral science.

This rough classification is clear enough. What is more doubtful is where certain subjects belong. History and anthropology are sometimes classed with literature and philosophy, sometimes with social science; symbolic logic has close affinities with mathematics and other "natural" sciences, just as these sciences have with philosophy. And where do we put psychology, geography and the history of the natural sciences? It is soon evident that all subjects are interrelated through the single mind of man, and that we shall never be able to carve up the domain of thought along fixed lines.

This conclusion is of capital importance, for one of the current clichés is that the humanities, as their name suggests, are more human than science and social science—in fact, the only form of thought that remains truly human in a civilization given over to mathematics and machinery. On reflection, these beliefs turn out to be mere verbalisms, the expression of impulses with which one may sympathize, but which must not be allowed to cloud the mind.

In the first place, etymology is a poor guide in this as in other arguments. The term "humanities," descended from the Renaissance catch phrase, *litterae humaniores*, can be appealed to as carrying the suggestion of "peculiarly human," but it is mere suggestion, not proof. If we respect fact and language, we must stop using the word "human" as an honorific term. Everything that men do is human; if an "especially" or "peculiarly" is to be added, it must apply to what men do with deliberation and intelligence. Accordingly, all subjects of research and instruction are human—peculiarly human—and so are a number of activities that the moral sense condemns, such as the deliberate and intelligent preparation of cruelty, criminal violence and war. Once again, to define the humanities by honorifics is a delusion.

But to understand the cause of that delusion is a step forward in their correct identification. For we have reached the point where the discussion of the humanities as academic subjects leads us to think again of culture at large, and notably of the arts, whose dwelling place is unlimited and whose life dare not be academic. The arts exist in the market place, in Bohemia, in journalism, as well as in the cultivated parts of society, and they belong to none exclusively. In recent years, for various reasons, more and more people have come to regard art as the principal justification of man's existence, the redemption of his follies through perfect and lasting creation. Whereas in religious times man is said to work for the greater glory of God, in the modern secular world he prides himself on being what we call creative; all his efforts are equated with—or at least measured by—the work of the artist. This produces another confusion among related but distinct activities—the arts, the humanities, creation and culture. And we can see why the dedicated students of the arts—particularly those who teach the humanities—claim special regard. Their work brings them in daily touch with what the world considers the highest embodiment of man's spirit.

As an immediate result of this pride, they experience the age-old distress of the priesthood, which is to see that though the world worships the true God, it carries its golden tribute to alien altars. The result, among our humanists, is the putting forth of those utilitarian arguments we noticed before; they promise personal happiness or social harmony as the by-product of studying the imagery of Shakespeare or digging in the midden heaps of Mesopotamia.

Unfortunately the promise, though honestly meant, is false; and what is worse, this missionary role puts the humanities in an untenable position, materially and spiritually. For the missionary must offer the ultimate word on mankind, the secret of salvation, which proves his special insight into the transcendent. What more, then, does he want? The world correctly considers that he has been paid in the coin he values most, and that it is only weakness in him to want power and wealth besides.

On top of this it turns out that his secret is a pious fraud. Experience has shown again and again that the humanities are as powerless as any other branch of learning to solve the riddle of the Sphinx or chart the course for Utopia. If they could, and if this were in fact their utility, their importance would come to an end in the very instant of success. For such is the fate of all mere devices.

But the humanities are not a mere device; they are not agencies for general improvement. The humanities in the broad cultural sense and in the narrow academic one have uses that are much more intimate and permanent. In any generation persons are born who, finding in the world books and music and works of art and theaters, are instinctively drawn to them. These people grow up with an ingrained desire for the objects of their interest and a preference for people of a like taste. A larger group, though less intent, takes from time to time similar pleasure in artistic activities. The two groups together are strong enough to impose on the remainder the daily presence of what delights them.

Thus the art of architecture and its decoration—the post-office mural or the restored Williamsburg—are forced on millions who, left to themselves, might live in a cave or a tent. Thus newspapers and magazines reproduce pictures, retell history, comment on art old and new, criticize music and books, write about the lives and opinions of artists—in short, cater for the minority who sway us all by their peculiar tastes.

Thus again, public libraries and museums and concerts in parks and dinner-hour broadcasts "make available to all" (as we say) the products of these special concerns. Consequently, when we repeat the commonplace that the modern world is ruled by science, we must at once add that that same world is given its shape and color by art, its most pleasing sounds and meanings by music and poetry, its categories, characters and catchwords by philosophy, fiction and history. Imagine all the devotees of the humanities suddenly withdrawing to a monastery, taking with them all that belongs to them, and the workaday world we know would turn before our astonished faces into something bleak, dark, soundless, bare of sensuous charm and empty of any meaning beyond that of immediate needs and their fulfillment by mechanic aids.

A few persons—many fewer than the humanities can count as devotees—might still enjoy intellectual contemplation and mathematical thrills, but even they might miss from the stripped stage of daily life the furniture we call civilization.

This contrast is at once instructive and comforting. It tells us that the arts produce objects for the senses and not only for the mind, which is one reason why the humanities are not interested in proofs or in statistics; in place of proof they give possession, and in place of averages they give uniqueness. And despite fashions in taste, these objects form an ever-enlarging treasury. We speak of 3000 years of literature, philosophy and architecture; of a vast collection of objects of art, of an impressive repertory of music—all of it as varied, new and mysterious as it ever was. This reality points to the true role, the indispensable function, of the *academic* humanities—they are the organizers of our huge inheritance of civilization. Without the continual work of humanistic scholars we should be living not in a culture full of distinct and vigorous traditions—national, religious, artistic, philosophical, scientific and political; rather, we should be rummaging about in an attic full of incomprehensible relics.

Let us take one or two examples, beginning with the simplest and most obvious, which is to say the commonest and least noticed. Take a man who lives in a small town, a businessman who is not aware of any intellectual interests, though he feels a sturdy patriotism, local and national. Such a man, contrary to all appearances, and whether he knows it or not, is a client of scholarship. With every commemorative stamp that reinforces his pride, he absorbs a product of art and research. Every political speech he hears invoking the memory of Jefferson or Lincoln implies his recognition of ideas and allusions that belong to the domain of the humanities. He need not belong to the county historical society to approve, as bank director, a decision to make the new bank building a replica of Independence Hall; he probably approves out of natural piety.

But this puts him at once in the grip of half a dozen humanities. Questions of art, of taste, of semantics, of period style, of historical accuracy bother his unaccustomed head. He begins to live at once in the present and in the past; his imagination adds to its work on discount rates visions of pediments and meditations on cracked bells. This Philistine, whom the learned world looks upon merely as census fodder, invades the library, reads books and compares old engravings. What is more, he may shortly be seen struggling with his native idiom in the course of preparing a prospectus for future visitors to the bank; he is but a step away from becoming an antiquarian and a numismatist. Meanwhile he has turned author after having become a consumer of scholarship, a defender of it to his exasperated family —indeed, a scholar in spite of himself.

As for the bank building, however foolishly inappropriate and pretentious it may be, it stands as a monument to the force of tradition and points to the need for its due ordering.

Next, consider the sophisticated citizen of the metropolis who goes to see an Old Vic production of Shakespeare. He enjoys the performance or he does not, but in either case he takes its availability for granted, like the arrival of his coffee at breakfast. Shakespeare is there, waiting; Shakespeare is always with us. It probably does not occur to this patron of the theater that between the blotted lines as they left Shakespeare's hand and their repetition on Broadway, thousands of minds have toiled to rescue perishable art from neglect and misunderstanding. If you mention to him the lighting effects, our spectator may give a fleeting thought to the scientific effort behind the development of electricity, but as he argues with you about the acting of the play, he has no notion that, like the clarity of the text, the production draws on three hundred years of critical thought, of which his own remarks are but echoes filtered through textbooks and newspapers. Shakespeare, then, exists for him only by the joint effort of many expert hands, which have, as a byproduct, fashioned the beholder's mind to perceptiveness.

Without this double action of humanistic scholarship repeated every generation, our heritage of art and thought would soon crumble into nothingness. All we need in order to be sure of this is to hear a publisher talk about book sales—if school adoption is likely, the work is printed and stays in print. This means that in addition to bringing order into the high products of civilization, the teaching and scholarship of the humanities keep that civilization in being. Let no word be said in school about Shakespeare and Doctor Johnson, let no pressure be put on youth to learn the familiar dates and names, the terms and meanings of past eras, and in ten years or less we should lapse into a kind of intellectual feudalism. Local groups and cliques would maintain particular cults, by oral tradition or with the aid of a few quickly perishable books, and local lore would soon replace what we now call common knowledge. The enterprise of learning would collapse as soon as the assumption of its unity and necessity was removed, leaving the individual at the mercy of chance encounters and without hope of light. The scientist and the statistician would be cut off from the rest of mankind—unless they diverted part of their energies to re-creating a common intellectual world—and those of whom I have spoken as being born with a passion for art and letters would be thrown back entirely on their own resources, like the survivors of a barbarian invasion.

When, therefore, the representative of a foundation expresses official skepticism about the humanities in the modern world (not ever speaking for himself, since he is a humanist at heart, but for his Board of Trustees, whose hardheadedness is reported as granitic), the argument against his skepticism is quite simple: The humanities are of no use in the social worker's sense of "useful." They are of use, unobtrusively, all day and every day, to those who respect and enjoy and require the evidences of civilization.

I have used the board of a foundation only as an example. The conflict between the "practical" sciences and the "superfluous" humanities is not a real conflict to those who know the realities they are talking about. Rather, it is a conflict with the thoughtless about the meaning of utility.

The spokesmen for the "practical" view that only science and social science are worth their cost, because they feed and cure and restrain mankind, have never measured any such costs or verified any results. They act on prejudice, or in fear of a popular opinion which has never been canvassed. They moreover limit the useful to large social necessities, such as national defense or the reduction of juvenile delinquency. But necessity is a strange test to apply in a society with pretensions such as ours, a society which might be described as in flight from necessity. Apply the test to the "practical" spokesman himself and he would soon cry mercy; no necessity exists for him to go fishing, for his wife to wear mink, for his office to be attractively decorated. If he is a man of business, he knows that trade depends on people's desire for products they could easily live without. The desire, the taste, establishes the utility of all man-made things, a fifth of whisky or a Fifth of Beethoven.

The use of the humanities, then, is proved and fixed by the ancient, unshakable, ever-spreading desire for them. On the surface these uses appear more individual than social, more self-indulgent than altruistic. Some men are so selfish that they read a book or go to a concert for their own sinister pleasure, instead of doing it to improve social conditions, as the good citizen does when drinking cocktails or playing bridge.

But one must take things as they are; the advocate of practicality is very unpractical if he does not. We may grant him the desirability of devoting human energies to killing viruses and improving our neighbors; but it does not follow that all rewards and research funds should go to projects for the immediate relief of pain and sorrow—the "studies" that promise to reduce nail biting among wallflowers and prevent dorsal decubitus in backsliders.

For if we drop the jargon of projects for a moment and look about us, we find that people have a perverse liking for simple satisfactions of their own choosing. They like singing and dancing and storytelling; they like to argue about the existence of God and the reality of their senses; they want to sit in a corner with a book, or outdoors with an easel and a box of paints; they collect coins and arrowheads; they trace their genealogy and develop an interest in the history of the iron-pipe industry. They read about foreign affairs and learn foreign languages for the sake of aimless travel abroad—there is no end to the silly scholarly interests that actual, living, modern, scientific, respectable American citizens will take up rather than do an honest day's work clearing slums and keeping down divorce.

The real state of affairs should now be plain. The humanities, which pander to these follies and which are perfectly useless as an antibiotic, are all about us, tempting our eye, ear and mind, and always adding, adding, to the load of mischief they stand for. Their practitioners seem to have no thought but to increase the sum of the things they deal in. True, these things do not cost any more than the undertakings of social science—rather less—and far less than the mighty enterprises of physical science. To that extent the humanities are unwise and perhaps undeserving of the attention of those entrusted with millions for educational purposes. Yet those same guardians, it is well known, give of their own money to the liberal-arts college of their youth, and send their children there to study chiefly the humanities. The practical man, it seems, has been too busy spinning dreams of medical and behavioral betterment to bring his opinions in line with his practice.

We might leave him in his muddle to reconcile his tongue and his pocketbook by himself, if it were not for one more confusion of ideas for which the humanists themselves are responsible and which helps to excuse the practical man. I refer to the habit of identifying the craftsman with his craft. The fact that the academic humanities provide the intellectual structure of the civilized life in no way guarantees that the humanistic scholar is a model of civilized intelligence and good taste. Any such view of him is an assumption that reality often dispels, which may explain why the public mistrusts the scholar; he does not look like the noble image one forms of *the* humanist, something like Holbein's portrait of Erasmus. The world is better prepared to find the artist an odd fish—in fact, it is disappointed if he isn't. And this expectation suggests to some that perhaps the scholar looks strange because he, too, is a kind of artist; from which it is only a step to saying that humanistic scholarship is creative.

The academic humanities undoubtedly deal with the arts; why, then, doesn't it follow that scholars and teachers in those fields are artists, or at least cultivated men? The fact is that they are not, or need not be. This must be bluntly said, if only to prevent the serious claims of the humanities from being understood as the claims of humanists to wisdom, elegance and glamour. Not long ago a well-known psychiatrist denounced the hu-

manities as a wasteful expense. Put the time and money into
mass psychoanalysis, he said, and the sum of individual happiness in this country would be immeasurably increased. This
sort of argument is unanswerable. It is also irrelevant. But it
shows the danger of perpetuating conventional nonsense about
the academic humanists and their work. They can be adequately rewarded and respected only when they appear in
their true colors.

The academic humanities, I repeat, are not a form of creation. It is really strange that one should have to say this, when
the very definition of the academic humanities is: The *study*
of art and thought. In a culture with less reverence for art than
ours, and freer of social anxiety about proving one's worthiness,
no sensible scholar would ever have decorated himself and his
fellows with the title of creator. The scholar, to be sure, often
possesses the intelligence, imagination, subtlety or other qualities that are found in artists. But a creator—a maker of something new that stands by itself—he is not. Observation shows
that the artistic and the scholarly temperaments rarely combine.
They are not even well paired within the university, and we have
yet to hear of any masterpiece hatched on a campus. I do not
mean a work that has been published or produced—I mean a
masterpiece.

It is because of this fundamental difference that works of attempted creation ought not to qualify for academic credit. I
know such crediting is an accepted practice, and I despair of
making clear the reasons why it is unjust and ludicrous, but no
matter. The point here is that the public must support the work
of the humanistic scholars, teachers and critics, not because they
produce art, but because they serve art. They serve art, as I have
shown, by introducing the new generations to it, thus keeping
alert the eye, ear and mind; they serve art by maintaining order
around it, thus preventing its obscuration by error and nonsense;
they serve art, finally, by tracing out connections and principles
throughout the whole domain, thus satisfying curiosity and en-
hancing pleasure. That is the practical service rendered in answer to the inborn need of man for art and thought.

In the course of doing this the scholarly humanities sometimes add to the sum of art by discovering or restoring lost works. It was only a short while ago that a lost Haydn mass was recovered by an American musicologist. His adroit, persistent search is worthy of all praise, but who can fail to see that his work called for qualities very different from those needed to write the mass itself? On his side, the artist has no business playing the scholar —a composer the equal of Haydn should not waste his time "going from monastery to monastery for lost music." On the contrary, lost music is his opportunity to supply fresh work.

Whatever mixture of aims and talents occurs in any individual life, professional obligations are distinct from personal. This is why a scholar need not even be a cultivated man. Many scholars qualify as both, but that remains their privilege, not their duty. This amounts to saying that scholarship, like teaching, is a special gift which does not necessarily imply any other. Richard Bentley, the seventeenth-century scholar, was a genius in his line; he did not merely know but he felt the classical languages, by ear as well as intellectually. Yet his edition of Milton shows that he hardly understood his native English idiom, and that off bounds his common sense completely deserted him.

It is, moreover, a fact that a large part of scholarship is drudgery, from which it follows that many scholars are drudges. Who shall say that they are not necessary, worthy, even admirable? The people who edit letters and annotate classics, who compile bibliographies, catalogues and lexicons, are as indispensable as the laboratory technicians who repeat minute determinations, or the tabulators who turn questionnaires into curves. None of them directly delight the mind; we must have them, nevertheless, and be grateful. It is as unfair to expect that he who compiles a concordance of a poet shall be lyrical as that he who drives fat oxen shall himself be fat.

The humanities, then, are not a Cinderella who goes forth into the world only with the aid of magic and has to scurry home when real life resumes its sway. Quite the contrary, the humanities are permanently abroad, and if in their academic setting they are poor, it is because their actual services are taken too much for granted; it is that by dint of living on their intellectual capital they look rich—rich in students, rich in enthusiasm, rich in intangible rewards. They are poor in means because they have not known how to make out their case on their own grounds. They have claimed powers that belong either to no man or to other men, and at the same time they have been culpably modest and retiring.

They have heard sanctimonious voices repeating *ad nauseam* that "man does not live by bread alone," and they have never interrupted to say, "Bakers and butchers, be quiet—and discharge your debt to us for the alchemy which makes your life behind the counter bearable."

That rejoinder, to be sure, is neither gracious nor ennobling, but it is at least honest and, when competition is the order of the day, it is appropriate. In more contemplative moments, the humanities can find other words to represent them, and it is with an approximation of such words that I want to close.

The humanities are a form of knowledge. Like other knowledge, this deals with man's life in nature and society, but it is acquired through the study of man's spiritual creations—language, art, history, philosophy and religion. This filtering of the subject, man, through the medium of mind has the effect of keeping always in the foreground the element of novelty, of uniqueness, of astonishing unpredictability. Whereas the study of nature assumes and finds its uniformities, and whereas the scientific study of society tries also to grasp what is regular and inevitable, the study of nature and man through the humanities dwells on what is individual and unlike and anarchic. It finds what does *not* conform to rule, what has no counterpart, what does not "behave," but simply is or acts—this is the splendid and refreshing spectacle of the humanities. It is the Antigone of Sophocles, who is like no other woman—which is like no other drama; the Athenian plague in Thucydides, which is at once unknown, vividly present and forever the past; the old woman painted by Rembrandt, whose like we shall never see again, but in that record; the adagio of Beethoven's Fourth Symphony, which rose from no formula and yields none; the Zarathustra of Nietzsche, which is an impossibility and a revelation; the lyrics of Thomas Hardy, which defy all the canons of diction and sentiment and prove them wrong; the languages of a thousand peo-

31

ples, which are each more illogical and more subtle than the next. These are the substance which the humanities present to us in the order of logic and veracity, combining thereby fixed reason with wayward spirit, and thus alone deserving the name of Misbehavioral Science.

Further reading:

> Barzun, Jacques: THE HOUSE OF INTELLECT. New York: Harper and Brothers; 1959.
>
> ———: TEACHER IN AMERICA. New York: Anchor Books; 1956.
>
> Starr, Nathan Comfort (ed.): THE PURSUIT OF LEARNING. New York: Harcourt, Brace and Company; 1956.
>
> Van Doren, Mark (ed.): THE NEW INVITATION TO LEARNING. New York: Random House; 1942.
>
> Whitehead, A. N.: SCIENCE IN THE MODERN WORLD. New York: New American Library.

The Riddle of Life

BY
WILLIAM S. BECK

*William S. Beck is one of the most articulate interpreters
of modern biology to the general reader. His recent book
Modern Science and the Nature of Life (1957), a searching study of science and the scientist, received high praise.
He has been affiliated with U.C.L.A., the Atomic Energy
Project, and N.Y.U. As assistant professor of medicine and
tutor in biochemical sciences at Harvard University and
chief of the Hematology Research Laboratory of the Massachusetts General Hospital, Dr. Beck is engaged in research on cell metabolism, enzymology, and mammalian-
cell genetics.*

There have been times, in years gone by, when the public
had an active interest in the great scientific and philosophical debates of the day. Men of affairs shared in the excitement aroused by new ideas, they helped create it, and in
many of history's more unforgettable intellectual free-for-alls, a
volatile and partisan public almost succeeded in forcing the
principal disputants out of the theater of battle, that noisy was
the din.

In general, these were the debates which followed upon any
contribution which directly or indirectly threatened to unseat
man from his throne at the center of the universe. It is said, for
example, that when Copernicus revealed that the earth moved

around the sun rather than the sun about man's earth, great hilarious parties were held in which reveling citizens would pretend they were too dizzy to walk upright, for who could keep his balance on an earth that moved? Similarly, an aroused public took sides in the great controversy between Pasteur and his opponents over whether bacteria could arise spontaneously out of sterile broths to make it a burning issue of the day. And who will forget the clamor which followed Huxley's declaration that the Darwinian theory of evolution applied as well to man, that man was a product of organic evolution as were all living beings, that, if you wished to phrase it bluntly, man descended from the ape? This, in Huxley's proud phrase, is man's place in nature.

Today, the interest shown by many literate people in the progress of science and its implications has ebbed very low, despite the fact that the content of contemporary science (particularly biology) has never been more uproariously exciting or profoundly significant for human life and thought. This is a paradox difficult to explain, though one may speculate that we are living in a time when personal security is so constantly threatened it is perhaps too disturbing for many of us to delve into questions whose answers may make us even more insecure.

But this is not the whole story. For many, the estrangement has arisen out of the fact that science has grown technical, impersonal, complicated, abstract and symbol-ridden. Communication has broken down, and it is perhaps hopeless to try to understand today's specialist when we are not sure we ever understood yesterday's schoolbooks. This is a pity because such views are seldom justified. Thought and effort may be necessary; one must raise his head if he wishes to look around. But the effort is worth while.

It is worth while if only for the joyous fun of it. One should savor great developments as they happen, for truly great contributions quickly enter the intellectual household of humanity. There they became commonplaces, yesterday's triumphs, and if we missed them yesterday, the exhilarating moment is passed. I share the view of most scientists: it is much more fun to discover knowledge than to possess it.

Science is, moreover, the outstanding feature of modern civilization. It is leading us, willingly or not, into strange new worlds where, if we are to live on in fulfillment and peace, we will have to understand what science is and what it is not, what it can and what it cannot do in helping us control the environment, what it tells us of man, his place in nature, and his destiny.

One of the remarkable and frustrating aspects of modern biology is the fact that the roaring tide of specialization has left no one who feels qualified to hold forth on the problem of life itself. Biology has its taxonomists, bacteriologists and biochemists, each an expert in his own domain, but no one wants to tackle the single overriding question common to all: what is life?

Of the several hypotheses that have been offered to explain life, none has been capable of decisive testing. Thus, we have not been able to do what one must always do with any hypothesis if it is to be meaningful: test it experimentally and then accept it, modify it or abandon it as the results dictate. For the only value of such notions lies in their potential usefulness in leading us to new hypotheses and new experiments. This is how knowledge is won and science progresses.

Actually, experimental data can at best contribute only indirectly to this problem. No one can enter a laboratory and undertake to study Life. We study examples of life, in specific areas of inquiry, by asking discrete questions of limited scope. The answers when taken together may provide a basis for generalization by whose reflected light we may hope to illuminate what has been called the biggest question of them all. It is a question which, in my opinion and in the light of what is now going on in science, is probably capable of an answer right now. It is not a very satisfying answer, for it suggests that this question may be one of the meaningless ones.

Since ancient times, a fatal fascination lay in the argument over whether the riddle of life could be explained by sophisticated combinations of physical and chemical laws, a view which is called mechanistic or materialistic, or, alternatively, by the workings of some extra-material agency which alone gives matter the spark of life. From the Age of Greece to the Age of Biochemistry, the battle has shuffled back and forth across traditional disciplinary boundaries, into and out of biology, physics and chemistry, back through theology, up and down the long, drafty corridors of metaphysics. Here, as perhaps in no other field of inquiry, can be seen the crazy quilt of frank speculation, honest application of scientific method, the paternity of wish to thought, the ceaseless kneading of modest but partial evidence into exorbitant theory. What is the question which has led to so many answers?

It is obvious to all that living things are physical objects. They have weight and solidity and exist in a physical matrix. No one has reliably experienced disembodied life. The materials which make up the organism are known to every chemist. We know how some of these substances are put together. We know also that all living things die, and after death, retain, at least momentarily, their same structure, weight and physical continuity. These two general assertions are perhaps indisputable. The question is: what accounts for the difference between living and nonliving physical objects, between the animate body and its corpse?

The *something* that transforms matter into life has been many things to many men. To the ancients, it was the psyche, the life principle, or the soul. To Aristotle, it was three souls. To the early philosopher Democritus, it was something made of atoms, as were all things in his view. Descartes, early in the seventeenth century, made his famous distinction between mind and matter wherein he pictured a dualistic world whose material half was strictly mechanistic. The mind or "rational soul" did not occupy space and was characterizable only by its function: it did the thinking, feeling and reasoning. And, though the rational soul (according to Descartes) did impinge directly upon the material body somewhere in the valve manifold of the pineal gland, the remainder of life's functions were all based on autonomous material mechanisms. Descartes actually gave such great impetus to mechanistic biology that many began to urge that the soul was merely a superfluous hypothesis.

Biology, however, was not purged of its spirits. Frank spookism did give way to more scientific-sounding concepts embodying the idea of *vital forces*—hypothetical agencies by whose indispensable presence and powers matter was made into living matter. Although it explained nothing, substituting mere verbal symbols for the answers still being sought, vitalism nevertheless came to include a large catalogue of nonmaterialistic points of view. In the later nineteenth and early twentieth centuries, the debate between mechanists and vitalists became strenuous and intemperate. Vitalists repeatedly pointed to the failure of strict Darwinian evolutionary theory to explain in detail the emergence of the human mind and consciousness. Moreover, vitalists began bringing from the laboratory long processions of dramatic observations. The German biologist, Hans Driesch, for example, demonstrated in newts the astonishing restitution of whole limbs after leg amputation. To Driesch this had a clear meaning: that some invisible controlling agency must reside within the living organism. No conception, stated Driesch, which views life as a physical or chemical machine, can account for the origin of a whole organism from a single fertilized egg or for the mind of man.

No biologist, of course, ever denied that newt limbs regenerate splendidly following amputation. Like all good experiments, this is the kind one can repeat for himself. The disagreement arises over the conclusions which can justifiably be drawn from this fact. Need one postulate invisible vital forces to explain what has been observed? If there are vital forces, what could one do to verify their existence? Here was the real problem: no possible biological observation could be made which would threaten the validity of this hypothesis. No situation could be imagined which was incompatible with the existence of the postulated vital force. Whatever one observed fitted nicely: it is the vital force at work. Even death could be explained as a giving up or giving out of the vital force, so that even death of the organism did not end the life of the hypothesis.

In contrast, for the mechanistic biologist, every natural occurrence arouses surprise and interest. All living phenomena require explanation in physiochemical terms since none are automatically pre-explained.

Because the progress which the mechanists achieved was undeniable, the extravagant and implausible vitalism of Driesch and his followers gradually passed from favor. It is usually stated, therefore, that vitalism is a dead issue in biology today. Yet, neither is a strict mechanistic viewpoint universally accepted. A number of biologists have taken an intermediate position that the essence of the organism is its wholeness and marvelous integration. According to this view, called *organicism*, life depends upon the complexity of organization of its material parts. To this extent, the doctrine is palatable to the most hardheaded of mechanists who agree that there are no pieces of living matter, but only intact, complex, living organisms.

But many organicists have not stopped there. They have added a variety of other beliefs which carry them beyond the ken of scientific inquiry—doctrines, for example, involving the purpose of life and the nature of thought processes. Thus it is not wholly accurate to state that the mechanism-vitalism controversy is dead.

During this debate, biologists have succeeded in setting the stage for what may be one of the most important moments in the history of science. Within recent years, scientific analysis of the living organism has moved forward with such giant steps that one must be audacious indeed to predict what will or will not be accessible to future scientific inquiry. Few scientists today would concede the existence of a secret of life or a life principle.

On what evidence is this position based? Let us consider some of the developments of biological science.

Despite boisterous controversies, the nineteenth century witnessed the firm establishment of a number of fundamental biological theories. One theory held that the basic living unit is the cell, that multicellular plants and animals are composed of individual cells which are essentially similar, and that all cells are formed by binary fission. Another was that, after its spontaneous origin, life could thenceforth arise only from life.

Still another theory was contributed by Darwin when he asserted that the evolution of species resulted from a struggle for existence among species and within species. And there was the epochal work of the Moravian monk, Gregor Mendel, whose breeding experiments on pea plants showed that heredity was controlled by sets of physical particles within the germ cells of each plant. When the germ cells of two parents were combined, their genetic particles mixed, and the combination that was transmitted to the offspring determined its hereditary character.

A key feature of Mendel's work was the demonstration that when an offspring showed a trait of one parent, say the color of the male, it might nevertheless hand on to the offspring the corresponding trait of the female. This proved that the genetic particles of female parent's color were present in the offspring all the while, even though masked by the particles of male parent's color. Not only were they present though hidden in one generation, they were stable, so that when they could finally reassert themselves in the character traits of a later generation, they were unaltered by their long stay in limbo. Thus it was concluded that heredity depends upon a mosaic of *separate and discrete physical particles* with a continuing existence in time. In 1909 the great Danish botanist Wilhelm Johannsen named them *genes*.

Darwin was one of the many who failed to grasp Mendel's work. And it was not appreciated until well into the present century that, though the discoveries of the two men seemed to be opposed, they were not. Whereas Mendel showed that genetic particles are stable and that genic stability is what guarantees that the offspring will be the same species as its parents, Darwin showed that species are not stable, but arise anew in evolution. How could these two views be reconciled? The answer is *mutation*—the occasional chance alteration of the gene itself.

When a gene mutates it is abruptly and permanently altered in an all-or-none fashion. And as we know of genes only by the results of their actions, by the so-called test of progeny, so we know of mutant genes only from the appearance of altered traits in the progeny which are transmitted to all subsequent generations. Mutations are fairly rare events, but in 1927 Prof. Hermann J. Muller showed in experiments on fruit flies that the frequency of mutations can be artificially increased. He did this by exposing the germ cells to x-ray irradiation; the higher the dose, the greater the frequency of induced mutations. This discovery led to the realization that it is the rare spontaneous mutation—caused primarily by the stray radiation always present in the environment—which is the operative factor in evolution.

Random mutation produces the variations that Darwin was talking about and mutation is, as far as we know, the only source of genetic variability and hence of evolution. Thus was it possible to reconcile Darwin's concept of biological variation with Mendel's concept of genic permanence. The gene *is* permanent unless it mutates. The mutant gene, once formed, is also permanent except for the small probability that it will mutate back to its original state. For despite their rarity, mutations occur in cell populations with a regular and predictable frequency.

Thus it became clear how the genes were transmitted to the offspring and how they might be altered. What was not known, however, was *how* the gene influences a specific organism to develop this or that trait. If the gene is pictured as a blueprint, how does it communicate with the builder?

The ingenious work of the California investigators, George W. Beadle and Edward L. Tatum, with a red bread mold provided an important clue. So that we can clearly understand their experiment, let us begin with some preliminary facts. The living organism is a self-regulating metabolic machine whose primary activity is the chemical conversion of nutrient materials to other compounds needed for growth and maintenance.

We may illustrate the essential character of metabolism quite simply:

$$A \rightarrow B \rightarrow C \rightarrow D \rightarrow E \rightarrow F$$

Let A in the schema represent an ingredient of the diet, and F a compound that the organism needs. The intermediate compounds are merely products and precursors in an orderly sequence of chemical conversions. Each step is made possible by a specific *enzyme* within the cell. The function of enzymes, which are special protein molecules, is to catalyze and control these reactions. For almost every one of the huge number of chemical reactions in the organism, there is one enzyme "in charge." There are indications that the high specificity of each enzyme results from an intricate spatial arrangement of the limited number of amino acids which make up all proteins.

We may, therefore, regard all biological traits as consequences of enzymatic reactions. For example, brown skin is brown because a brown pigment has been synthesized by a collection of enzymes in the cells of the skin. In other words, the presence or absence of specific enzymes determines the appearances which we call traits. The question then becomes: what is the relationship between genes and enzymes?

Beadle and Tatum took a sample of mold that could make substance F from A. The mold needed a supply of F for growth, but if cultivated on a medium containing A alone, it could flourish because it possessed the enzymes needed to convert A to F. They found then that if they irradiated the mold, many off-spring appeared which would no longer grow on a medium containing only A, but would grow if F was added to the culture. In other words, the F requirement for growth remained, but the mold had lost the ability to convert A to F.

By closer analysis, they demonstrated that this radiation-in duced loss occurred in just *one* of the sequential steps; that is, the organism could not now convert C to D, for example, while the other steps remained unaltered. This could be shown in two ways: by demonstrating normal growth on a medium containing only D (proving that $D \rightarrow E \rightarrow F$ was intact); and by showing a large pile-up of C when the medium contains only A —proving that A was still being converted into C, although C was not being converted to D. These results suggested that x-irradiation of the mold results in offspring which lack a single enzyme. When an actual search was made for the "$C \rightarrow D$ en-zyme," it was indeed found to be missing. Furthermore, when mold growth was sustained by artificially providing the missing ingredient, normal reproduction followed and subsequent generations lacked the same enzyme. Beadle and Tatum, therefore, postulated that for each enzyme, there is one gene—the "one gene, one enzyme hypothesis."

Their work clarified several other mysteries. For example, the red mold needs vitamin B_1 just as we do; but *it* can make B_1 from simpler compounds, whereas we cannot. When Beadle and Tatum produced a mutant unable to make its own B_1, they had to provide it artificially. Since our B_1 must be ready made, B_1 is for us a vitamin, because by definition a vitamin is a substance the organism needs but cannot manufacture. We may reasonably speculate that our ancestors once could make B_1, but by a mutation the enzymatic machinery needed for its synthesis was lost forever. Had there been no organisms in our environment which could make it for us, like the bread mold or other living organisms, we might have perished then and there.

The question now comes down to the nature of the relationship between the gene and enzymes. Conceivably, the gene is some kind of master pattern which is replicated in the manufacture of specific enzyme molecules. Since such high specificity is conveyed from the gene to the enzyme, we may postulate a physical relationship such as occurs in printing. Thus, the gene might be an intricate pattern mold for stamping the specificity into its enzyme. If the gene were physically damaged, the corresponding enzyme would then be lost.

This postulate pointed a new approach: what is the gene made of chemically—or, more precisely, what are chromosomes made of? The gene is an abstract assumption while chromosomes are the microscopically visible structures in which, we believe, genes are located. It had been known for years that a substance could be extracted from cell nuclei which, being acidic, was named *nucleic acid*. It was then discovered that there are two kinds of nucleic acid: the one found only in the nucleus, desoxyribonucleic acid or DNA, and the other, which may be outside the nucleus, ribonucleic acid or RNA.

The molecules of nucleic acid were seen to be extraordinarily long chainlike structures whose links consisted of numerous units called *nucleotides*. The nucleotides, in turn, are fairly complicated compounds of four kinds, differing only in the identity of attached substances known as nitrogenous bases. For convenience, we may refer to these as 1,2,3, and 4. Thus, chemically speaking, DNA appeared to be a long chain of four repeating units such as:

. . . –1–2–3–4–1–2–3–4 or perhaps . . . 3–2–1–4 . . .

The exact sequence of these units was unresolved. Having recorded these observations, biochemists placed nucleic acid on the shelf to gather dust, a mysterious gummy white powder of unknown significance.

In time, however, nucleic acid reappeared on the scene in several unexpected places. Investigators found that viruses consist of nothing more than minute pieces of nucleic acid with a protein coating. When a virus enters a cell, as it must to reproduce, the protein remains outside. This suggested that it is nucleic acid alone when stimulates the production of new and complete viruses within the host cell. The blueprints for virus synthesis, it appeared, therefore, must reside within the nucleic acid. Since the acid evidently determines when and how a cell turns out new viruses, it alone must carry the hereditary information which guarantees that the new viruses will be replicas of their parent.

Meanwhile another phenomenon was being observed. Two strains of the same bacterial species were cultured, differing only in that one had trait *x*, the other did not. (We are here using *x* as a convenient symbol to denote any of several hereditary traits —penicillin-resistance, for example. Thus, in this context, *x*-bacteria would be penicillin-resistant; non-*x*-bacteria penicillin-sensitive.) An extract of the *x*-bacteria culture free of whole bacteria, particles or other debris was prepared and added to the growing culture of non-*x*-bacteria. The results were quite startling. The treated culture developed many colonies of *x*-bacteria. Moreover, the new *x*-bacteria bred true, showing that their newly acquired trait was hereditary. This phenomenon was called *transformation* and the active ingredient in the extract was called the *transforming* principle or TP. It was further shown that TP is DNA. Once again, DNA apparently turns up as a carrier of genetic information.

An avalanche of questions followed these discoveries. Are the properties of the gene explained by the properties of DNA? How does DNA carry genetic information when no *chemical* difference can be detected between the DNA nucleotides of different species? When a cell makes new DNA, what preserves the genetic information? What could not be questioned was the dramatic fact that, at last, a fateful meeting had occurred between biology, chemistry and physics. All lines of demarcation were now erased. For DNA is a *chemical* compound carrying *biological* information somewhere within its *physical* structure.

The stage was now set for a unified attack on one of the greatest enigmas of science. In 1953, James D. Watson and F. H. C. Crick reported that examination of DNA by x-ray diffraction revealed it to be not a mere string of nucleotides, but a highly organized helical structure. The most exciting part of their discovery was that the helix involved not one, but two parallel nucleotide strands. It was also concluded that any given sequence of nucleotides in one strand determined the order in the other strand, since in the limited space of the tightly joined structure only certain pairs of nitrogenous bases could fit together side by side.

Here was a picture which could explain a great deal. A double set of strands suggests a self-duplicating mechanism. The two strands could separate and each could serve as a mold for the formation of the other, since each nitrogenous base in the chain could accommodate only the correct complementary base. Thus, the daughter DNA would be similarly double-stranded with the same order of nucleotides. The preservation of this *order* is crucial, for every indication points to base order as the code in which all of heredity is written. Theorists were quick to note that if the DNA chain contained only 100 sets of four nucleotides each (it actually contains thousands), the number of possible linear arrangements would be considerably larger than the number of atoms in the solar system. Such a range of variations would be more than enough to account for the specificity of enzymes *if one makes the obvious deduction*, to wit: nucleotides confer specificity on enzymes by assembling their constituent amino acids in the correct sequences. Nucleotide sequence thus determines which enzymes will be present and therefore which traits will occur in each generation.

According to the latest evidence, DNA does not preside directly over the synthesis of enzymes. Instead it somewhat resembles the process by which phonograph records are manufactured. First, the artist makes a master. To duplicate the master, a negative pressing is made, which is used to press out positives. Here, the master is DNA, whose basic character has been shaped by evolution. The negative which transfers the sequence pattern is RNA, and the matrix into which it stamps a specific pattern is the protein which thereby becomes an enzyme.

Biochemists have now learned to synthesize artificial nucleotide chains and are seeking to arrange them in specific order patterns. One might call this an attempt to create life, but such a statement adds little to our understanding of what has been done and what remains to be done. We are working with physical phenomena entirely accessible to our understanding, and in this light the words "life" and "living" have pallid complexions. We have now entered a zone where such words serve us no longer. It is a zone of ambiguity where there is no meaning or purpose in debating where life begins and nonlife ends. What occurs occurs; the rest relates to one's state of mind. There are, in fact, none but metaphysical reasons to assume *a priori* that an absolute and unbridgeable gap must separate animate and inanimate matter. The evidence rather points in the opposite direction and suggests that "life" and "nonlife" may be words like "hot" and "cold." They are positions on a spectrum graduated from the simple to the complex: life is on the complex end, nonlife on the simple. The middle ground is neither one nor the other.

To the vitalistic argument that mechanists have not yet created a living organism, there are two answers. One is that neither has the astronomer created a solar system, nor has the evolutionist evolved an elephant, although both understand their systems in mechanistic terms. The other is that "not yet" is not the same as "never." Nothing so far discovered warrants the final conclusion that biological events will *never* be totally explained in the language of physics and chemistry.

However, substantial and nonmystical reasons exist for suspecting that the goal of mechanistic biology may never be reached, though vitalists rarely mention these reasons. There are two basic methods of studying the living organism, the behavioral and the analytical. In order to elucidate biological phenomena it may be essential to make both types of observations simultaneously. But the two methods are mutually exclusive. We would, for example, have difficulty studying the brain by dissection or chemical analysis while at the same time observing its behavior by the interview method—the only method available for examining a mind at work. The final explanation of one in terms of the other would call for simultaneous observation. Likewise, it would be difficult to study the nucleotide order of a DNA molecule during the act of genetic recombination, as long as such recombination can occur only in the intact cell. Base analysis is destructive of biological organization, while behavioral analysis requires the organism to be intact. This problem is particularly frustrating in cancer research. Here we seek to attribute abnormal patterns of growth behavior to events within cells. But test-tube analysis conducted on shreds of cancer cells can show no growth pattern—since growth requires that the cell be intact. If cancer is due to genetic mutation brought on by radiation, noxious chemicals or viruses (as many of us believe), we may be hard pressed to relate a DNA alteration to abnormal growth.

Yet the problem may not be insoluble. A clue to a possible solution may lie in the laboratory synthesis of infective virus nucleic acid. If we can *first* synthesize nucleic acids to our own specification and *then* observe their genetic behavior, we could then dispense with the necessity of simultaneous observation.

This is not to suggest that we may someday possess the "secret of life," whatever that phrase may mean. But an adequate explanation of organismic behavior may be possible in terms of physics and chemistry. Indeed, as we have seen, such an explanation may be close at hand.

Further reading:

Beck, *William S.*: MODERN SCIENCE AND THE NATURE OF LIFE. New York: Harcourt, Brace and Company; 1957.

McElroy, *William D., and Bentley Glass* (*eds.*): THE CHEMICAL BASIS OF DEVELOPMENT. Baltimore: The Johns Hopkins Press; 1958.

———: THE CHEMICAL BASIS OF HEREDITY. Baltimore: The Johns Hopkins Press; 1957.

Feigl, *Herbert, and May Brodbeck* (*eds.*): READINGS IN THE PHILOSOPHY OF SCIENCE. New York: Appleton-Century-Crofts; 1953.

Reichenbach, *Hans*: THE RISE OF SCIENTIFIC PHILOSOPHY. Berkeley: University of California Press; 1951.

Simpson, *George Gaylord, Colin S. Pittendrigh, and Lewis H. Tiffany*: LIFE: AN INTRODUCTION TO BIOLOGY. New York: Harcourt, Brace and Company; 1957.

The Lost Dimension in Religion

BY

PAUL TILLICH

Paul Tillich, university professor at Harvard and a member of the Divinity School faculty, centers his theology "on the method of correlation between the questions arising out of the human predicament and the answers given in the classical symbols of religion." Holding teaching posts in philosophy and theology in many of the leading German universities, he was forced to leave his native land upon the rise of Hitler because of his outspoken criticism of Nazism, and in 1933 came to this country at the invitation of Union Theological Seminary, where he taught until 1955. Principal writings include Systematic Theology; The Courage to Be; Love, Power and Justice; Dynamics of Faith.

Every observer of our Western civilization is aware of the fact that something has happened to religion. It especially strikes the observer of the American scene. Everywhere he finds symptoms of what one has called religious revival or, more modestly, the revival of interest in religion. He finds them in the churches with their rapidly increasing membership. He finds them in the mushroomlike growth of sects. He finds them on

47

college campuses and in the theological faculties of universities. Most conspicuously, he finds them in the tremendous success of men like Billy Graham and Norman Vincent Peale, who attract masses of people Sunday after Sunday, meeting after meeting. The facts cannot be denied, but how should they be interpreted? It is my intention to show that these facts must be seen as expressions of the predicament of Western man in the second half of the twentieth century. But I would even go a step further. I believe that the predicament of man in our period gives us also an important insight into the predicament of man generally—at all times and in all parts of the earth.

There are many analyses of man and society in our time. Most of them show important traits in the picture, but few of them succeed in giving a general key to our present situation. Although it is not easy to find such a key, I shall attempt it and, in so doing, will make an assertion which may be somewhat mystifying at first hearing. The decisive element in the predicament of Western man in our period is his loss of the dimension of depth. Of course, "dimension of depth" is a metaphor. It is taken from the spatial realm and applied to man's spiritual life. What does it mean?

It means that man has lost an answer to the question: What is the meaning of life? Where do we come from, where do we go to? What shall we do, what should we become in the short stretch between birth and death? Such questions are not answered or even asked if the "dimension of depth" is lost. And this is precisely what has happened to man in our period of history. He has lost the courage to ask such questions with an infinite seriousness—as former generations did—and he has lost the courage to receive answers to these questions, wherever they may come from.

I suggest that we call the dimension of depth the religious dimension in man's nature. Being religious means asking passionately the question of the meaning of our existence and being willing to receive answers, even if the answers hurt. Such an idea of religion makes religion universally human, but it certainly differs from what is usually called religion. It does not describe religion as the belief in the existence of gods or one

48

God, and as a set of activities and institutions for the sake of relating oneself to these beings in thought, devotion and obedience. No one can deny that the religions which have appeared in history are religions in this sense. Nevertheless, religion in its innermost nature is more than religion in this narrower sense. It is the state of being concerned about one's own being and being universally.

There are many people who are ultimately concerned in this way who feel far removed, however, from religion in the narrower sense, and therefore from every historical religion. It often happens that such people take the question of the meaning of their life infinitely seriously and reject any historical religion just for this reason. They feel that the concrete regions fail to express their profound concern adequately. They are religious while rejecting the religions. It is this experience which forces us to distinguish the meaning of religion as living in the dimension of depth from particular expressions of one's ultimate concern in the symbols and institutions of a concrete religion. If we now turn to the concrete analysis of the religious situation of our time, it is obvious that our key must be the basic meaning of religion and not any particular religion, not even Christianity. What does this key disclose about the predicament of man in our period?

If we define religion as the state of being grasped by an infinite concern we must say: Man in our time has lost such infinite concern. And the resurgence of religion is nothing but a desperate and mostly futile attempt to regain what has been lost.

How did the dimension of depth become lost? Like any important event, it has many causes, but certainly not the one which one hears often mentioned from ministers' pulpits and evangelists' platforms—namely, that a widespread impiety of modern man is responsible. Modern man is neither more pious nor more impious than man in any other period. The loss of the dimension of depth is caused by the relation of man to his world and to himself in our period, the period in which nature is being subjected scientifically and technically to the control of man. In this period, life in the dimension of depth is replaced by life

49

in the horizontal dimension. The driving forces of the industrial society of which we are a part go ahead horizontally and not vertically. In popular terms this is expressed in phrases like "better and better," "bigger and bigger," "more and more." One should not disparage the feeling which lies behind such speech. Man is right in feeling that he is able to know and transform the world he encounters without a foreseeable limit. He can go ahead in all directions without a definite boundary.

A most expressive symbol of this attitude of going ahead in the horizontal dimension is the breaking through of the space which is controlled by the gravitational power of the earth into the world-space. It is interesting that one calls this world-space simply "space" and speaks, for instance, of space travel, as if every trip were not travel into space. Perhaps one feels that the true nature of space has been discovered only through our entering into indefinite world-space. In any case, the predominance of the horizontal dimension over the dimension of depth has been immensely increased by the opening up of the space beyond the space of the earth.

If we now ask what does man do and seek if he goes ahead in the horizontal dimension, the answer is difficult. Sometimes one is inclined to say that the mere movement ahead without an end, the intoxication with speeding forward without limits, is what satisfies him. But this answer is by no means sufficient. For on his way into space and time man changes the world he encounters. And the changes made by him change himself. He transforms everything he encounters into a tool; and in doing so he himself becomes a tool. But if he asks, a tool for what, there is no answer.

One does not need to look far beyond everyone's daily experience in order to find examples to describe this predicament. Indeed our daily life in office and home, in cars and airplanes, at parties and conferences, while reading magazines and watching television, while looking at advertisements and hearing radio, are in themselves continuous examples of a life which has lost the dimension of depth. It runs ahead, every moment is filled with something which must be done or seen or said or planned. But no one can experience depth without stopping and becoming aware of himself. Only if he has moments in which he does not care about what comes next can he experience the meaning of this moment here and now and ask himself about the meaning of his life. As long as the preliminary, transitory concerns are not silenced, no matter how interesting and valuable and important they may be, the voice of the ultimate concern cannot be heard. This is the deepest root of the loss of the dimension of depth in our period—the loss of religion in its basic and universal meaning.

If the dimension of depth is lost, the symbols in which life in this dimension has expressed itself must also disappear. I am speaking of the great symbols of the historical religions in our Western world, of Judaism and Christianity. The reason that the religious symbols became lost is not primarily scientific criticism, but it is a complete misunderstanding of their meaning; and only because of this misunderstanding was scientific critique able, and even justified, in attacking them. The first step toward the non-religion of the Western world was made by religion itself. When it defended its great symbols, not as symbols, but as literal stories, it had already lost the battle. In doing so the theologians (and today many religious laymen) helped to transfer the powerful expressions of the dimension of depth into objects or happenings on the horizontal plane. There the symbols lose their power and meaning and become an easy prey to physical, biological and historical attack.

If the symbol of creation which points to the divine ground of everything is transferred to the horizontal plane, it becomes a story of events in a removed past for which there is no evidence, but which contradicts every piece of scientific evidence. If the symbol of the Fall of Man, which points to the tragic estrangement of man and his world from their true being is transferred to the horizontal plane, it becomes a story of a human couple a few thousand years ago in what is now present-day Iraq. One of the most profound psychological descriptions of the general human predicament becomes an absurdity on the horizontal plane. If the symbols of the Saviour and the salvation through Him which point to the healing power in history and personal life are transferred to the horizontal plane, they become stories of a half-divine being coming from a heavenly place and returning to it. Obviously, in this form, they have no meaning whatsoever for people whose view of the universe is determined by scientific astronomy.

If the idea of God (and the symbols applied to Him) which expresses man's ultimate concern is transferred to the horizontal plane, God becomes a being among others whose existence or nonexistence is a matter of inquiry. Nothing, perhaps, is more symptomatic of the loss of the dimension of depth than the permanent discussion about the existence or nonexistence of God—a discussion in which both sides are equally wrong, because the discussion itself is wrong and possible only after the loss of the dimension of depth.

When in this way man has deprived himself of the dimension of depth and the symbols expressing it, he then becomes a part of the horizontal plane. He loses his self and becomes a thing among things. He becomes an element in the process of manipulated production and manipulated consumption. This is now a matter of public knowledge. We have become aware of the degree to which everyone in our social structure is managed, even if one knows it and even if one belongs himself to the managing group. The influence of the gang mentality on adolescents, of the corporation's demands on the executives, of the conditioning of everyone by public communication, by propaganda and advertising under the guidance of motivation research, et cetera, have all been described in many books and articles.

Under these pressures, man can hardly escape the fate of becoming a thing among the things he produces, a bundle of conditioned reflexes without a free, deciding and responsible self. The immense mechanism, set up by man to produce objects for his use, transforms man himself into an object used by the same mechanism of production and consumption.

But man has not ceased to be man. He resists this fate anxiously, desperately, courageously. He asks the question, for what? And he realizes that there is no answer. He becomes aware of the emptiness which is covered by the continuous movement ahead and the production of means for ends which become means again without an ultimate end. Without knowing what has happened to him, he feels that he has lost the meaning of life, the dimension of depth.

Out of this awareness the religious question arises and religious answers are received or rejected. Therefore, in order to describe the contemporary attitude toward religion, we must first point to the places where the awareness of the predicament of Western man in our period is most sharply expressed. These places are the great art, literature and, partly at least, the philosophy of our time. It is both the subject matter and the style of these creations which show the passionate and often tragic struggle about the meaning of life in a period in which man has lost the dimension of depth. This art, literature, philosophy is not religious in the narrower sense of the word; but it asks the religious question more radically and more profoundly than most directly religious expressions of our time.

It is the religious question which is asked when the novelist describes a man who tries in vain to reach the only place which could solve the problem of his life, or a man who disintegrates under the memory of a guilt which persecutes him, or a man who never had a real self and is pushed by his fate without resistance to death, or a man who experiences a profound disgust of everything he encounters.

It is the religious question which is asked when the poet opens up the horror and the fascination of the demonic regions of his soul, or if he leads us into the deserts and empty places of our being, or if he shows the physical and moral mud under the surface of life, or if he sings the song of transitoriness, giving words to the ever-present anxiety of our hearts.

It is the religious question which is asked when the playwright shows the illusion of a life in a ridiculous symbol, or if he lets the emptiness of a life's work end in self-destruction, or if he confronts us with the inescapable bondage to mutual hate and guilt, or if he leads us into the dark cellar of lost hopes and slow disintegration.

It is the religious question which is asked when the painter breaks the visible surface into pieces, then reunites them into a great picture which has little similarity with the world at which we normally look, but which expresses our anxiety and our courage to face reality.

53

It is the religious question which is asked when the architect, in creating office buildings or churches, removes the trimmings taken over from past styles because they cannot be considered an honest expression of our own period. He prefers the seeming poverty of a purpose-determined style to the deceptive richness of imitated styles of the past. He knows that he gives no final answer, but he does give an honest answer.

The philosophy of our time shows the same hiddenly religious traits. It is divided into two main schools of thought, the analytic and the existentialist. The former tries to analyze logical and linguistic forms which are always used and which underlie all scientific research. One may compare them with the painters who dissolve the natural forms of bodies into cubes, planes and lines; or with those architects who want the structural "bones" of their buildings to be conspicuously visible and not hidden by covering features. This self-restriction produces the almost monastic poverty and seriousness of this philosophy. It is religious —without any contact with religion in its method—by exercising the humility of "learned ignorance."

In contrast to this school the existentialist philosophers have much to say about the problems of human existence. They bring into rational concepts what the writers and poets, the painters and architects, are expressing in their particular material. What they express is the human predicament in time and space, in anxiety and guilt and the feeling of meaninglessness. From Pascal in the seventeenth century to Heidegger and Sartre in our time, philosophers have emphasized the contrast between human dignity and human misery. And by doing so, they have raised the religious question. Some have tried to answer the question they have asked. But if they did so, they turned back to past traditions and offered to our time that which does not fit our time. Is it possible for our time to receive answers which are born out of our time?

Answers given today are in danger of strengthening the present situation and with it the questions to which they are supposed to be the answers. This refers to some of the previously mentioned major representatives of the so-called resurgence of religion, as for instance the evangelist Billy Graham and the counseling and healing minister, Norman Vincent Peale.

Against the validity of the answers given by the former, one must say that, in spite of his personal integrity, his propagandistic methods and his primitive theological fundamentalism fall short of what is needed to give an answer to the religious question of our period. In spite of all his seriousness, he does not take the radical questions of our period seriously.

The effect that Normal Peale has on large groups of people is rooted in the fact that he confirms the situation which he is supposed to help overcome. He heals people with the purpose of making them fit again for the demands of the competitive and conformist society in which we are living. He helps them to become adapted to the situation which is characterized by the loss of the dimension of depth. Therefore, his advice is valid on this level; but it is the validity of this level that is the true religious question of our time. And this question he neither raises nor answers.

In many cases the increase of church membership and interest in religious activities does not mean much more than the religious consecration of a state of things in which the religious dimension has been lost. It is the desire to participate in activities which are socially strongly approved and give internal and a certain amount of external security. This is not necessarily bad, but it certainly is not an answer to the religious question of our period.

Is there an answer? There is always an answer, but the answer may not be available to us. We may be too deeply steeped in the predicament out of which the question arises to be able to answer it. To acknowledge this is certainly a better way toward a real answer than to bar the way to it by deceptive answers. And it may be that in this attitude the real answer (within available limits) is given. The real answer to the question of how to regain the dimension of depth is not given by increased church membership or church attendance, nor by conversion or healing experiences. But it is given by the awareness that we have lost the decisive dimension of life, the dimension of depth, and that there is no easy way of getting it back. Such awareness is in itself a state of being grasped by that which is symbolized in the term, dimension of depth. He who realizes that he is separated from the ultimate source of meaning shows by this realization that he is not only separated but also reunited. And this is just our situation. What we need above all—and partly have—is the radical realization of our predicament, without trying to cover it up by secular or religious ideologies. The revival of religious interest would be a creative power in our culture if it would develop into a movement of search for the lost dimension of depth.

This does not mean that the traditional religious symbols should be dismissed. They certainly have lost their meaning in the literalistic form into which they have been distorted, thus producing the critical reaction against them. But they have not lost their genuine meaning—namely, of answering the question which is implied in man's very existence in powerful, revealing and saving symbols. If the resurgence of religion would produce a new understanding of the symbols of the past and their relevance for our situation, instead of premature and deceptive answers, it would become a creative factor in our culture and a saving factor for many who live in estrangement, anxiety and despair. The religious answer has always the character of "in spite of." In spite of the loss of dimension of depth, its power is present, and most present in those who are aware of the loss and are striving to regain it with ultimate seriousness.

Further reading:

    Tillich, Paul: DYNAMICS OF FAITH. New York: Harper and Brothers; 1957.

    ——: THE PROTESTANT ERA. Chicago: Phoenix Books.

    ——: THE RELIGIOUS SITUATION. New York: Meridian Books.

    Heinemann, F. H.: EXISTENTIALISM AND THE MODERN PREDICAMENT. New York: Harper and Brothers; 1953.

    Spiegelberg, Frederic: LIVING RELIGIONS OF THE WORLD. New York: Prentice-Hall; 1956.

    Fromm, Erich: MAN FOR HIMSELF. New York: Rinehart and Company; 1947.

The Mystery
of Matter

BY

J. ROBERT OPPENHEIMER

*J. Robert Oppenheimer has been director of the Institute
for Advanced Study at Princeton since 1947. Trained as
a physicist at Harvard, Cambridge, and Göttingen universities, Dr. Oppenheimer served for eighteen years as
a professor of physics at the University of California and
the California Institute of Technology. Between 1943 and
1945 he was director of the laboratory at Los Alamos,
where the first atomic bombs were made. For his contribution to this project Dr. Oppenheimer was awarded the
Medal for Merit. Subsequently he served as adviser to the
Atomic Energy Commission, the White House, and the
departments of State and Defense. In 1954, after hearings
which are still the subject of intense controversy, Dr. Oppenheimer was denied security clearance. His most recent
book was* The Open Mind *(1955).*

What I have undertaken to write here, about an active
but very small part of the scene in contemporary
science, must leave me troubled, touched with misgivings and
some concerns of conscience. I have written this account for

those who may be interested, but who are neither professionally active nor professionally trained. Many of the words that I have used may mean the wrong things to such a reader; all will mean far less than they should for a good understanding.

This can hardly be otherwise. We must consider objects like electrons and mesons, processes like collision and radioactive decay. Behind each of these words is an epic of experiment, equipment, observation, error, analysis, imagination and work. None of these words corresponds to anything manifest in daily life, or even in experience close to that of daily life. We must refer to arguments whose rigor and scope can hardly, in practical terms, be comprehended without some use of mathematics, and often mathematics not available to a lay, well-educated contemporary. Here and there I have tried to make a small exposition of what a word or a notion means, but this in turn has rested on familiarity and knowledge with earlier parts of science that were in their day also at the frontier and that are even now far removed by the specialized experience of the laboratory, by the abstract logic of mathematical argument and by the happy interplay between these, from the common experience of man.

There is another side. In natural science, discovery has led to invention, invention to technique and practice; and the shape of our world has changed its day-to-day character almost as much as our knowledge of nature. But by virtue of the fact that these are practical changes, that they satisfy, or are intended to satisfy, human needs and interests, they can be described, even to those who are far from the tradition in which they had their origin.

The consequences of nuclear power for man can be described without reference to physics. If these consequences are hard to describe, that is because they involve things that will happen in the future: human choice and decision and motivation, and the tangled institutions of our economic and political world. Weapons can be described without reference to the physics or the mathematics or the chemistry that goes into them. If they are hard to describe, it is for the same reasons, and the further reason that essential things are often kept secret.

Scientists seek new truth about the world; but science has traits in common with other human activities. It has its long cumulative experience, the present building on the past, the future resting on the present. It has its record of error, astonishment, invention and understanding that, taken as a whole, constitutes its tradition. These largely separate traditions are as essential to an understanding of a part of biology or astronomy or physics as is our general human tradition to the existence of civilized human life and intercourse among us. All of us in our years of learning, many if not most of us throughout our lives, need some apprenticeship in the specialized traditions, which will make us better able to understand one another, and clearer as to the extent to which we do not. This will not be easy. To me it seems necessary for the coherence of our culture, and for our future as a free civilization.

The contemporary scientific phase to which I have alluded centers around the giant accelerators—the so-called atom-smashers—now under construction in the United States, the Soviet Union and Western Europe. They are intended to advance one special aspect of physics, which we term particle physics. The aim here is to answer the fundamental question—of what is matter made?

This special aspect of physics is today a very fashionable one among physicists. There are at least three reasons for this: it involves problems of extraordinary difficulty and, also, it involves novelty and thus adventure. Then, too, many signs indicate that if we can solve the problems involved, we shall have achieved new concepts of natural harmony and order.

The notion that matter consists of atoms is an ancient one. The curious speculated about it long before they could be sure such things as atoms existed, let alone what they were or how they behaved. It was not until the nineteenth century that the atomic hypothesis achieved some progress. This was due partly to the discoveries of chemical laws determining what elements combine with which, and in what proportions; and partly to theoretical studies of how matter in bulk behaves in terms of the motions and properties of the atoms and molecules composing it. Yet even at the beginning of the twentieth century distinguished physical scientists doubted the truth of the atomic hypothesis.

The last doubts vanished early in this century. We began to get direct evidence of how atoms behaved. The principal agent of discovery was a new set of experimental techniques for inducing and recording phenomena that could be traced to an atomic process in which only one atom took part. These techniques show that atoms are not, in the literal Greek sense of the word, atoms at all. That is, they are not indivisible and immutable. They do, contrary to earlier beliefs, split up or disintegrate; profound spontaneous changes occur in their structure. The simplest division of an atom is the removal of an electron. Electrons are very light particles which have a negative electrical charge. (When electric current is made by a battery, electrons flow out of the negative terminal carrying their negative electric charge.) The electrons fill most of the space of an atom and determine its chemical behavior and the color of the light it emits and absorbs.

Radiations from radioactive materials, which are themselves products of atomic disintegration, revealed alterations, not in the outer electronic part of the atom, but in the atomic nucleus itself. Such radiations proved to be powerful tools for exploring the atoms they strike. It was through these radiations that Ernest Rutherford, early in the century, discovered the atomic nucleus, which contains almost the entire atomic mass, yet is perhaps a hundred thousand times smaller than the complete atomic structure. The nucleus, Rutherford found, has a positive electric charge. The nucleus of a hydrogen atom (called the proton) has a single positive charge, opposite to that of the electron; that of the helium atom has a double positive charge. This nuclear charge continues to increase up through the 100-odd elements so far discovered.

After 1900 our atomic knowledge grew fast. One phase of investigation concentrated on electrons. Rutherford discovered what force a nucleus exerts on the electrons in an atom. The next step was to discover how the electrons responded to those forces. This seemed at first comparatively simple. The investigators applied Newton's laws, which describe the motions of bodies subject to forces. They had a rude shock. Those laws proved to be inapplicable.

It took two decades to find out why this was so. It was cleared up by the discovery of the wave properties of electrons. Electron behavior, it seemed, could be described only in terms of both particles and waves. Because of the great variety of wave forms which may represent an electron, there are some waves which represent a precisely located particle and others which represent a particle with a definite velocity; but there are none which represent both of these properties.

A new approach to physical phenomena recognizing these facts was needed. It had to transcend Newtonian mechanics, replacing its strict determinism with statistical laws, reconciling the wave and particle behavior of all matter. This new approach had to recognize limitations on the possibility of observing the physical systems. Prediction of probability had to replace predictions of certainty. This theory is called the quantum theory of the atom.

This great atomic theory, which rivals Einstein's theory of relativity as an intellectual achievement, pointed up the narrowness of all earlier sceintific descriptions and was indispensable to later progress. It did not, however, dispose of the question, what constitutes matter? Atoms, we know, consist of a central nucleus and enough circumambient electrons to neutralize the nuclear charge. The forces at play are familiar electrical attractions and repulsions of charges and currents, very much like the forces of gravity. But the finer properties of the atomic nucleus hardly entered into this stage of the atomic theory. The properties of the electron itself, its mass and charge, could be found by experiment—but they were still not understood. Even the fact that electrons weigh so very much less than the nuclei was just a curious observation.

The next act was the study of the atomic nucleus. This was made possible by the development of the first accelerators. The accelerators were designed to accelerate simple nuclei, like the proton, so that they moved with very high speed. They are then shot against a target. Sometimes the accelerated nuclei will hit and penetrate the nucleus of an atom in the target. One then observes the particles emerging from this encounter. Almost all the nuclear properties thus disclosed can be understood on a simple basis. Nuclei are also not, it developed, atomic in the literal sense. They are composite, consisting of neutrons and protons bound together by complex, predominantly attractive forces.

This picture of atomic nuclei took a long time to clarify. The forces between the protons and neutrons that make up the nucleus are not nearly as simple as those acting on electrons in the atom. Many of the nuclei's most interesting traits become observable only when the nuclei contain numerous neutrons and protons, involving all the aspects of a complex system. A great deal still remains to be learned about nuclear structure and behavior. Few of us expect to be profoundly startled by what we may learn, or to have to change profoundly the methods of description evolved during recent decades. Why then, when we know that matter consists of nuclei, made up of neutrons and protons, with electrons surrounding them, can we not name these particles as the answer to the question of what constitutes matter?

The properties of the three particles—neutrons, protons and electrons—seem puzzling and arbitrary as we observe them in nature. If we had no physical means of altering them, if they were really immutable, we should have no basis at all for understanding their properties. We should have to content outselves with storing them in our memory as arbitrary elements of the natural world. But such is not the case. Just as radioactive tools earlier established the mutability of individual atoms and nuclei, so the accelerators showed electrons, neutrons and protons to be mutable.

In these discoveries a key role was played by cosmic rays, the products of the galactic super-accelerators of outer space. When these rays strike matter, they produce particles present neither in the rays nor in ordinary matter—particles which can be seen, for instance, as tracks in photographic emulsion or as tracks of droplets in wet air. These tracks show that the new particles come apart and form others. This proved that no particles of ordinary matter—and indeed none that can be made from it— are unchangeable. All particles can appear or disappear under the proper conditions. Many can change into each other, though the rules of the game limit this play. Protons can turn into neutrons, neutrons into protons, and both can turn into quite different particles. Electrons can come and go very much like the quanta of light emitted by a candle and then absorbed by a dark cloth.

The study of high-energy collisions of particles in accelerators also revealed a surprising picture. In general, the products of such collisions are not the same as the particles which originally collided. If the energy is very high, many particles will be created that did not exist before. Many of these created particles had never been seen before. All, except the familiar protons and electrons, are unstable. Eventually these new particles disintegrate or decay, producing in the process other lighter particles. Even those which do not decay are impermanent. They may vanish in a collision with other particles.

Of great importance in understanding this picture is the interchangeability, or equivalence, of mass and energy. This enables particles to materialize when we provide energy, or to change into energy. The light quantum itself is a particle created when an atom has enough energy to radiate. One of the most vivid early examples of matter created from energy was the production of a negative electron and its positively charged twin, the positron, when X rays of high energy were passed through matter. The many radioactive processes wherein a nucleus emits an electron or positron are best understood thus: creation of the particles occurs when the nucleus has more than enough energy to correspond to the mass of the created particles according to Einstein's famous formula—that energy is equivalent to mass times the square of the velocity of light.

All particles that have an electric charge have a mate oppositely charged, but otherwise identical. So do many with no total charge but some electric properties. We recognize these particles by several characteristics—mass, charge, electrical properties, the time they take to disintegrate or decay, the kind of new particles they produce, and their behavior when they collide with ordinary matter.

This assortment of particles offers a tentative solution to the mystery of matter. Matter, as we know it, consists of impermanent objects—a view which is quite unlike the ancient concept of immutable objects with attractions or forces between them.

Our new atomic menagerie of thirty particles consists of the electron, the proton and the neutron and their electrically opposite counterparts or antiparticles. Additionally, we know of nine other groups. Three are weightless—the light quanta of Einstein, and the neutrinos and antineutrinos of Enrico Fermi which appear in radioactive processes. Three groups, a pair, a triplet and a quadruplet, called mesons, have a mass several hundred times that of the electron. Three groups, the hyperons, a pair, a quadruplet and a sextuplet, are heavier than the proton.

Mesons and hyperons generally live less than a millionth of a second. Broadly speaking, their rate of decay can be understood in terms of the energy released by the difference between their mass and that of the new particles created. The more energy, the shorter the life of the decaying particle. Yet their lives seem very long compared to the millionth of a billionth of a billionth of a second it takes for products of their decay to move apart.

These comparatively long lives are among the major mysteries of particle physics. They indicate that the forces producing spontaneous disintegration must be extremely weak. Two years ago we learned, to our great astonishment, that these same forces discriminate sharply between left-handed and right-handed configurations of their products of decay. Most students of particle physics were delighted when the suggestion that this might be the case turned out to be right and two young Chinese physicists —Tsung Dao Lee, of Columbia University, and Chen Ning Yang, of the Princeton Institute for Advanced Study—were awarded the 1957 Nobel Prize for their contribution to this theory.

Do the thirty particles complete the list? We can't be sure. There have been no additions for some time, though the energies of the accelerators and the diligence of cosmic-ray research have both increased. This is a question on which the more powerful accelerators now building may shed light.

Atomic particles show many regularities of behavior and structure which hint at a kind of order. To trace and formulate these regularities is another focal problem of particle physics. All the particles are characterized by their mass, ranging from the heavy hyperon through the proton and neutron and the mesons to the electron, 2000 times lighter than the proton, and the neutrino with no mass at all. The neutrino thus constitutes a packet of energy traveling with the speed of light—186,000 miles per second. The masses themselves only partly suggest order. But there are other regularities. All known elementary particles have either no electric charge, or a charge the same as the electron's, or a charge of the same magnitude, but of opposite sign. All particles appear, when moving freely and not colliding, to be describable by a few simple types of wave motion. Also, as noted before, the particles occur in groups—the electron and its mate, the groups of hyperons and mesons—and in these groups have many similar properties, and almost equal masses.

There is still more striking evidence of regularity. Though mutable, not all particles can change into all others, not everything can happen in a reaction, even if enough energy is present. We attribute these missing reactions to a selection rule. Normally we try to characterize such a selection rule by identifying —and sometimes inventing—a quantity which does not alter in collision, which remains constant, invariant, immutable. The sum of energy and mass is such a quantity which cannot change in any physical process. There are many others. The total electric charge of the products of reaction, for example, is always equal to the total charge of the ingredients.

Another example of regularity involves the stability of matter. Though the rather massive neutrons and protons have ample energy to change into lighter particles, in ordinary matter they do not do so. If they did, matter—the whole universe as we know it—would not exist. Thus we learn that whereas neutrons and protons can change into each other, the nucleon number, the sum of the number of neutrons and protons involved in a physical process, never changes. When dealing with other reactions this law must be generalized. But it still persists, and must be about as strictly maintained as the law of the conservation of charge, for in the long era of cosmological time no significant deviations from it have ever occurred—as we see from the light that matter emitted a billion years ago and that reaches us today from outer space.

How tentative have been our efforts to sort out and identify the atomic factors that do not change can be inferred from one example. To describe the nonoccurrence of a large class of reactions involving nuclei, hyperons and mesons, it was necessary to find, or postulate, a new attribute of immutability. Its discoverers named it "strangeness."

The conservation of charge and the conservation of nucleon number appear to be absolute physical laws. In no physical process do they alter; no forces exist to promote their alteration. There is a larger body of attributes that do change, though not readily. The concept of "strangeness" is one of these. The forces working on these attributes are weak. In particular, there are very weak forces which appear in radioactivity; we do not understand why some of these weak forces change properties that strong forces, manifested in the collision of particles, do not change. To one such slow change, almost prohibited by a selection rule— an occasional collision in the vast interior of the sun in which two protons form a deuteron and a positive electron—we owe most of the heat and light reaching the earth.

Of course, the laws of selection and of conservation, whether absolute or only approximate, help us to describe what happens, and to predict what will happen. On this ground alone they would be a part of physics. But they play a further role. When no forces exist that will change a certain quantity like the total charge or total energy and mass, the absence of these forces implies that the laws of physics must have a corresponding simplicity. In ordinary mechanics, if no forces act on a system from outside, the system will neither speed up nor slow down; its total momentum or impulse will not change. This we attribute to the simplicity or symmetry of empty space, wherein no forces act. With a little mathematics it is easy to give a general proof of this connection between symmetry and changelessness; I have not found a way to make it clear in a few words.

Every selection rule we learn from nature teaches us something about the symmetry of physical laws—a valuable clue when we do not know what those laws may be, or what sort of quantities they govern. This provides one of the very few theoretical procedures now available to us for solving the problem of the constitution of matter.

Another way of attacking such a problem is to search for descriptions of unfamiliar phenomena which are analogous to descriptions of phenomena already familiar to physicists. Thus the quantum theory, for all its strangeness, is still based on an analogy with Newtonian mechanics; it must and does give the familiar correct answers when applied to the large-scale events of ordinary life. Radioactive processes were described by Fermi in analogy with what he had learned about the emission and absorption of the light by which we all live. This analogy, like most, of course, required correction and refinement.

This use of analogy—adapting a familiar mode of description to a new situation, finding the points of difference, and ultimately determining whether anything remains to the analogy—seems essential to the progress of understanding. But at the moment, all fundamental questions as to its validity for particle physics are still open and subject to anxious doubts.

At the same time a sense of expectancy, of impending change, hovers over this area of the scientific scene. What we hope for is that the newly discovered particles, their existence, properties and attributes, and the selection rules dominating their interaction, will eventually appear less arbitrary, more united and intelligible. We do not know why these particles exist, nor whether there maybe others like or unlike them. We do not know why they have their particular masses. The attributes needed to describe their changeless features are not yet fully understood. We may compare our present state of knowledge with that of nineteenth-century chemistry, when the chemical properties and atomic weights of many elements and the rules of their combination were known, but when each fact was learned by laboratory analysis and could not be reduced to simple laws. With the development of atomic mechanics, empiricism was complemented by theory. Today all that earlier knowledge, and much besides, can be expressed in terms of a very few empirical constants and one law of nature—a law which describes the action of electrons under the influence of the electric field of an atomic nucleus.

Two views prevail as to how a comparable understanding of fundamental particles may be attained. According to one, all the particles are manifestations of special states of a primordial matter. This view holds that when we uncover the proper laws for this matter, they will imply the existence of precisely the particles that do exist, with just the properties they have, and exclude all others.

According to a radically different view, our future description of this part of the physical world will refer to the elementary particles themselves, and to laws linking their properties and behavior, and will not refer to a more basic substance. In this view, not merely the behavior, but the very existence of the particles would emerge as a necessary part of the description. If that description can be achieved, it would have to include some limitations on the fineness of the scale in time and space with which we can hope to follow the course of physical events. For we should have to use for our observations the elementary particles which, as we know them, are finite in number.

If our history is any guide, our guesses as to the future of physics will turn out not to have been very clever. They should perhaps be considered an account of present efforts and the hopes that inspire them, rather than predictions. Regarding the two views, their merits and demerits—which are spectacular—a warm debate goes on.

The history of physics may be no guide. In particle physics we may have to accept an arbitrary, complicated, not very orderly set of facts, without seeing behind them the harmony in terms of which they might be understood. It is the special faith and dedication of our profession that we will not lightly concede such a defeat.

The Lessons of the Past

BY

EDITH HAMILTON

*Edith Hamilton is among the world's leading authorities
on the Graeco-Roman civilization, a study which has occupied her for more than half her years (she was born in
1867). Her The Greek Way and The Roman Way have
become classics in the field. She received her advanced
education at Bryn Mawr College and the universities of
Leipzig and Munich. She was headmistress of the Bryn
Mawr School in Baltimore from 1896 to 1922. In 1957,
in recognition of her devotion and scholarship, the Greek
government made her an honorary citizen of Athens.*

I s there an ever-present past? Are there permanent truths
which are forever important for the present? Today we are
facing a future more strange and untried than any other generation has faced. The new world Columbus opened seems small
indeed beside the illimitable distances of space before us, and
the possibilities of destruction are immeasurably greater than
ever. In such a position can we afford to spend time on the past?
That is the question I am often asked. Am I urging the study of
the Greeks and Romans and their civilizations for the atomic
age?

Yes; that is just what I am doing. I urge it without qualifications. We have a great civilization to save—or to lose. The greatest civilization before ours was the Greek. They challenge us and we need the challenge. They, too, lived in a dangerous world. They were a little, highly civilized people, the only civilized people in the west, surrounded by barbarous tribes and with the greatest Asiatic power, Persia, always threatening them. In the end they succumbed, but the reason they did was not that the enemies outside were so strong, but that their own strength, their spiritual strength, had given way. While they had it they kept Greece unconquered and they left behind a record in art and thought which in all the centuries of human effort since has not been surpassed.

The point which I want to make is not that their taste was superior to ours, not that the Parthenon was their idea of church architecture nor that Sophocles was the great drawing card in the theaters, nor any of the familiar comparisons between fifth-century Athens and twentieth-century America, but that Socrates found on every street corner and in every Athenian equivalent of the baseball field people who were caught up by his questions into the world of thought. To be able to be caught up into the world of thought—that is to be educated.

How is that great aim to be reached? For years we have eagerly discussed ways and means of education, and the discussion still goes on. William James once said that there were two subjects which if mentioned made other conversation stop and directed all eyes to the speaker. Religion was one and education the other. Today Russia seems to come first, but education is still emphatically the second. In spite of all the articles we read and all the speeches we listen to about it, we want to know more; we feel deeply its importance.

There is today a clearly visible trend toward making it the aim of education to defeat the Russians. That would be a sure way to defeat education. Genuine education is possible only when people realize that it has to do with persons, not with movements.

When I read educational articles it often seems to me that this important side of the matter, the purely personal side, is not emphasized enough; the fact that it is so much more agreeable and interesting to be an educated person than not. The sheer pleasure of being educated does not seem to be stressed. Once long ago I was talking with Prof. Basil L. Gildersleeve of Johns Hopkins University, the greatest Greek scholar our country has produced. He was an old man and he had been honored everywhere, in Europe as well as in America. He was just back from a celebration held for him in Oxford. I asked him what compliment received in his long life had pleased him most. The question amused him and he laughed over it, but he thought too. Finally he said, "I believe it was when one of my students said, 'Professor, you have so much fun with your own mind.'" Robert Louis Stevenson said that a man ought to be able to spend two or three hours waiting for a train at a little country station when he was all alone and had nothing to read, and not be bored for a moment.

What is the education which can do this? What is the furniture which makes the only place belonging absolutely to each one of us, the world within, a place where we like to go? I wish I could answer that question. I wish I could produce a perfect decorator's design warranted to make any interior lovely and interesting and stimulating; but, even if I could, sooner or later we would certainly try different designs. My point is only that while we must and should change the furniture, we ought to throw away old furniture very cautiously. It may turn out to be irreplaceable. A great deal was thrown away in the last generation or so, long enough ago to show some of the results. Furniture which had for centuries been foremost, we lightly, in a few years, discarded. The classics almost vanished from our field of education. That was a great change. Along with it came another. There is a marked difference between the writers of the past and the writers of today who have been educated without benefit of Greek and Latin. Is this a matter of cause and effect? People will decide for themselves, but I do not think anyone will question the statement that clear thinking is not the characteristic which distinguishes our literature today. We are more and more caught up by the unintelligible. People like it. This argues an inability to think, or, almost as bad, a disinclination to think.

Neither disposition marked the Greeks. They had a passion for thinking things out, and they loved unclouded clarity of statement as well as of thought. The Romans did, too, in their degree. They were able to put an idea into an astonishingly small number of words without losing a particle of intelligibility. It is only of late, with a generation which has never had to deal with a Latin sentence, that we are being submerged in a flood of words, words, words. It has been said that Lincoln at Gettysburg today would have begun in some such fashion as this: "Eight and seven-tenths decades ago the pioneer workers in this continental area implemented a new group based on an ideology of free boundaries and intitial equality," and might easily have ended, "That political supervision of the integrated units, for the integrated units, by the integrated units, shall not become null and void on the superficial area of this planet." Along with the banishment of the classics, gobbledegook has come upon us —and the appalling size of the Congressional Record, and the overburdened mail service.

Just what the teaching in the schools was which laid the foundation of the Greek civilization we do not know in detail; the result we do know. Greek children were taught, Plato said, to "love what is beautiful and hate what is ugly." When they grew up their very pots and pans had to be pleasant to look at. It was part of their training to hate clumsiness and awkwardness; they loved grace and practiced it. "Our children," Plato said, "will be influenced for good by every sight and sound of beauty, breathing in, as it were, a pure breeze blowing to them from a good land."

All the same, the Athenians were not, as they showed Socrates when he talked to them, preoccupied with enjoying lovely things. The children were taught to think. Plato demanded a stiff examination, especially in mathematics, for entrance to his Academy. The Athenians were a thinking people. Today the scientists are bearing away the prize for thought. Well, a Greek said that the earth went around the sun, sixteen centuries before Copernicus thought of it. A Greek said if you sailed out of Spain and kept to one latitude, you would come at last to land, seventeen hundred years before Columbus did it. Darwin said,

"We are mere schoolboys in scientific thinking compared to old Aristotle." And the Greeks did not have a great legacy from the past as our scientists have; they thought science out from the beginning.

The same is true of politics. They thought that out, too, from the beginning, and they gave all the boys a training to fit them to be thinking citizens of a free state that had come into being through thought.

Basic to all the Greek achievement was freedom. The Athenians were the only free people in the world. In the great empires of antiquity—Egypt, Babylon, Assyria, Persia—splendid though they were, with riches beyond reckoning and immense power, freedom was unknown. The idea of it never dawned in any of them. It was born in Greece, a poor little country, but with it able to remain unconquered no matter what manpower and what wealth were arrayed against her. At Marathon and at Salamis overwhelming numbers of Persians had been defeated by small Greek forces. It had been proved that one free man was superior to many submissively obedient subjects of a tyrant. Athens was the leader in that amazing victory, and to the Athenians freedom was their dearest possession. Demosthenes said that they would not think it worth their while to live if they could not do so as free men, and years later a great teacher said, "Athenians, if you deprive them of their liberty, will die."

Athens was not only the first democracy in the world, it was also at its height an almost perfect democracy—that is, for men. There was no part in it for women or foreigners or slaves, but as far as the men were concerned it was more democratic than we are. The governing body was the Assembly, of which all citizens over eighteen were members. The Council of Five Hundred which prepared business for the Assembly and, if requested, carried out what had been decided there, was made up of citizens who were chosen by lot. The same was true of the juries. Minor officials also were chosen by lot. The chief magistrates and the highest officers in the army were elected by the Assembly. Pericles was a general, very popular, who acted for a long time as if he were head of the state, but he had to be elected every year. Freedom of speech was the right the Athenians prized most and there has never been another state as free in that respect. When toward the end of the terrible Peloponnesian War the victorious Spartans were advancing upon Athens, Aristophanes caricatured in the theater the leading Athenian generals and showed them up as cowards, and even then as the Assembly opened, the herald asked, "Does anyone wish to speak?"

There was complete political equality. It was a government of the people, by the people, for the people. An unregenerate old aristocrat in the early fourth century, B.C., writes: "If you *must* have a democracy, Athens is the perfect example. I object to it because it is based on the welfare of the lower, not the better, classes. In Athens the people who row the vessels and do the work have the advantage. It is their prosperity that is important." All the same, making the city beautiful was important too, as were also the great performances in the theater. If, as Plato says, the Assembly was chiefly made up of cobblers and carpenters and smiths and farmers and retail-business men, they approved the construction of the Parthenon and the other buildings on the Acropolis, and they crowded the theater when the great tragedies were played. Not only did all free men share in the government; the love of the beautiful and the desire to have a part in creating it were shared by the many, not by a mere chosen few. That has happened in no state except Athens.

But those free Greeks owned slaves. What kind of freedom was that? The question would have been incomprehensible to the ancient world. There had always been slaves; they were a first necessity. The way of life everywhere was based upon them. They were taken for granted; no one ever gave them a thought. The very best Greek minds, the thinkers who discovered freedom and the solar system, had never an idea that slavery was evil. It is true that the greatest thinker of them all, Plato, was made uncomfortable by it. He said that slaves were often good, trustworthy, doing more for a man than his own family would, but he did not follow his thought through. The glory of being the first one to condemn it belongs to a man of the generation before Plato, the poet Euripides. He called it, "That thing of evil," and in several of his tragedies showed its evil for all to see. A few centuries later the great Greek school of the Stoics denounced it.

Greece first saw it for what it is. But the world went on in the same way. The Bible accepts it without comment. Two thousand years after the Stoics, less than a hundred years ago, the American Republic accepted it.

Athens treated her slaves well. A visitor to the city in the early fourth century, B.C., wrote: "It is illegal here to deal a slave a blow. In the street he won't step aside to let you pass. Indeed you can't tell a slave by his dress; he looks like all the rest. They can go to the theater too. Really, the Athenians have established a kind of equality between slaves and free men." They were never a possible source of danger to the state as they were in Rome. There were no terrible slave wars and uprisings in Athens. In Rome, crucifixion was called "the slave's punishment." The Athenians did not practice crucifixion, and had no so-called slave's punishment. They were not afraid of their slaves.

In Athens' great prime Athenians were free. No one told them what they must do or what they should think—no church or political party or powerful private interests or labor unions. Greek schools had no donors of endowments they must pay attention to, no government financial backing which must be made secure by acting as the government wanted. To be sure, the result was that they had to take full responsibility, but that is always the price for full freedom. The Athenians were a strong people, they could pay the price. They were a thinking people; they knew what freedom means. They knew—not that they were free because their country was free, but that their country was free because they were free.

A reflective Roman traveling in Greece in the second century A.D. said, "None ever throve under democracy save the Athenians; *they* had sane self-control and were law-abiding." He spoke truly. That is what Athenian education aimed at, to produce men who would be able to maintain a self-governed state because they were themselves self-governed, self-controlled, self-reliant. Plato speaks of "the education in excellence which makes men long to be perfect citizens, knowing both how to rule and be ruled." "We are a free democracy," Pericles said. "We do not allow absorption in our own affairs to interfere with participation in the city's; we yield to none in independence

75

of spirit and complete self-reliance, but we regard him who holds aloof from public affairs as useless." They called the useless man a "private" citizen, *idiotes*, from which our word "idiot" comes.

They had risen to freedom and to ennoblement from what Gilbert Murray calls "effortless barbarism"; they saw it all around them; they hated its filth and fierceness; nothing effortless was among the good things they wanted. Plato said, "Hard is the good," and a poet hundreds of years before Plato said,

> *Before the gates of Excellence the high gods have placed*
> *sweat.*
> *Long is the road thereto and steep and rough at the first,*
> *But when the height is won, then is there ease.*

When or why the Greeks set themselves to travel on that road we do not know, but it led them away from habits and customs accepted everywhere that kept men down to barbaric filth and fierceness. It led them far. One example is enough to show the way they took. It was the custom—during how many millenniums, who can say?—for a victor to erect a trophy, a monument of his victory. In Egypt, where stone was plentiful, it would be a slab engraved with his glories. Farther east, where the sand took over, it might be a great heap of severed heads, quite permanent objects; bones last a long time. But in Greece, though a man could erect a trophy, it must be made of wood and it could never be repaired. Even as the victor set it up he would see in his mind how soon it would decay and sink into ruin, and there it must be left. The Greeks in their onward pressing along the steep and rough road had learned a great deal. They knew the victor might be the vanquished next time. There should be no permanent records of the manifestly impermanent. They had learned a great deal.

An old Greek inscription states that the aim of mankind should be "to tame the savageness of man and make gentle the life of the world." Aristotle said that the city was built first for safety, but then that men might discover the good life and lead it. So the Athenians did according to Pericles. Pericles said that

Athens stood for freedom and for thought and for beauty, but in the Greek way, within limits, without exaggeration. The Athenians loved beauty, he said, but with simplicity; they did not like the extravagances of luxury. They loved the things of the mind, but they did not shrink from hardship. Thought did not cause them to hesitate, it clarified the road to action. If they had riches they did not make a show of them, and no one was ashamed of being poor if he was useful. They were free because of willing obedience to law, not only the written, but still more the unwritten, kindness and compassion and unselfishness and the many qualities which cannot be enforced, which depend on a man's free choice, but without which men cannot live together.

If ever there is to be a truly good and great and enduring republic it must be along these lines. We need the challenge of the city that thought them out, wherein for centuries one genius after another grew up. Geniuses are not produced by spending money. We need the challenge of the way the Greeks were educated. They fixed their eyes on the individual. We contemplate millions. What we have undertaken in this matter of education has dawned upon us only lately. We are trying to do what has never been attempted before, never in the history of the world—educate all the young in a nation of 170 millions; a magnificent idea, but we are beginning to realize what are the problems and what may be the results of mass production of education. So far, we do not seem appalled at the prospect of exactly the same kind of education being applied to all the school children from the Atlantic to the Pacific, but there is an uneasiness in the air, a realization that the individual is growing less easy to find; an idea, perhaps, of what standardization might become when the units are not machines, but human beings.

Here is where we can go back to the Greeks with profit. The Athenians in their dangerous world needed to be a nation of independent men who could take responsibility, and they taught their children accordingly. They thought about every boy. Someday he would be a citizen of Athens, responsible for her safety and her glory, "each one," Pericles said, "fitted to meet life's chances and changes with the utmost versatility and grace." To them education was by its very nature an individual

77

matter. To be properly educated a boy had to be taught music; he learned to play a musical instrument. He had to learn poetry, a great deal of it, and recite it—and there were a number of musical instruments and many poets; though, to be sure, Homer was the great textbook.

That kind of education is not geared to mass production. It does not produce people who instinctively go the same way. That is how Athenian children lived and learned while our millions learn the same lessons and spend hours before television sets looking at exactly the same thing at exactly the same time. For one reason and another we are more and more ignoring differences, if not trying to obliterate them. We seem headed toward a standardization of the mind, what Goethe called "the deadly commonplace that fetters us all." That was not the Greek way.

The picture of the Age of Pericles drawn by the historian Thucydides, one of the greatest historians the world has known, is of a state made up of people who are self-reliant individuals, not echoes or copies, who want to be let alone to do their own work, but who are also closely bound together by a great aim, the commonweal, each one so in love with his country—Pericles' own words—that he wants most of all to use himself in her service. Only an ideal? Ideals have enormous power. They stamp an age. They lift life up when they are lofty; they drag down and make decadent when they are low—and then, by that strange fact, the survival of the fittest, those that are low fade away and are forgotten. The Greek ideals have had a power of persistent life for twenty-five hundred years.

Is it rational that now when the young people may have to face problems harder than we face, is it reasonable that with the atomic age before them, at this time we are giving up the study of how the Greeks and Romans prevailed magnificently in a barbaric world; the study, too, of how that triumph ended, how a slackness and softness finally came over them to their ruin? In the end, more than they wanted freedom, they wanted security, a comfortable life, and they lost all—security and comfort and freedom.

Is not that a challenge to us? Is it not true that into our education have come a slackness and softness? Is hard effort prominent? The world of thought can be entered in no other way. Are we not growing slack and soft in our political life? When the Athenians finally wanted not to give to the state, but the state to give to them, when the freedom they wished most for was freedom from responsibility, then Athens ceased to be free and was never free again. Is not that a challenge?

Cicero said, "To be ignorant of the past is to remain a child." Santayana said, "A nation that does not know history is fated to repeat it." The Greeks can help us, help us as no other people can, to see how freedom is won and how it is lost. Above all, to see in clearest light what freedom is. The first nation in the world to be free sends a ringing call down through the centuries to all who would be free. Greece rose to the very height, not because she was big, she was very small; not because she was rich, she was very poor; not even because she was wonderfully gifted. So doubtless were others in the great empires of the ancient world who have gone their way leaving little for us. She rose because there was in the Greeks the greatest spirit that moves in humanity, the spirit that sets men free.

Plato put into words what that spirit is. "Freedom" he says, "is no matter of laws and constitutions; only he is free who realizes the divine order within himself, the true standard by which a man can steer and measure himself." True standards, ideals that lift life up, marked the way of the Greeks. Therefore their light has never been extinguished.

"The time for extracting a lesson from history is ever at hand for them who are wise." Demosthenes.

Further reading:
> Hamilton, Edith: THE ECHO OF GREECE. New York: W. W. Norton and Company; 1957.
> ——: THE GREEK WAY. New York: W. W. Norton and Company; 1930.

————: THE ROMAN WAY. New York: W. W. Norton and Company; 1932.

Dodds, E. R.: THE GREEKS AND THE IRRATIONAL. Berkeley: University of California Press; 1956.

Kitto, H. D. F.: GREEK TRAGEDY: A LITERARY STUDY. Second revised edition. New York: Barnes and Noble; 1950.

————: THE GREEKS. Baltimore: Penguin Books.

Drugs That Shape Men's Minds

BY

ALDOUS HUXLEY

Essayist, satirist, critic, literary journalist, and prolific novelist (Antic Hay, Point Counter Point, Brave New World, The Genius and the Goddess, *and so on*), *Aldous Huxley has familial roots in the sciences. His grandfather was* T. H. Huxley, *the famed English zoologist, and his brother is Sir Julian Huxley, contemporary biologist. Aldous Huxley's interest in mind-changing drugs led him, some years ago, to become an experimental subject for research on the effects of mescaline and similar drugs. He wrote two books on this experience and its implications. English-born and Oxford-educated, Huxley now lives in Los Angeles.*

In the course of history many more people have died for their drink and their dope than have died for their religion or their country. The craving for ethyl alcohol and the opiates has been stronger, in these millions, than the love of God, of home, of children; even of life. Their cry was not for liberty or death; it was for death preceded by enslavement. There is a paradox here, and a mystery. Why should such multitudes of men and women be so ready to sacrifice themselves for a cause so utterly hopeless and in ways so painful and so profoundly humiliating?

To this riddle there is, of course, no simple or single answer. Human beings are immensely complicated creatures, living simultaneously in a half dozen different worlds. Each individual is unique and, in a number of respects, unlike all the other members of the species. None of our motives is unmixed, none of our actions can be traced back to a single source and, in any group we care to study, behavior patterns that are observably similar may be the result of many constellations of dissimilar causes.

Thus, there are some alcoholics who seem to have been biochemically predestined to alcoholism. (Among rats, as Prof. Roger Williams, of the University of Texas, has shown, some are born drunkards; some are born teetotalers and will never touch the stuff.) Other alcoholics have been foredoomed not by some inherited defect in their biochemical make-up, but by their neurotic reactions to distressing events in their childhood or adolescence. Again, others embark upon their course of slow suicide as a result of mere imitation and good fellowship because they have made such an "excellent adjustment to their group" —a process which, if the group happens to be criminal, idiotic or merely ignorant, can bring only disaster to the well-adjusted individual. Nor must we forget that large class of addicts who have taken to drugs or drink in order to escape from physical pain. Aspirin, let us remember, is a very recent invention. Until late in the Victorian era, "poppy and mandragora," along with henbane and ethyl alcohol, were the only pain relievers available to civilized man. Toothache, arthritis and neuralgia could, and frequently did, drive men and women to become opium addicts.

De Quincey, for example, first resorted to opium in order to relieve "excruciating rheumatic pains of the head." He swallowed his poppy and, an hour later, "What a resurrection from the lowest depths of the inner spirit! What an apocalypse!" And it was not merely that he felt no more pain. "This negative effect was swallowed up in the immensity of those positive effects which had opened up before me, in the abyss of divine enjoyment thus suddenly revealed. . . . Here was the secret of happiness, about which the philosophers had disputed for so many ages, at once discovered."

"Resurrection, apocalypse, divine enjoyment, happiness. . . ." De Quincey's words lead us to the very heart of our paradoxical mystery. The problem of drug addiction and excessive drinking is not merely a matter of chemistry and psychopathology, of relief from pain and conformity with a bad society. It is also a problem in metaphysics—a problem, one might almost say, in theology. In The Varieties of Religious Experience, William James has touched on these metaphysical aspects of addiction:

> *The sway of alcohol over mankind is unquestionably due to its power to stimulate the mystical faculties in human nature, usually crushed to earth by the cold facts and dry criticisms of the sober hour. Sobriety diminishes, discriminates and says no. Drunkenness expands, unites and says yes. It is in fact the great exciter of the Yes function in man. It brings its votary from the chill periphery of things into the radiant core. It makes him for the moment one with truth. Not through mere perversity do men run after it. To the poor and the unlettered it stands in the place of symphony concerts and literature; and it is part of the deeper mystery and tragedy of life that whiffs and gleams of something that we immediately recognize as excellent should be vouchsafed to so many of us only through the fleeting earlier phases of what, in its totality, is so degrading a poison. The drunken consciousness is one bit of the mystic consciousness, and our total opinion of it must find its place in our opinion of that larger whole.*

William James was not the first to detect a likeness between drunkenness and the mystical and premystical states. On the day of Pentecost there were people who explained the strange behavior of the disciples by saying, "These men are full of new wine."

Peter soon undeceived them: "These are not drunken, as ye suppose, seeing it is but the third hour of the day. But this is that which was spoken by the prophet Joel. And it shall come to pass in the last days, saith God, I will pour out of my Spirit upon all flesh."

And it is not only by "the dry critics of the sober hour" that the state of God-intoxication has been likened to drunkenness. In their efforts to express the inexpressible, the great mystics themselves have done the same. Thus, St. Theresa of Avila tells us that she "regards the centre of our soul as a cellar, into which God admits us as and when it pleases Him, so as to intoxicate us with the delicious wine of His grace."

Every fully developed religion exists simultaneously on several different levels. It exists as a set of abstract concepts about the world and its governance. It exists as a set of rites and sacraments, as a traditional method for manipulating the symbols, by means of which beliefs about the cosmic order are expressed. It exists as the feelings of love, fear and devotion evoked by this manipulation of symbols.

And finally it exists as a special kind of feeling or intuition—a sense of the oneness of all things in their divine principle, a realization (to use the language of Hindu theology) that "thou art That," a mystical experience of what seems self-evidently to be union with God.

The ordinary waking consciousness is a very useful and, on most occasions, an indispensable state of mind; but it is by no means the only form of consciousness, nor in all circumstances the best. Insofar as he transcends his ordinary self and his ordinary mode of awareness, the mystic is able to enlarge his vision, to look more deeply into the unfathomable miracle of existence.

The mystical experience is doubly valuable; it is valuable because it gives the experiencer a better understanding of himself and the world and because it may help him to lead a less self-centered and more creative life.

In hell, a great religious poet has written, the punishment of the lost is to be "their sweating selves, but worse." On earth we are not worse than we are; we are merely our sweating selves, period.

Alas, that is quite bad enough. We love ourselves to the point of idolatry; but we also intensely dislike ourselves—we find ourselves unutterably boring. Correlated with this distaste for the idolatrously worshiped self, there is in all of us a desire, sometimes latent, sometimes conscious and passionately expressed, to escape from the prison of our individuality, an urge to self-transcendence. It is to this urge that we owe mystical theology, spiritual exercises and yoga—to this, too, that we owe alcoholism and drug addiction.

Modern pharmacology has given us a host of new synthetics, but in the field of the naturally occurring mind changers it has made no radical discoveries. All the botanical sedatives, stimulants, vision revealers, happiness promoters and cosmic-consciousness arousers were found out thousands of years ago, before the dawn of history.

In many societies at many levels of civilization attempts have been made to fuse drug intoxication with God intoxication. In ancient Greece, for example, ethyl alcohol had its place in the established religion. Dionysus, or Bacchus, as he was often called, was a true divinity. His worshipers addressed him as *Lusios,* "Liberator," or as *Theoinos,* "Godwine." The latter name telescopes fermented grape juice and the supernatural into a single pentecostal experience. "Born a god," writes Euripides, "Bacchus is poured out as a libation to the gods, and through him men receive good." Unfortunately they also receive harm. The blissful experience of self-transcendence which alcohol makes possible has to be paid for, and the price is exorbitantly high.

Complete prohibition of all chemical mind changers can be decreed, but cannot be enforced, and tends to create more evils than it cures. Even more unsatisfactory has been the policy of complete toleration and unrestricted availability. In England, during the first years of the eighteenth century, cheap untaxed gin—"drunk for a penny, dead drunk for two-pence"—threatened society with complete demoralization. A century later, opium, in the form of laudanum, was reconciling the victims of the Industrial Revolution to their lot—but at an appalling cost in terms of addiction, illness and early death. Today most civilized societies follow a course between the two extremes of total prohibition and total toleration. Certain mind-changing drugs, such as alcohol, are permitted and made available to the public on payment of a very high tax, which tends to restrict their consumption. Other mind changers are unobtainable except under doctors' orders—or illegally from a dope pusher. In this way the problem is kept within manageable bounds. It is most certainly not solved. In their ceaseless search for self-transcendence, millions of would-be mystics become addicts, commit scores of thousands of crimes and are involved in hundreds of thousands of avoidable accidents.

Do we have to go on in this dismal way indefinitely? Up until a few years ago, the answer to such a question would have been a rueful "Yes, we do." Today, thanks to recent developments in biochemistry and pharmacology, we are offered a workable alternative. We see that it may soon be possible for us to do something better in the way of chemical self-transcendence than what we have been doing so ineptly for the last seventy or eighty centuries.

Is it possible for a powerful drug to be completely harmless? Perhaps not. But the physiological cost can certainly be reduced to the point where it becomes negligible. There are powerful mind changers which do their work without damaging the taker's psychophysical organism and without inciting him to behave like a criminal or a lunatic. Biochemistry and pharmacology are just getting into their stride. Within a few years there will probably be dozens of powerful but—physiologically and socially speaking—very inexpensive mind changers on the market.

In view of what we already have in the way of powerful but nearly harmless drugs; in view, above all, of what unquestionably we are very soon going to have—we ought to start immediately to give some serious thought to the problem of the new mind changers. How ought they to be used? How can they be abused? Will human beings be better and happier for their discovery? Or worse and more miserable?

The matter requires to be examined from many points of view. It is simultaneously a question for biochemists and physicians, for psychologists and social anthropologists, for legislators and law-enforcement officers. And finally it is an ethical question and a religious question. Sooner or later—and the sooner, the better—the various specialists concerned will have to meet, discuss and then decide, in the light of the best available evidence and the most imaginative kind of foresight, what should be done. Meanwhile let us take a preliminary look at this many-faceted problem.

Last year American physicians wrote 48,000,000 prescriptions for tranquilizing drugs, many of which have been refilled, probably more than once. The tranquilizers are the best known of the new, nearly harmless mind changers. They can be used by most people, not indeed with complete impunity, but at a reasonably low physiological cost. Their enormous popularity bears witness to the fact that a great many people dislike both their environment and "their sweating selves." Under tranquilizers the degree of their self-transcendence is not very great; but it is enough to make all the difference, in many cases, between misery and contentment.

In theory, tranquilizers should be given only to persons suffering from rather severe forms of neurosis or psychosis. In practice, unfortunately, many physicians have been carried away by the current pharmacological fashion and are prescribing tranquilizers to all and sundry. The history of medical fashions, it may be remarked, is at least as grotesque as the history of fashions in women's hats—at least as grotesque and, since human lives are at stake, considerably more tragic. In the present case, millions of patients who had no real need of the tranquilizers have been given the pills by their doctors and have learned to resort to them in every predicament, however triflingly uncomfortable. This is very bad medicine and, from the pill taker's point of view, dubious morality and poor sense.

There are circumstances in which even the healthy are justified in resorting to the chemical control of negative emotions. If you really can't keep your temper, let a tranquilizer keep it for you. But for healthy people to resort to a chemical mind changer every time they feel annoyed or anxious or tense is neither sensible nor right. Too much tension and anxiety can reduce a man's efficiency—but so can too little. There are many occasions when it is entirely proper for us to feel concerned, when an excess of placidity might reduce our chances of dealing effectively with a ticklish situation. On these occasions, tension mitigated and directed from within by the psychological methods of self-control is preferable from every point of view to complacency imposed from without by the methods of chemical control.

And now let us consider the case—not, alas, a hypothetical case—of two societies competing with each other. In Society A, tranquilizers are available by prescription and at a rather stiff price—which means, in practice, that their use is confined to that rich and influential minority which provides the society with its leadership. This minority of leading citizens consumes several billions of the complacency-producing pills every year. In Society B, on the other hand, the tranquilizers are not so freely available, and the members of the influential minority do not resort, on the slightest provocation, to the chemical control of what may be necessary and productive tension. Which of these two competing societies is likely to win the race? A society whose leaders make an excessive use of soothing syrups is in danger of falling behind a society whose leaders are not over-tranquilized.

Now let us consider another kind of drug—still undiscovered, but probably just around the corner—a drug capable of making people feel happy in situations where they would normally feel miserable. Such a drug would be a blessing, but a blessing fraught with grave political dangers. By making harmless chemical euphoria freely available, a dictator could reconcile an entire population to a state of affairs to which self-respecting human beings ought not to be reconciled. Despots have always found it necessary to supplement force by political or religious propaganda. In this sense the pen is mightier than the sword. But mightier than either the pen or the sword is the pill. In mental hospitals it has been found that chemical restraint is far more effective than strait jackets or psychiatry. The dictatorships of tomorrow will deprive men of their freedom, but will give them in exchange a happiness none the less real, as a subjective experience, for being chemically induced. The pursuit of happiness is one of the traditional rights of man; unfortunately, the achievement of happiness may turn out to be incompatible with another of man's rights—namely, liberty.

It is quite possible, however, that pharmacology will restore with one hand what it takes away with the other. Chemically induced euphoria could easily become a threat to individual liberty; but chemically induced vigor and chemically heightened intelligence could easily be liberty's strongest bulwark. Most of us function at about 15 per cent of capacity. How can we step up our lamentably low efficiency?

Two methods are available—the educational and the biochemical. We can take adults and children as they are and give them a much better training than we are giving them now. Or, by appropriate biochemical methods, we can transform them into superior individuals. If these superior individuals are given a superior education, the results will be revolutionary. They will be startling even if we continue to subject them to the rather poor educational methods at present in vogue.

Will it in fact be possible to produce superior individuals by biochemical means? The Russians certainly believe it. They are now halfway through a Five Year Plan to produce "pharmacological substances that normalize higher nervous activity and heighten human capacity for work." Precursors of these future mind improvers are already being experimented with. It has been found, for example, that when given in massive doses some of the vitamins—nicotinic acid and ascorbic acid are examples—sometimes produce a certain heightening of psychic energy. A combination of two enzymes—ethylene disulphonate and adenosine triphosphate, which, when injected together, improve carbohydrate metabolism in nervous tissue—may also turn out to be effective.

Meanwhile good results are being claimed for various new synthetic, nearly harmless stimulants. There is iproniazid, which, according to some authorities, "appears to increase the total amount of psychic energy." Unfortunately, iproniazid in large doses has side effects which in some cases may be extremely serious! Another psychic energizer is an amino alcohol which is thought to increase the body's production of acetylcholine, a substance of prime importance in the functioning of the nervous system. In view of what has already been achieved, it seems quite possible that, within a few years, we may be able to lift ourselves up by our own biochemical bootstraps.

In the meantime let us all fervently wish the Russians every success in their current pharmacological venture. The discovery of a drug capable of increasing the average individual's psychic energy, and its wide distribution throughout the U.S.S.R., would probably mean the end of Russia's present form of government. Generalized intelligence and mental alertness are the most powerful enemies of dictatorship and at the same time the basic conditions of effective democracy. Even in the democratic West we could do with a bit of psychic energizing. Between them, education and pharmacology may do something to offset the effects of that deterioration of our biological material to which geneticists have frequently called attention.

From these political and ethical considerations let us now pass to the strictly religious problems that will be posed by some of the new mind changers. We can foresee the nature of these future problems by studying the effects of a natural mind changer, which has been used for centuries past in religious worship; I refer to the peyote cactus of Northern Mexico and the Southwestern United States. Peyote contains mescaline—which can now be produced synthetically—and mescaline, in William James' phrase, "stimulates the mystical faculties in human nature" far more powerfully and in a far more enlightening way than alcohol and, what is more, it does so at a physiological and social cost that is negligibly low. Peyote produces self-transcendence in two ways—it introduces the taker into the Other World of visionary experience, and it gives him a sense of solidarity with his fellow worshipers, with human beings at large and with the divine nature of things.

The effects of peyote can be duplicated by synthetic mescaline and by LSD (lysergic acid diethylamide), a derivative of ergot. Effective in incredibly small doses, LSD is now being used experimentally by psychotherapists in Europe, in South America, in Canada and the United States. It lowers the barrier between conscious and subconscious and permits the patient to look more deeply and understandingly into the recesses of his own mind. The deepening of self-knowledge takes place against a background of visionary and even mystical experience.

When administered in the right kind of psychological environment, these chemical mind changers make possible a genuine religious experience. Thus a person who takes LSD or mescaline may suddenly understand—not only intellectually but organically, experientially—the meaning of such tremendous religious affirmations as "God is love," or "Though He slay me, yet will I trust in Him."

It goes without saying that this kind of temporary self-transcendence is no guarantee of permanent enlightenment or a lasting improvement of conduct. It is a "gratuitous grace," which is neither necessary nor sufficient for salvation, but which if properly used, can be enormously helpful to those who have received it. And this is true of all such experiences, whether occurring spontaneously, or as the result of swallowing the right kind of chemical mind changer, or after undertaking a course of "spiritual exercises" or bodily mortification.

Those who are offended by the idea that the swallowing of a pill may contribute to a genuinely religious experience should remember that all the standard mortifications—fasting, voluntary sleeplessness and self-torture—inflicted upon themselves by the ascetics of every religion for the purpose of acquiring merit, are also, like the mind-changing drugs, powerful devices for altering the chemistry of the body in general and the nervous system in particular. Or consider the procedures generally known as spiritual exercises. The breathing techniques taught by the yogi of India result in prolonged suspensions of respiration. These in turn result in an increased concentration of carbon dioxide in the blood; and the psychological consequence of this is a change in the quality of consciousness. Again, meditations involving long, intense concentration upon a single idea or image may also result—for neurological reasons which I do not profess to understand—in a slowing down of respiration and even in prolonged suspensions of breathing. Many ascetics and mystics have practiced their chemistry-changing mortifications and spiritual exercises while living, for longer or shorter periods, as hermits. Now, the life of a hermit, such as Saint Anthony, is a life in which there are very few external stimuli. But as Hebb, John Lilly and other experimental psychologists have recently shown in the laboratory, a person in a limited environment, which provides very few external stimuli, soon undergoes a change in the quality of his consciousness and may transcend his normal self to the point of hearing voices or seeing visions, often extremely unpleasant, like so many of Saint Anthony's visions, but sometimes beatific.

That men and women can, by physical and chemical means, transcend themselves in a genuinely spiritual way is something which, to the squeamish idealist, seems rather shocking. But, after all, the drug or the physical exercise is not the cause of the spiritual experience; it is only its occasion.

Writing of William James' experiments with nitrous oxide, Bergson has summed up the whole matter in a few lucid sentences. "The psychic disposition was there, potentially, only waiting a signal to express itself in action. It might have been evoked spiritually by an effort made on its own spiritual level. But it could just as well be brought about materially, by an inhibition of what inhibited it, by the removing of an obstacle; and this effect was the wholly negative one produced by the drug." Where, for any reason, physical or moral, the psychological dispositions are unsatisfactory, the removal of obstacles by a drug or by ascetic practices will result in a negative rather than a positive spiritual experience. Such an infernal experience is extremely distressing, but may also be extremely salutary. There are plenty of people to whom a few hours in hell—the hell that they themselves have done so much to create—could do a world of good.

Physiologically costless, or nearly costless, stimulators of the mystical faculties are now making their appearance, and many kinds of them will soon be on the market. We can be quite sure that, as and when they become available, they will be extensively used. The urge to self-transcendence is so strong and so general that it cannot be otherwise. In the past, very few people have had spontaneous experiences of a premystical or fully mystical nature; still fewer have been willing to undergo the psychophysical disciplines which prepare an insulated individual for this kind of self-transcendence. The powerful but nearly costless mind changers of the future will change all this completely. Instead of being rare, premystical and mystical experiences will become common. What was once the spiritual privilege of the few will be made available to the many. For the ministers of the world's organized religions, this will raise a number of unprecedented problems. For most people, religion has always been a matter of traditional symbols and of their own emotional, intellectual and ethical response to those symbols. To men and women who have had direct experience of self-transcendence into the mind's Other World of vision and union with the nature of things, a religion of mere symbols is not likely to be very satisfying. The perusal of a page from even the most beautifully written cookbook is no substitute for the eating of dinner. We are exhorted to "*taste* and see that the Lord is good."

In one way or another, the world's ecclesiastical authorities will have to come to terms with the new mind changers. They may come to terms with them negatively, by refusing to have anything to do with them. In that case, a psychological phenomenon, potentially of great spiritual value, will manifest itself outside the pale of organized religion. On the other hand, they may choose to come to terms with the mind changers in some positive way—exactly how, I am not prepared to guess.

My own belief is that, though they may start by being something of an embarrassment, these new mind changers will tend in the long run to deepen the spiritual life of the communities in which they are available. That famous "revival of religion," about which so many people have been talking for so long, will not come about as the result of evangelistic mass meetings or the television appearances of photogenic clergymen. It will come about as the result of biochemical discoveries that will make it possible for large numbers of men and women to achieve a radical self-transcendence and a deeper understanding of the nature of things. And this revival of religion will be at the same time a revolution. From being an activity mainly concerned with symbols, religion will be transformed into an activity concerned mainly with experience and intuition—an everyday mysticism underlying and giving significance to everyday rationality, everyday tasks and duties, everyday human relationships.

Further reading:

Huxley, Aldous: THE DOORS OF PERCEPTION. New York: Harper and Brothers; 1954.

——: HEAVEN AND HELL. New York: Harper and Brothers; 1956.

James, William: THE VARIETIES OF RELIGIOUS EXPERIENCE. New York: Modern Library.

——: THE WILL TO BELIEVE AND HUMAN IMMORTALITY. New York: Dover Publications.

Rolin, Jean: POLICE DRUGS. New York: Philosophical Library; 1952.

de Ropp, Robert E.: DRUGS AND THE MIND. New York: St. Martin's Press; 1957.

Slotkin, J. S.: THE PEYOTE RELIGION. Chicago: The Free Press of Glencoe, Illinois; 1956.

The Decline of
Heroes

BY

ARTHUR M. SCHLESINGER, JR.

For The Crisis of the Old Order, *the first volume in his continuing study of the Rooseveltian era, Arthur M. Schlesinger, Jr., won the Society of American Historians' Francis Parkman Prize. His* The Age of Jackson, *published in 1945, won the Pulitzer Prize. Like his father, who has written fifteen important social and historical studies, Arthur Schlesinger, Jr., is professor of history at Harvard University. He is married and has four children.*

O urs is an age without heroes—and, when we say this, we suddenly realize how spectacularly the world has changed in a generation. Most of us grew up in a time of towering personalities. For better or for worse, great men seemed to dominate our lives and shape our destiny. In the United States we had Theodore Roosevelt, Woodrow Wilson, Franklin Roosevelt. In Great Britain, there were Lloyd George and Winston Churchill. In other lands, there were Lenin, Stalin, Hitler, Mussolini, Clemenceau, Gandhi, Kemal, Sun Yat-sen. Outside of politics there were Einstein, Freud, Keynes. Some of these great men influenced the world for good, others for evil; but, whether for good or for evil, the fact that each had not died at birth made a difference, one believed, to everyone who lived after them.

Today no one bestrides our narrow world like a colossus; we have no giants who play roles which one can imagine no one else playing in their stead. There are a few figures on the margin of uniqueness, perhaps: Adenauer, Nehru, Tito, De Gaulle, Chiang Kai-shek, Mao Tse-tung. But there seem to be none in the epic style of those mighty figures of our recent past who seized history with both hands and gave it an imprint, even a direction, which it otherwise might not have had. As De Gaulle himself remarked on hearing of Stalin's death, "The age of giants is over." Whatever one thought, whether one admired or detested Roosevelt or Churchill, Stalin or Hitler, one nevertheless felt the sheer weight of such personalities on one's own existence. We feel no comparable pressures today. Our own President, with all his pleasant qualities, has more or less explicitly renounced any desire to impress his own views on history. The Macmillans, Khrushchevs and Gronchis have measurably less specific gravity than their predecessors. Other men could be in their places as leaders of America or Britain or Russia or Italy without any change in the course of history. Why ours should thus be an age without heroes, and whether this condition is good or bad for us and for civilization, are topics worthy of investigation.

Why have giants vanished from our midst? One must never neglect the role of accident in history; and accident no doubt plays a part here. But too many accidents of the same sort cease to be wholly accidental. One must inquire further. Why should our age not only be without great men but even seem actively hostile to them? Surely one reason we have so few heroes now is precisely that we had so many a generation ago. Greatness is hard for common humanity to bear. As Emerson said, "Heroism means difficulty, postponement of praise, postponement of ease, introduction of the world into the private apartment, introduction of eternity into the hours measured by the sitting-room clock." A world of heroes keeps people from living their own private lives.

Moreover, great men live dangerously. They introduce extremes into existence—extremes of good, extremes of evil—and ordinary men after a time flinch from the ultimates and yearn for undemanding security. The Second World War was the climax of an epoch of living dangerously. It is no surprise that it precipitated a universal revulsion against greatness. The war itself destroyed Hitler and Mussolini. And the architects of victory were hardly longer-lived. After the war, the British repudiated Churchill, and the Americans (with the adoption of the 22nd Amendment), Roosevelt. In due course, the French repudiated De Gaulle (they later repented, but it took the threat of civil war to bring him back); the Chinese, Chiang Kai-shek; and the Russians, Stalin. Khrushchev, in toppling Stalin from his pedestal, pronounced the general verdict against the uncommon man: the modern world, he said, had no use for the "cult of the individual." And, indeed, carried to the excesses to which the worshipers of Hitler and Stalin carried it, even to the much milder degree to which admirers of Roosevelt and Churchill sometimes carried it, the cult of the individual was dangerous. No man is infallible, and every man needs to be reminded of this on occasion. Still, our age has gone further than this—it objects not just to hero worship but to heroes. The century of the common man has come into its own.

This term, "common man," suggests the deeper problem. There is more involved than simply a dismissal of those colossi whom the world identified with a season of blood and agony. The common man has always regarded the great man with mixed feelings—resentment as well as admiration, hatred as well as love. The Athenian who refused to vote for Aristides because he was so tired of hearing him called "the Just" expressed a natural reaction. Great men make small men aware of their smallness. Rancor is one of the unavowed but potent emotions of politics; and one must never forget that the envy of the havenots can be quite as consuming when the haves have character or intelligence as it is when they have merely material possessions.

Modern democracy inadvertently gave envy new scope. While the purpose of democracy was to give everyone a fair chance to rise, its method enabled rancorous men to invoke "equality" as an excuse for keeping all down to their own level. "I attribute the small number of distinguished men in political life," wrote Alexis de Tocqueville after visiting the United States in the 1830's, "to the ever-increasing despotism of the majority. . . . The power of the majority is so absolute and irresistible that one must give up one's rights as a citizen and almost abjure one's qualities as a human being, if one intends to stray from the track which it prescribes." James Bryce even titled a chapter in his American Commonwealth, Why Great Men Are Not Chosen President.

History has shown these prophets unduly pessimistic. Distinguished men do enter American politics; great men have been chosen President. Democracy demonstrates a capability for heroic leadership quite as much as it does a tendency toward mediocrity. Yet Tocqueville and the others were correct enough in detecting the dislike of great men as a permanent potentiality in a democracy. And the evolution of industrial society appears to have given this sentiment new force. More and more of us live and work within great organizations; an influential book has already singled out the organization man as the American of the future. The bureaucratization of American life, the decline of the working class, the growth of the white-collar class, the rise of suburbia—all this has meant the increasing homogeneity of American society. Though we continue to speak of ourselves as rugged individualists, our actual life has grown more and more collective and anonymous. As a Monsanto Chemical film put it, showing a group of technicians at work in a laboratory: "No geniuses here; just a bunch of average Americans working together." Our ideal is increasingly smooth absorption into the group rather than self-realization in the old-fashioned, strong-minded, don't-give-a-damn sense. Where does the great man fit into our homogenized society?

"The greatness of England is now all collective," John Stuart Mill wrote a century ago: "individually small, we only appear capable of anything great by our habit of combining." He might have been writing about contemporary America; but where we Americans are inclined to rejoice over the superiority of the "team," Mill added somberly, "It was men of another stamp than this that made England what it has been; and men of another stamp will be needed to prevent its decline."

But was Mill right? Do individuals really have impact on history? A powerful school of philosophers has denied any importance at all to great men. Such thinkers reject heroes as a childish hangover from the days when men ascribed everything to the action of gods. History, they assert, is not made by men, but by inexorable forces or irrevocable laws: if these forces or laws do not manifest themselves through one individual, they will do so through another. What has happened already has comprehensively and absolutely decided what will happen in the future. "If there is a single human action due to free will," wrote Tolstoi, "no historical law exists, and no conception of historical events can be formed." If all this is so, obviously the presence or absence of any particular "hero" at any particular time cannot make the slightest difference.

This view of history is a form of fatalistic determinism; and Tolstoi's War and Peace offers one of its most eloquent statements. Why, Tolstoi asked, did millions of men in the time of Napoleon, repudiating their common sense and their human feelings, move from west to east, slaughtering their fellows? The answers provided by historians seemed to him hopelessly superficial. His own answer was: "The war was bound to happen simply because it was bound to happen"; all previous history predetermined it. Where did this leave the great men? In Tolstoi's view, they were the most deluded figures of all. Great men, he said, "are but the labels that serve to give a name to an event and, like labels, they have the least possible connection with the event itself." The greater the man, "the more conspicuous is the inevitability and predestination of every act he commits." The hero, said Tolstoi, "is the slave of history."

There are many forms of historical fatalism. Toynbee and Spengler, with their theory of the inexorable growth and decay of civilizations, represent one form. The Marxists, with their theory that changes in the modes of production control the course of history, represent another. When Khrushchev denounced the practice of making "a hero" out of "a particular leader" and condemned the cult of the individual as "alien to the spirit of Marxism-Leninism," he was speaking the true spirit of his faith. And Marxism is not the only form of economic determinism; there are also, for example, economic determinists of the laissez-faire school who believe that all civilization is dependent on rigid adherence to a certain theory of the sacredness of private property.

Fatalists differ greatly among themselves. But, however much they differ, they unite in the conclusion that the individual plays no role of his own in history. If they are right, then nothing could matter less whether or not this is an age without heroes.

But they are not right. The philosophy of historical fatalism rests on serious fallacies. For one thing, it supposes that, because a thing happens, it had to happen. But causation is one matter; predestination another. The construction of a causal explanation after an event merely renders that event in some sense intelligible. It does not in the least show that this particular event, and no other, had to take place; that nothing else could possibly have occurred in its stead. The serious test of the fatalist case must be applied before the event. The only conclusive proof of fatalism would lie in the accurate prediction of events that have not yet happened. And to say, with Tolstoi, that all prior history predetermines everything that follows is to say nothing at all. It is to produce an explanation which applies equally to everything—and thus becomes so vague and limitless as to explain nothing.

Fatalism raises other difficulties. Thus it imputes reality to mystical historical "forces"—class, race, nation, the will of the people, the spirit of the times, history itself. But there are no such forces. They are merely abstractions or metaphors with no existence except in the mind of the beholder. The only evidence for them is deduction from the behavior of individuals. It is therefore the individual who constitutes the basic unit of history. And, while no individual can be wholly free—and, indeed, recent discoveries of the manifold ways in which we are unconsciously conditioned should constitute a salutary check on human vanity—one must assume the reality of an area of free choice until that assumption is challenged, not by metaphysical affirmation, but by verifiable proof—that is, consistently accurate prediction of the future.

Fatalism, moreover, is incompatible with human psychology and human morality. Anyone who rigorously accepted a deterministic view of life, for example, would have to abandon all notions of human responsibility, since it is manifestly unfair to praise or punish people for acts which are by definition beyond their control. But such fatalism is belied by the assumption of free choice which underlies every move we make, every word we utter, every thought we think. As Sir Isaiah Berlin observes of determinism, "If we begin to take it seriously, then, indeed, the changes in our language, our moral notions, our attitudes toward one another, our views of history, of society and of everything else will be too profound to be even adumbrated." We can no more imagine what the universe of the consistent determinist would be like than we can imagine what it would be like to live in a world without time or one with seventeen-dimensional space.

For the historian concerned with concrete interpretation of actual events, he can easily demonstrate the futility of fatalism by trying to apply it to specific historical episodes. According to the extreme determinist view, no particular individual can make the slightest difference. As slaves of history, all individuals are, so to speak, interchangeable parts. If Napoleon had not led his armies across Europe, Tolstoi implies, someone else would have. William James, combating this philosophic fatalism, once asked the determinists whether they really believed "the convergence of sociological pressures to have so impinged on Stratford on Avon about April 23, 1564, that a W. Shakespeare, with all his mental peculiarities, had to be born there." And did they further believe, James continued, that "if the aforesaid W. Shakespeare had died of cholera infantum, another mother at Stratford on Avon would needs have engendered a duplicate copy of him to restore the sociologic equilibrium?" Who could believe such stuff? Yet, if the determinists do not mean exactly this, how can they read the individual out of history?

In December, 1931, a British politician, crossing Fifth Avenue in New York between 76th and 77th streets around ten-thirty at night, was knocked down and gravely injured by an automobile. Fourteen months later an American politician, sitting in an open car in Miami, Florida, was fired on by an assassin; a man standing beside him was killed. Would the next two decades of history have been the same had Contasini's car killed Winston Churchill in 1931 and Zangara's bullets killed Franklin Roosevelt in 1933? Suppose, in addition, that Adolf Hitler had been killed in the street fighting during the Munich *Putsch* of 1923, and that Lenin and Mussolini had died at birth. Where would our century be now?

Individuals, of course, must operate within limits. They cannot do everything. They cannot, for example, propel history into directions for which the environment and the human material are not prepared: no genius, however heroic, could have brought television to ancient Troy. Yet, as Sidney Hook has convincingly argued in his thoughtful book, The Hero in History, great men can count decisively "where the historical situation permits of major alternative paths of development."

This argument between fatalism and heroism is not one on which there is a lot to be said on both sides. The issue is far too sharp to be straddled. Either history is rigidly determined and foreordained, in which case individual striving does not matter; or it is not, in which case there is an essential role for the hero. Analysis of concrete episodes suggests that history is, within limits, open and unfinished; that men have lived who did what no substitute could ever have done; that their intervention set history on one path rather than another. If this is so, the old maxim, "There are no indispensable men," would seem another amiable fallacy. There is, then, a case for heroes.

To say that there is a case for heroes is not to say that there is a case for hero worship. The surrender of decision, the unquestioning submission to leadership, the prostration of the average man before the Great Man—these are the diseases of heroism, and they are fatal to human dignity. But, if carried too far, hero worship generates its own antidote. "Every hero," said Emerson, "becomes a bore at last." And we need not go too far.

History amply shows that it is possible to have heroes without turning them into gods.

And history shows, too, that, when a society, in flight from hero worship, decides to do without great men at all, it gets into troubles of its own. Our contemporary American society, for example, has little use for the individualist. Individualism implies dissent from the group; dissent implies conflict; and conflict suddenly seems divisive, un-American and generally unbearable. Our greatest new industry is evidently the production of techniques to eliminate conflict, from positive thoughts through public relations to psychoanalysis, applied everywhere from the couch to the pulpit. Our national aspiration has become peace of mind, peace of soul. The symptomatic drug of our age is the tranquilizer. "Togetherness" is the banner under which we march into the brave new world.

Obviously society has had to evolve collective institutions to cope with problems that have grown increasingly complex and concentrated. But the collective approach can be overdone. If Khrushchev worried because his collectivist society developed a cult of the individual, maybe we Americans should start worrying as our so-called individualist society develops a cult of the group. We instinctively suppose that the tough questions will be solved by an interfaith conference or an interdisciplinary research team or an interdepartmental committee or an assembly of wise men meeting at Arden House. But are not these group tactics essentially means by which individuals hedge their bets and distribute their responsibilities? And do they not nearly always result in the dilution of insight and the triumph of mishmash? If we are to survive, we must have ideas, vision, courage. These things are rarely produced by committees. Everything that matters in our intellectual and moral life begins with an individual confronting his own mind and conscience in a room by himself.

A bland society will never be creative. "The amount of eccentricity in a society," said John Stuart Mill, "has generally been proportional to the amount of genius, mental vigor and moral courage it contained. That so few now dare to be eccentric marks the chief danger of the time." If this condition frightened Mill in Victorian England, it should frighten us much more. For our national apotheosis of the group means that we systematically lop off the eccentrics, the originals, the proud, imaginative, lonely people from whom new ideas come. What began as a recoil from hero worship ends as a conspiracy against creativity. If worship of great men brings us to perdition by one path, flight from great men brings us there just as surely by another. When we do not admire great men, then our instinct for admiration is likely to end by settling on ourselves. The one thing worse for democracy than hero worship is self-worship.

A free society cannot get along without heroes, because they are the most vivid means of exhibiting the power of free men. The hero exposes to all mankind unsuspected possibilities of conception, unimagined resources of strength. "The appearance of a great man," wrote Emerson, "draws a new circle outside of our largest orbit and surprises and commands us." Carlyle likened ordinary, lethargic times, with their unbelief and perplexity, to dry, dead fuel, waiting for the lightning out of heaven to kindle it. "The great man, with his free force direct out of God's own hand, is the lightning. . . . The rest of men waited for him like fuel, and then they too would flame."

Great men enable us to rise to our own highest potentialities. They nerve lesser men to disregard the world and trust to their own deepest instinct. "In picking out from history our heroes," said William James, "each one of us may best fortify and inspire what creative energy may lie in his own soul. This is the last justification of hero worship." Which one of us has not gained fortitude and faith from the incarnation of ideals in men, from the wisdom of Socrates, from the wondrous creativity of Shakespeare, from the strength of Washington, from the compassion of Lincoln, and above all, perhaps, from the life and the death of Jesus? "We feed on genius," said Emerson. "Great men exist that there may be greater men."

Yet this may be only the smaller part of their service. Great men have another and larger role—to affirm human freedom against the supposed inevitabilities of history. The first hero was Prometheus, who defied the gods and thus asserted the independence and autonomy of man against all determinism. Zeus punished Prometheus, chaining him to a rock and encouraging a vulture to pluck at his vitals.

Ever since, man, like Prometheus, has warred against history. It has always been a bitter and remorseless fight; for the heavy weight of human inertia lies with fatalism. It takes a man of exceptional vision and strength and will—it takes, in short, a hero—to try to wrench history from what lesser men consider its preconceived path. And often history tortures the hero in the process, chains him to a rock and exposes him to the vulture. Yet, in the model of Prometheus, man can still hold his own against the gods. Brave men earn the right to shape their own destiny.

An age without great men is one which acquiesces in the drift of history. Such acquiescence is easy and seductive; the great appeal of fatalism, indeed, is as a refuge from the terror of responsibility. Where a belief in great men insistently reminds us that individuals can make a difference, fatalism reassures us that they can't. It thereby blesses our weakness and extenuates our failure. Fatalism, in Berlin's phrase, is "one of the great alibis" of history.

Let us not be complacent about our supposed capacity to get along without great men. If our society has lost its wish for heroes and its ability to produce them, it may well turn out to have lost everything else as well.

Further reading:

Berlin, Sir Isaiah: THE HEDGEHOG AND THE FOX. New York: Simon and Schuster; 1953.

——: HISTORICAL INEVITABILITY. New York: Oxford University Press; 1954.

Carlyle, Thomas: SARTOR RESARTUS AND HEROES AND HERO-WORSHIP. Everyman Library. New York: E. P. Dutton and Company.

Emerson, Ralph Waldo: ENGLISH TRAITS, AND REPRESENTATIVE MEN. Everyman Library. New York: E. P. Dutton and Company.

Hook, Sydney: THE HERO IN HISTORY. New York: Humanities Press; 1950.

James, William: THE WILL TO BELIEVE AND HUMAN IMMORTALITY. New York: Dover Publications; 1956.

Mill, John Stuart: ON LIBERTY. Chicago: Henry Regnery Company.

The Poet's Vision

BY
EDITH SITWELL

*Dame Edith Sitwell, English poet, critic, social noncon-
formist, and literary controversialist, is the sister of Osbert
and Sacheverell Sitwell, and with them has formed an
iconoclastic triumvirate which has roiled the cultural waters of England and America for the past four decades.
A prolific poet with a highly individual style, Dame Edith
has written verse ranging from the eccentric to passages
of great power and perception; as a critic she is a widely
acknowledged defender of the poetical faith. A colorful
and astringent personality at seventy-one, Dame Edith
lives in Yorkshire, at Renishaw Park, which has been a
Sitwell family estate for more than six hundred years.*

A great deal of nonsense is being written in England at this
time, declaring that modern poets and the reading public
are out of touch with each other, and take no interest in each
other. It is being written mainly by bad poets who, not having
received the acclaim for which they had hoped, turn critics on
the chance of abolishing the work of their more successful
brethren.

But it is an indisputable fact that the public enjoys poetry
unless it is lethally boring, or unless they are frightened out of
doing so by bad critics. As for the poet taking no interest in his

fellow human beings, the poet is not the coldly bored observer, or the enemy of, the sneerer at, his readers. He is a brother speaking to a brother of "a moment of their other lives"—a moment that had been buried beneath the dust of the busy world. The poet supports his brothers' flagging footsteps, telling them, as Shakespeare's Antony said to Cleopatra before darkness fell, "Come on, my queen; there's sap in't yet." Sap in the event, sap in the heart of man.

All great poetry is dipped in the dyes of the heart, and is, in Emerson's phrase, "a larger imbibing of the common heart."

The poet is the complete lover of mankind. "Now he has passed that way," wrote Walt Whitman, "see after him! There is not left any vestige of despair or misanthropy or cunning or exclusiveness, or the ignominy of a nativity or colour or delusion of hell or the necessity of hell; and no man thenceforth shall be degraded for ignorance or weakness or sin."

To Shakespeare, only that which was too cold for hell is to be condemned. Only the hard heart offends. He sees the fundamental splendour of all living beings.

So, too, the artist. "The line in Michelangelo," said the painter Henry Fuseli, "is uniformly grand . . . the child, the female, meanness, deformity, were indiscriminately stamped with grandeur. A beggar rose from his hand the patriarch of poverty, the hump of his dwarf is impressed with dignity; his women are moulds of generation, his infants teem with the man, his men are a race of giants."

The love that is in the soul of the poet stamps mankind indiscriminately, also, with grandeur. "Little children, love one another." This is the poet's message to his brothers. To him, every day is holy.

Again, it is a part of the poet's lifework to find the rays of the universe that connect vision and reality. "Genius," said Emerson, "is the naturalist or geographer of the supersensible regions, and draws their map, acquainting them with new fields of activity."

"The first sensation an infant gets," wrote William James, "is for him the universe . . . the infant encounters an object in which all the categories of the intellect are contained.". . . The first time we see light, we *are* it, rather than *see* it. But all our later optical knowledge is about what the experience gives."

The great artist in each of the arts retains *spiritually* (even if he is physically blind as Milton, physically deaf as Beethoven) the child's wondering vision of the glories of the world. His vision, his hearing, are closer to the quintessence of reality than any other vision or hearing. Like Moses, he sees God in the burning bush when the half-opened or myopic physical eye sees only the gardener's diurnal task—the burning of leaves on a garden path.

As Blake wrote in his Vision of the Last Judgment: " 'What,' it will be Question'd, 'When the Sun rises, do you not see a round disk of fire somewhat like a guinea?' 'O no, no, I see an Innumerable company of the Heavenly host crying, "Holy, Holy, Holy, is the Lord God Almighty!" I Question not my Corporeal or Vegetative Eye any more than I would Question a Window concerning a Sight. I look thro' it, and not with it.' "

It is a part of the poet's work to give each man his own view of the world—show him what he sees but does not know that he sees. The poet, like the painter, harmonizes what seems to the "Vegetative Eye" irreconcilable aspects of the world, into a great design, a great balance. He shows the quintessence of the thing seen. His imagination is not a pretty fancy, but is the quintessence of reality. In Carl Jung's words, "Imagination is a concentrated extract of all the forces of life."

Of course, from time to time, difficulties arise between the poet and his readers. These may derive from various causes. Sometimes the difficulty may be the result of the poet's inspiration's not having completely found its way out of the unconscious in which all poetry is conceived.

But everything which opens out to us a new world is bound to appear strange at first. We must not confuse the obscurity which arises from great complexity, from multitudinous forces of life, and that which arises from emptiness. Of course, poems must be clarified as far as possible. Yet even when they appear, at first, strange, they may, in the end, warm us with their beauty. "The unimaginable remoteness and energy of the Dog Star, Sirius, with its amazing attendant sun, are of the liveliest interest to the intellect," wrote Walter de la Mare; and even before we understand it completely, "its beauty and its splendour are a comfort and an exaltation to every solitary winter heart."

It must be remembered, also, when we find difficulties because of the complexity of a poem, that sometimes a phrase may bear two meanings. What did Shakespeare mean when he wrote, "Men have died . . . and worms have eaten them, but not for love"? Did he mean that men have died, but not for love? Or that worms have eaten them, but not out of love? Perhaps he meant both. The poet needs the collaboration of his audience. The reader must not sit back and expect the poet to do all the work. To read poetry with enjoyment entails the use of all the reader's powers of concentration, sensibility and sympathy. A poem may sometimes appear difficult simply because the reader has determined that it *shall* be difficult.

If it is said that certain of the images in modern poems are strange, this may be the result of condensation or because where the sense of one language does not contain the full meaning, the full sensation, the poet sometimes uses the language of another sense. The senses of poets are like those of primitive peoples, at once acute and uncovered.

William James, in Principles of Psychology, wrote, "Bleuler and Lehmann, some years ago, called attention to a strange idiosyncrasy found in certain persons, and consisting in the fact that impressions on the eye, skin, etc., were accompanied by distinct sensations of sound. Coloured hearing is the name sometimes given to the phenomenon, which has been frequently described. . . . The Viennese aurist Urbantschitsch has proved that these cases are only extreme cases of a very general law, and that all our sense-organs influence each other's sensations. The hue of patches of colour so distant as not to be recognised was immediately, in Urbantschitsch's patients, perceived when a tuning-fork was sounded close to the ear. Sometimes, on the contrary, the field was darkened by the sound. The acuity of vision was increased, so that letters, too far to be read, could be read when the tuning-fork was heard. Urbantschitsch, varying experiments, found that their results were mutual, and that sounds which were on the limits of audibility, became audible when lights of various colours were exhibited to the eye. Smell, taste, touch, sense, and temperature, etc., were all found to fluctuate when lights were seen and sounds were heard."

The use of this sense transfusion in poetry is scarcely new. Dante, in Canto 5 of The Inferno, has the line *Io venni in luogo d'ogni luce muto* (I came into a place of all light dumb).

Lafcadio Hearn, in a letter to a fellow author, said, "When you wrote of the deep bass of that green I could see, feel, smell, taste, and chew the leaf; it was rather bitter in taste, and dense, and faintly odorous. . . ."

When I myself was young, certain lines of mine were received by a mingled shower of bouquets and brickbats—with a strong preponderance of brickbats. One was the line "The morning light creaks down again." But is that really so strange?

"I do not remember," wrote Samuel Hearne, in his Journey from Hudson's Bay to the Northern Ocean, "to have met with any travellers into high northern altitudes, who remarked their having heard the Northern Lights make any noise in the air as they vary their colours or position; which may probably be owing to the want of perfect silence at the time they made their observations on these meteours. I can positively affirm that on still nights I have heard them make a rustling and crackling noise, like the waving of a large flag in a fresh gale of wind."

The reason why I said "the morning light creaks" is this: After rain, the early light seems as if it does not run quite smoothly. Also, it has a quality of great hardness and seems to present a physical obstacle to the shadows—and this gives me the impression of a creaking sound because it is at once hard and uncertain.

An initial feeling of strangeness in poetry may, also, be due to our attempts to pierce down to the essence of the thing seen, producing or heightening the significance by discovering in it attributes which at first sight appear alien, but which are acutely related, by producing its quintessential colour (sharper, brighter, than that seen by an eye grown stale), and by stripping it of all unessential details.

A beautiful early example of this acute and piercing visual apprehension, this concentration into essence by the means of which I have been speaking, may be found in those lovely lines from Gerard Manley Hopkins' The May Magnificat:

> *Star-eyed strawberry-breasted*
> *Throstle above her nested*
> *Cluster of bugle-blue eggs thin.*

In this sharply seen image, Hopkins says "strawberry-breasted" because of the freckles on the thrush's breast. In the enhanced and deepened colour of the bugle-blue eggs (bugle being a country name for the wild flower, bugloss), the sharp U of "bugle" melting into the softer U of "blue" gives the reflection of one in the other, the sisterhood of the deep blue heavens, the flower and the egg, their colours changing and shifting in the clear light.

In a notebook I published some years ago, I have a quotation about a painter who, painting a tree, *became* a tree. This condensation of essence, this power of becoming a tree, helped to make Dylan Thomas a great poet. It also made his poems appear strange at first sight. But if you heard a tree speak in its own voice, would not that voice seem strange?

All poems should be inherent in, rooted in, the language. That does not mean that they cannot be translated into another language by a great translator. But they cannot be translated into other words in the original language. If the poet had not chosen the exact words he needed for his meaning, he would have been no poet.

Dylan Thomas's poems are rooted in the language. But one can, at least, speak of the themes. Take that great poem, A Refusal to Mourn the Death, by Fire, of a Child in London.

> *Never until the mankind-making*
> *Bird beast and flower*
> *Fathering and all humbling darkness*
> *Tells with silence the last light breaking*
> *And the still hour*
> *Is come of the sea tumbling in harness*

And I must enter again the round
Zion of the water bead
And the synagogue of the ear of corn
Shall I let pray the shadow of a sound
Or sow my salt seed
In the least valley of sackcloth to mourn

The majesty and burning of the child's death.
I shall not murder
The mankind of her going with a grave truth
Nor blaspheme down the stations of the breath
With any further
Elegy of innocence and youth.

Deep with the first dead lies London's daughter,
Robed in the long friends,
The grains beyond age, the dark veins of her mother,
Secret by the unmourning water
Of the riding Thames.
After the first death, there is no other.

In this poem, with its dark, magnificent movement, we see Death in its reality, as a return to the beginning of things, as a robing, a sacred investiture in those who have been our friends since the beginning of time.

In the first lines the poet is saying that the nature of bird, beast, and flower went to the making of man, and like mankind, these spring from, and must return to, the "fathering and all humbling darkness," that is, the loving and healing darkness in which all are equal.

The line, "Tells with silence the last light breaking," means that the noisy day, the toil, are over.

"And the still hour Is come of the sea tumbling in harness": These lines speak, I think, of the wandering, questing spirit that was harnessed by the body, finding peace. But I am puzzled by the use of the word "of." Perhaps this means that the final quiet is always within us.

The poem is an affirmation of faith in that ultimate safety

with our first friends. Never, therefore, until the world ends for the poet, as for the child, and he must ". . . enter again the round Zion of the water bead And the synagogue of the ear of corn" will he darken the grandeur of the child's going with his tears ("my salt seed")—tears that are yet a begetting. The "water bead" is holy, the "ear of corn" a place of prayer, the "stations of the breath" are the Stations of the Cross.

W. H. Auden is a very complex poet, but should, I think, present no difficulties to the reader.

He is the Way.
Follow Him through the Land of Unlikeness;
You will see rare beasts, and have unique adventures.

He is the Truth.
Seek Him in the Kingdom of Anxiety;
You will come to a great city that has expected your return
    for years.

He is the Life.
Love Him in the World of the Flesh;
And at your marriage all its occasions shall dance for joy.
                    [Chorus from For The Time Being]

We might summarise the central core of Auden's work as the humanising of the holy, "a genial radiation," as Emerson said of Plato . . . "skilful to discriminate power from form, essence from accident, and opening, by its terminology, and definition, high roads into nature."

When I and my contemporaries began to write, a change in the direction, imagery, and rhythms in poetry had become necessary, owing to the rhythmical flaccidity, the verbal deadness, the dead and expected patterns of some of the poetry immediately preceding us.

The history of the changes in poetry is unvarying. After one school of great poets has died, there is a host of bad, little, incompetent, or else lifelessly competent imitators. Meanwhile, the great new poets arise, and as it is necessary for poetry to cast its dead skin, like a snake casting its slough, they produce something which appears an innovation, although in all probability it has gone back to a tradition of two hundred years before.

In Victorian England the obstructionists were busy insulting Walt Whitman, one of the greatest poets in the language, and Swinburne, also a very great poet. Whilst insulting these, they went into ecstasies over the tea-table tintinnabulation of the silver spoons born in the mouths of such a Victorian aunt of poetry as Austin Dobson. It was in this age, too, that the desire first rose among minor poets to fit in, poetically, with boring ordinary occasions—not to transmute these, but to copy them faithfully in miniature. There was a frightened rush to conform to the point of view of the Man-in-the-Street, to provide a simple dress for his simple thoughts, and thin cotton gloves to protect his hands from the touch of real life. And it is to this state that the bad English minor poets of today are returning.

Such was the sensibility of the admired late-nineteenth-century poets that strong men used to cry publicly if they saw a few ducks on a pond. And not only cry when they saw them, but cry about it for years afterwards.

> *Four ducks on a pond.*
> *A grass bank beyond.*
> *A blue sky of Spring*
> *White clouds on the wing;*
> *What a little thing*
> *To remember for years—*
> *To remember, with tears!*

Well, my readers may agree with me that it *was* a little thing, and that the poet was a great big sissy to cry about it.

In England and America at this moment, side by side with those poets who are revivifying the language and revitalising rhythms, there is a group of versifiers who are trying half consciously to drag poetry back to the devitalised state of poetry of the Victorian age.

One of these modern versifiers, Robert Conquest, the editor of an anthology, wrote recently that the principle by which the anthology was governed was "simply a preference for poets who

were prepared to use (in widely different ways) the whole resources of language, intellect, and feeling." Mr. Conquest is the
author of these lines:

> *Is it, when paper roses make us sneeze,*
> *A mental or a physical event?*

We do, indeed, find "the whole resources of language, intellect, and feeling" used here!

Another gentleman wrote a poem in which "the whole resources of language, intellect, and feeling" were used, on the
subject of finding a spider in his bath!

A danger inherent in much verse by the *lesser* younger
writers is their misunderstanding of the uses of concentration—
a quality which when used properly is amongst the most valuable and necessary qualities in poetry. But it is necessary, in the
first place, to have something to concentrate. When there are
neither ideas of any consequence, nor passion, all you get is a
form of stinginess.

Another danger is the deficient technique of these lesser
writers. They write, for the most part, in lifeless quatrains, or
else produce attempts at geometrical designs so easy to manage
that any schoolboy could do so.

Yet see what can be done with quatrains by a great master,
T. S. Eliot. The poem from which this quatrain is taken is
Sweeney among the Nightingales:

> *Apeneck Sweeney spreads his knees*
> *Letting his arms hang down to laugh,*
> *The zebra stripes along his jaw*
> *Swelling to maculate giraffe.*

In this poem, there is the spiritual and physical horror of a
society where man is part braying beast, part ape—a society of
which Apeneck Sweeney is the epitome. And that spiritual and
physical horror is conveyed by the sound of the verse.

After the first line there is only hollowness, blankness, lazy
abysses of emptiness, stretches of vacancy, contractions into

shrunken nothingness, and, in the line "The zebra stripes along his jaw," the hoarse animal sound of the A in "jaw."

We may remark, too, on the inspiration and genius that, in the line "Apeneck Sweeney spreads his knees," uses minute sharp pin-points of vowels, like the beginning of a pin-point of brain and, in the line "letting his arms hang down to laugh," produces a gross sagging sensuality by the contrasted dark, heavy vowels.

But to return to the question of incompetent quatrains and little geometrical designs. These have taken the place of the flabby so-called free verse, which was actually only bad prose cut into uneven lengths with blunt scissors—free verse such as this:

> *For time is up, you have upset the table.*
> *Time is up, your red trousers are burnt.*
> *Time is up, the wireless is smashed.*
> *Oh, helpless now, I see*
> *This is reality.*

Well, if it *is* reality, that is just too bad!

Such writers think free verse is easy to manage. Actually, it is appallingly difficult. But listen to the melodic beauty of the following free verse handled by a great master of the medium, Sacheverell Sitwell. (Yes, I know the poor man is my brother, but that does not prevent him from being a wonderful poet.)

> *Such are the clouds—*
> *They float with white coolness and sunny shade,*
> *Sometimes preening their flightless feathers.*
> *Float, proud swans, on the calm lake*
> *And wave your clipped wings in the azure air,*
> *Then arch your neck, and look into the deep for pearls,*
> *Now can you drink dew from tall trees and sloping fields*
>   *of Heaven,*
> *Gather new coolness for tomorrow's heat*
> *And sleep through the soft night with folded wing!*

Is that not as melodious as any rhymed verse? The lovely floating movement is not due only to the fluctuations, the flowing forward and backward of the varying lengths of the lines. We feel, actually, a faint air wandering from time to time, between, under and above certain words, due to the exquisite and incredibly subtle pauses, resulting from the different wave lengths of the vowels as well as from the use of liquids and sibilants.

Poetry has many aspects, many landscapes, and there is as much room for the butterfly as for the lion. Nor does tragedy always wear funereal garb. Walter de la Mare reminded us that there is "the tragedy at one extreme of Dr. Faustus, and that of poor gay Mr. Punch and his dog Toby." Or again, we may have a poet's mind that is like "the joyful heedless mind of summer, beneath as above thought, the intense sensation of life, with its lights and colours, coming and going in the head."

"In art," said the painter Braque, "progress does not consist in extension, but in the knowledge of limits. Limitation of means determines style, engenders new forms, and gives impulse to creation."

The poetry of Marianne Moore is a case in point. She knows exactly what she *wants* to do and she does it. She is among the most exquisite and accurate observers of our time.

"Sir George Beaumont," said Coleridge, "found advantage in learning to draw through gauze spectacles." This is the true mark of the amateur, who invariably softens and blurs. Miss Moore is the exact antithesis of the amateur; the humming bird is not better equipped to pierce down to the essence of the flower than is Miss Moore.

She sees in a flash, reproduces in a flash, and all is delight, containing a kernel of loving wisdom. Nothing is too humble for love, and for the comprehension of the creature's life source, the joy, for instance, of the "small desert rat" who has "a shining silver house" that to many people is only sand. But to Miss Moore it is beautiful, as is the "fog-coloured skin" of the elephant.

To consider her technical proficiency, let us take these lines about the trunk of an elephant:

that tree-trunk without
roots, accustomed to shout
   its own thoughts to itself like a shell, maintained intact
   by who knows what strange pressure of the atmosphere;
     that
spiritual
brother to the coral—
   plant, absorbed into which, the equable sapphire light
   becomes a nebulous green. The I of each is to
the I of each
a kind of fretful speech
   which sets a limit on itself; the elephant is
   black earth preceded by a tendril? . . .

Leaving aside its visual strangeness and beauty, this is a technical marvel—essence and form being indissoluble. Miss Moore has here, I think, found what the Spanish poet Lorca called "not only form, but the marrow of form."

The slow gait of the elephant, its deliberation—these are obtained partly, I think, by the short lines which begin each verse, partly by the T's which end each line of the first verse and which seem to bring each line to a full stop, and to produce between one line and the next the effect of the space between two gigantic and deliberate footfalls. After the short lines come long lines that seem to carry the lumbering creature into the distance.

Sir Kenneth Clark, in his great work on Leonardo da Vinci, wrote "To the end of his life he continued to draw patterns of squares, circles, and arcs, trying to exhaust every possible combination, rather as an alchemist might try every possible combination of fluids in order to discover the elixir of life."

Also, poetry should, as Ben Jonson said, "speak somewhat above a mortal mouth." Consider the difference between this lovely passage: Byron's

So we'll go no more a-roving
By the light of the moon.

And this flat one, from King James the Fifth of Scotland's "The Jolly Beggar":

> *And we'll gang nae mair a-roving*
> *A rovin in the nicht.*

Therein lies the difference between poetry and platitude. Without live words, we cannot hope for live rhythms, the Tongues of Fire that came to the Apostles. "Coleridge's father," de Quincey tells us, "used to delight his flock on Sunday, with Hebrew quotations, which he always introduced as 'the immediate language of the Holy Ghost.'"

We do not need the Hebrew language. The English language will serve us well enough. But we do need the Tongues of Fire.

Further reading:
> Sitwell, Dame Edith (ed.): THE ATLANTIC BOOK OF BRITISH AND AMERICAN POETRY. Boston: Little, Brown, and Company; 1958.
> ——: POET'S NOTEBOOK. Boston: Little, Brown, and Company; 1950.
> Auden, W. H.: COLLECTED POETRY. New York: Random House; 1951.
> Eliot, T. S.: THE WASTE LAND AND OTHER POEMS. Harvest Books. New York: Harcourt, Brace, and Company; 1955.
> Moore, Marianne: COLLECTED POEMS. New York: The Macmillan Company; 1951.
> Thomas, Dylan: COLLECTED POEMS. Augmented edition. New York: New Directions; 1956.

The End of Empire

BY

D. W. BROGAN

D. W. (for Denis William) Brogan, an Irishman born in Scotland at the turn of the century, was educated at Glasgow University, Oxford, and Harvard, and is now professor of political science at Peterhouse, Cambridge University. Professor Brogan has published seventeen books of political and historical interpretation, including a number which treat the American scene with friendly warmth and understanding. Reinhold Niebuhr has praised Professor Brogan's "extraordinary gift for understanding and illuminating the woof of constitutional principles and the warp of political tactics in the fabric of democratic history." Professor Brogan is married to Olwen Kendall, the anthropologist. The couple have four sons and a daughter and live in Cambridge, England.

More than one foreign observer has noted, admired and envied the unconditional loyalty of the average American to the American political tradition. And as a source of internal, of external strength, the loyalty that sends boys and girls on pious pilgrimage to the National Archives to revere the Declaration of Independence and the Constitution is wholly admirable. But when the good American transfers his gaze to the outer world, when he innocently looks for equivalent institutions in that less fortunate part of the globe, when he takes as having the same meaning as he gives them inside America such common words as "freedom," "good government," "progress," he asks for trouble. And with the promptitude of superservice, he is given it. His plate is filled with problems, and he is driven to realize that he is the victim of the old Chinese curse. He "is living in interesting times."

The good American is confronted all over the world today with two linked phenomena, the decline of empires and the rise of nations. He can, as a good American, have no doubts as to the sentiments he must feel at the news and noise of these phenomena. He must rejoice that empires are falling (did not America give the first push in 1776?) and rejoice that new nations devoted to freedom are arising (did not America set the example in the same fateful and admirable year?).

But having paid this respect to the national tradition, the American notes with bewilderment and often with downright annoyance that peace, progress, good will, order and liberty don't seem to be in any greater supply than in the bad old days. He hears doubts expressed as to whether some free nations (Indonesia, Burma) are as well off as they were in the days of imperialist tyranny. He notices that there are two nations on very bad terms with each other in that land called India that was united under British rule, and that their creation was the signal for massacre, rape and exile on a colossal scale. He has to face in his morning paper news of bloody rioting in Ceylon, led, with a high degree of inconsistency, by Buddhist monks. New nations in Africa such as Ghana threaten to suppress internal opposition by methods very reminiscent of the bad old days. Even after paying, during an American visit, homage to Washington, Jefferson and Lincoln, Doctor Sukarno of Indonesia, returns home via Moscow much more impressed by the relevance of Soviet experience than of American. Newly enfranchised nations such as Egypt gladly dicker for arms with the Soviet Union. An Indian state elects a Communist government, and each area, liberated from imperial slavery, seems to develop odd ways of attaining those unalienable rights proclaimed in

1776. Indeed, some of them seem very easily alienable under the pressures of "freedom."

Nothing can be done to make the world easily and automatically safe for democracy (as Chesterton pointed out in 1918, "The world will never be made safe for democracy, it is a dangerous trade"). The good American will have to get used to seeing his principles parroted and parodied. But he will suffer less and be less tempted to angry and foolish reactions if he can bring himself to think that maybe the decline of empires, at the speed at which it has taken place, is not an unmitigated benefit, and if he also can bring himself to accept the fact that a nation which gets its "freedom"—that is, is freed from foreign rule— gains that and nothing more. What it gains may have little or no relevance to its real economic or social problems, except to make them worse, and even if it is evident that the gains are well worth the price, the price may yet be very high. And if the price includes poverty, disorder and division, the United States in its own interest may be forced to pick up the tab.

The United States may have to step in to fill the gap in common defense made by the withdrawal of the imperial power. It may have to spend men, money and patience (patience will be the hardest to come by) to prop up a new, free, but rickety governmental structure. It may even, as a last aggravation of its sad state, have to receive, with what self-control it can, charges of exploitation and imperialism made by peoples in complete control, as far as the American goes, of their own destiny. Bewildered and bothered, the American in the street—or in the White House—will be less bewildered, if no less annoyed, if he accepts the fact that the end of empires is the end of an epoch that suited the United States pretty well, and that the wicked, grasping imperial powers were doing a job (possibly from the worst of motives) that somebody had to do—a job that now must be done mainly by the United States, the reluctant legatee of the old firms now in liquidation.

For the decline of empire means the passing of a crude form of solution to a real problem. "All nations are equal, but some are more equal than others." Since this cynical view happens to be true, it means that nations have very different resources, degrees of competence, are at very different stages in historical development (but want to be at the same stage) and, in defiance of all objective assessments, are ready to assert that this stage of real equality has been reached—that Liberia is a republic in the sense that the United States is; that Ceylon is a state in the sense that Holland is. The old, condemned imperial order denied this. It asserted that nations were unequal, that they were at different stages of development and that the advanced nations had the right, the opportunity and the duty to bring the backward areas, forcibly if need be, up to scratch—a laborious and expensive process for which it was only reasonable to charge a fee.

I am well aware that this appears to contradict the formal doctrines of the Declaration of Independence and that such doctrines would be shocking if developed inside the United States. California and Mississippi are equal and are at the same stage of progress; the peoples of the two states are equal, if not identical, and law and custom make no difference between one group of inhabitants and another. Such is the theory; I beg to be excused from comment on the fact. But outside the United States, until very modern times, this was neither theory nor fact. No one thought that Egypt (legally then a Turkish possession) should be allowed a free hand in controlling the way from Europe to Asia simply because it "owned" the Isthmus of Suez. (The United States, nonimperialist as she was, took much the same line about Colombia's claim to own Panama.)

There was a practical justification for this high and mighty attitude. All the new techniques that transformed the world in the last 150 years originated in Europe or North America. The owners of the new machines and the new weapons faced a world that lay lapped in immemorial slumber. Briskly, like the proprietor of a health farm, the white world insisted on wakening the sleepers, by ruling them directly, as in India; by insisting on a highly privileged position, as in China; or by frightening the more alert into imitating the white man before he took over, as in Japan. Conquest, empire was as old as human society. What was new was the expanding technical superiority of the conquerors that ate into the "cake of custom," prodded the sleepers wide awake and bred, in reaction, the force that has undone the empires—nationalism.

It is desirable at this point to proclaim that I am too much disposed to accept the unavoidable to protest against this state of affairs. As the wise Bishop Butler put it, "Things and actions are what they are, and the consequences of them will be what they will be; why then should we seek to be deceived?" Why indeed? But it is a part of deception not to notice what follows from "things and actions being what they are," and there is some danger of such error being committed.

The first error in which it is tempting to fall is to assume that the end of imperialism, the arrival on the stage of nationalism, is necessarily accompanied by material or even by moral progress. For it is too often forgotten that the basic article of the nationalist creed is that progress, good government, liberty and civilization have no meaning except in nationalist terms. It is true that nationalist propaganda usually promises lots of goodies as well as national "freedom," but they are not of the essence of the contract, and the promise is often not kept. For example, material progress may be accelerated, usually is accelerated when the economic area of a state is large. The size of the United States is one reason for its wealth. But nationalism usually breaks up existing economic units (usually, not always), for, to the nationalist, progress in material well-being is empty if it does not mean progress in *national* well-being. A man can be *emotionally* well off only in a nation state to which he belongs, even if he could be *materially* better off in his mere material command of goods in a vaster nonnational or antinational area.

Thus, although not a perfect economic unit, the old Austro-Hungarian empire was a more satisfactory one than that created by the "succession" states. Yet it is now—and was in 1918—useless to point out this fact to the emergent nationalities. What they wanted was not well-being, but national well-being. It was a choice that the peoples of the old empire were free to make as a result of the Allied victory in the First World War. They made it, and no wisdom from above the battle, from Woodrow Wilson or Herbert Hoover, could have altered that fact.

After all, no such decision is as irrational as the decision to wage and endure war, and we are all conditioned to make that decision. "Give me liberty or give me death" is not only Patrick Henry's slogan. The same uneconomic choice can be seen nearer to the United States. What rational justification is there for the frontiers of Central America? The little republics round the waist of the Americas are "obviously" designed to be united or even to be united under Mexico. But suggest that to them! I am quite prepared to believe that even Panama, invented for the convenience of the United States, has bred in the past fifty years a genuine national feeling that will last—and may become a real nuisance to the United States, at any rate from a propaganda point of view. Why should Panama not imitate Egypt? And, from the nationalist point of view, there is no easy answer to that one.

The greatest single gift of British rule to India, perhaps the only one, was the creation of India. For it did not exist before the East India Company and then the British Indian government by war, by road, by railway, by law made a united government and a united economy for a subcontinent never before united in history under an effective central Indian government. But the first result of freedom for the India thus created was suicide. We now have India and Pakistan, the latter state a nation that did not exist, even as a name, fifty years ago. The one great good thing imperialism did was undone. The unity the French imposed on Indochina has not survived their defeat, and it is not certain that the unity of Indonesia (another artificial, imported name) will survive Dutch rule for long. All of these breakdowns in unity may have been worth while; they were certainly nearly, if not quite, inevitable, but they had a high price.

Nor is that all. The division of the imperial units suggests something about nationalism that is novel and ominous. Nationalism often, too often, *breeds* nationalism. Peoples who have got along more or less with each other under foreign rule suddenly develop violent antagonism when foreign rule is withdrawn or is threatened with collapse. For under the foreign tyrant some kind of neutrality could be imposed from above. If neither group ruled itself, it had not to worry about being ruled by its neighbors. But if those neighbors were on the way to becoming the ruling class, then the prospect of *local* foreign rule became intolerable. So the Indian Moslems revolted against the prospect of Hindu rule; Turkish turned on Greek Cypriots; and in once peaceful Ceylon, Sinhalese turned on Tamils as self-government, "freedom," got more complete. Nationalism, that is to say, is often the result of a reaction. If a government claims to embody a national tradition, a way of life, a language, a religion, or all of them, people have got to ask themselves is it really *their* way of life, language, religion? Often the answer given in blood and rapine is "No, a thousand times no." "Freedom" in these situations—and they are common enough—brings not peace, but a sword.

And this leads to the invention of nationalities, to the creation of new human groups cut off from the mass of mankind by new feuds, new and carefully fostered differences. It is, of course, too easy to be critical and cynical about the history manufactured for new nations or old nations making new claims. Popular history in all countries is full of comforting legend. It is largely because they have their nationalist growing pains far behind them that western European and North American nations can afford to be scholarly, critical; can debunk national heroes and legends, remember that Washington swore, and doubt the cherry tree. Some Americans in the South may even doubt whether Lee made the right choice in "going with his state" in 1861 instead of sticking with the United States, and some Germans may believe that Bismarck's temporary triumph was a long-run catastrophe for Germany and for Europe.

We cannot expect this kind of critical history from the new nations. We should be more struck with admiration than we are when we get an approach to it as we do in India in the educated classes, or when we think of Thomas Masaryk exposing the Dvur and Hora forgeries of the country's literary past, despite the fact that they flattered Czech national vanity. But we must be prepared today for a high degree of fiction in all or almost all nationalist propaganda, and the American people, full of kindness and credulity, must not be shocked when they discover that some interesting spokesmen for some interesting countries are prone to the use of what Huck Finn called "stretchers."

What is more important is the not infrequent case where historical fiction conceals from a long-suppressed and now renascent nation that its misfortunes are also largely its own fault. Except where the preponderance of power is overwhelmingly on the imperial side, and possibly not always then, the fact of subjection is a fact about the oppressed nation. It suggests weaknesses that mere freedom will not necessarily cure. Freedom may be (I think today it almost always is) the necessary preliminary to curing the weakness, but the weakness of resources, traditions, social habits is there to be cured. Waving a new flag makes you feel good, but that is about all.

It is difficult for Americans to realize that for a great part of the world, the views of poets and philosophers, of orators and legend makers are more important than the views of businessmen or scientists or economists. The Arabs are dazzled by their own past, seen in a golden haze. For two generations they have been asking the question why they, who once ruled the Mediterranean and brought civilization to the Christian barbarians, have been kicked around and subjected to foreign rule in their homelands. And the answer they expect must be encouraging. It must exaggerate the unity of the Arabs and suggest that only Western tyranny or local corruption prevents the creation of a great Arab nation stretching from the Atlantic to the Persian Gulf. It must ignore permanent and desperate problems of inadequate resources (as in Egypt and Algeria); of undoubtedly Arab but totally anachronistic social structures (as in Yemen and Saudi Arabia). It must find in hatred of Israel a substitute for difficult problems of social and religious readjustment. It must be uncritical of the social results of Islam. And it must give a great place to treason. For all suppressed nations have a deep conviction of betrayal.

Let Erin remember the days of old
Ere her faithless sons betrayed her,
When Malachi wore the collar of gold
That he won from the proud invader.

What the Irish sang the new nationalities still sing, and so every national leader has to look over his shoulder to keep an eye on his countrymen, who may see in the possibly inevitable failures and limited successes of "freedom" not a result of the nature of things, but treachery. So Nuri-as-Said is butchered, so Gandhi is assassinated.

And the leaders who have to be watchful often become leaders by negation rather than by affirmation; they are against something (foreign rule) rather than for something, for basic changes in the internal structure of the nation, eradication of the very weaknesses that helped to produce foreign rule in the beginning. Of course, this is not always so. Nationalist leaders are sometimes preachers, as was Gandhi, of self-reform as well as of the expulsion of the foreigner. The Gaelic League, the chief begetter of modern Ireland, had as one of its slogans: "And as we are shall Banba (Ireland) be." But it is easier to damn the imperialists than to go in for fundamental self-criticism, and when the imperialist has been heaved out or has left under his own steam, the basic problems remain.

So the world is faced with the new states with inadequate economic resources, with erratic frontiers, with dissident minorities, with delusions of grandeur and, what is worse, of goodness. And all this is in a world where the new nations are almost all arising in poor regions where, even with the best and most rational government, the headaches would be frightful, where the problem of keeping abreast of the birth rate and of not actually going backward in well-being is serious enough to daunt the bravest. It is not being offensive or aggressive to assert that half the nations whose delegates give parties in New York round the United Nations building are too poor and too backward to give their peoples in the next generation even as good a government and as adequate a standard of life as the most backward European nation (let us say Portugal) or the most backward American state (let us say Mississippi) possesses.

Freedom from imperial yoke may even be a luxury some of them (which could be named) can hardly afford. There are areas in the dwindling British and French empires that are a dead loss to the imperial power; regions that cannot afford freedom, although only the most prudent of their leaders know this. For there is nothing in "the law of Nature and of Nature's God" that provides that an area with the linguistic and cultural unity that demands nationhood and will not be denied will have any of the other resources for even frugal well-being.

The great problem of the concentration of most of the world's wealth and technical competence in a small area of the globe has many nonpolitical aspects. It is to be noted that there is *no* first-class industrial power outside the temperate zones. But the political problem of the replacement of the empires by the nations is one of the governing conditions of any attempt to redress the imbalance that is so deeply and dangerously dividing the world. And it is the beginning of wisdom for Americans, conditioned as they are by their own largely irrelevant history of nation-making, to recognize that national freedom may be an obstacle to a quick redressing of the balance, both by creating doubtfully viable national units and by transferring authority to leaders whose competence has lain in the exploiting (all right, the heroic undoing) of a national grievance.

But if this is the beginning, it is not the end of wisdom. For it is not only a fact, if not a totally welcome fact, that the days of empire are over; it is a fact that the nation state offers possibilities of improvement that the empires either never did (which I doubt) or have ceased to do (which I admit). There is another fact. If one political truth is established today, it is that once the nationalist bug bites a group of human beings they cannot be cured except by national freedom, with all the possible social and economic disadvantages it may bring. Once an Algerian, for instance, decides that he is not a Frenchman and doesn't want to be one, rational economic argument is wasted. Bernard Shaw usually talked nonsense on political questions, but he occasionally talked sense, and his Irish origin illuminated much of this question for him. So, he wrote sense in his preface to John Bull's Other Island, the only play he ever devoted to his native land. "A conquered nation is like a man with a cancer: he can think of nothing else, and is forced to place himself, to the exclusion of all better company, in the hands of quacks who profess to treat or cure cancer." This is true, and the first great gain of freedom is that thought and effort can be devoted to something more immediately relevant than "freedom."

It does not follow, of course, that it will be. There are few greater emotional losses than a grievance that explains why things have gone wrong in terms of another's fault. Any father of a family can testify to that (and his children can testify, too, in another sense). To get freedom is to lose a grievance, and some nations have firmly refused to give up their darling excuse. Thus, if the people of the Argentine Republic devoted a tenth as much rational thought to the causes of their serious, but quite curable troubles that they have wasted on irrelevant and unjust spleen about "Yanqui" imperialism, they would be a great deal better off. If a patriotic Cuban put to himself the question, "Would we not have been materially better off if we had had more Yanqui imperialism?" and then admitted that some, if not all, of the troubles of Cuba are homemade, freedom would be an unmitigated good. Can any candid observer, looking at Haiti and the Dominican Republic, pretend that freedom is always an unmitigated good?

The beneficial effects of freedom can be seen in two such different former jewels of the English crown as Ireland and India. For more than a generation of freedom has taught most of the inhabitants of the Irish Republic that their troubles are no longer of England's making, that "the border" is neither here nor there in the bookkeeping of a declining nation, that the Gaelic League was right: "And as we are shall Banba be." Even an act which, seen from the outside, seems one of the most foolish ever perpetrated by a rational community—the exit from the Commonwealth in 1948—may have been worth the price in making plain to the Irish people that a republic left them where they were, with the basic problem of why the Irish won't, if they can help it, live in Ireland.

The problems of India are so gigantic that courage fails the spectator (but not the Indians). But one great gain is the creation of a government that does not hesitate to face Indian abuses such as the caste system. The government of Nehru makes many mistakes, but it can, through the mouth of the Prime Minister, preach to the Indians the lesson that it is now up to them. No

British government could do that. It can risk appearing "anti-religious" as no British government dared risk appearing. It has not succeeded in abolishing untouchability or in winning over all the primitive tribes of India. It has not undone many centuries of limitations on the role of women. It has not succeeded in giving India what India needs badly, a competent and enlightened business class. But it has made beginnings in all these fields. It has kept India from becoming a mere "Hindustan." And it has made it possible for Indians to borrow from the West with no feeling of humiliation.

There is nothing that the new Indian government did that enlightened British officials didn't see as desirable. But, in this century, the British government in India had lost the power to innovate. An imperial power that begins to doubt its mission is rightly doomed. The old, confident, authoritarian British rulers stamped out the burning of widows, the religious murders of the Thugs, abolished backward kingdoms like Oudh and introduced in a fine philistine fashion the English language as the *lingua franca* of all India. These things, with the Indian army (obedient to civilian authority) and civil service (uniquely honest and competent in Asia), were great British legacies, but it was time for the British to go. Talk to an Indian who is now liberated from the need to think, all the time, in terms of national freedom, and you see the gain. He may even think that Macaulay, imposing English, had something to be said for him as he contemplates the bloody riots over languages that freedom has brought and the danger that an "Indian" national language such as Hindi may be a source of disunion and breed a new Pakistan in the south.

If this is the first, it is not the only gain. Indian nationalism may be simply the fruit of anti-British feeling, but it is a fact and gives India a new unity most necessary in a land divided by language, race, caste. It gives the Indian a new feeling of not being looked down on, and so a new freedom in his attitude to the outer world into which India has been dragged. True, the kind of dignity that nationalism breeds may be touchy, offensive, unrealistic, but there is no substitute for it. As the American Negro is no longer content to be grateful for concessions made from above, all over the world hundreds of millions of men are finding a new meaning in life, a new loyalty to something bigger than the village, the caste, the tribe.

It is not in solving immediate technical problems of well-being that the nations score over the empires. They often handle them, for quite a long time, worse than the imperial rulers did. It is in creating a new type of human being, who may not, it is true, adjust himself adequately to the new world, but at least is not doomed to fail in that adjustment as the empires finally became doomed to fail.

If the American abandons the fallacious parallel with the facts of the American Revolution (as apart from the spirit of '76) and contemplates the new world that is coming into being, he will be forced to avoid snap and easily systematic judgments (especially the judgment that assesses the worth and prospects of a new nation by its willingness to be noisily anti-Communist). He will see many nations running before they can walk— and so falling; demanding steel mills when what they need is more wells and better seed; aspiring after the heights of atomic cannon when they need to learn how to maintain a truck; above all, pouring out endless floods of what it may be too unkind to call mendacity, but can justly be called nonobjective information.

He will find few nations willing—or able—to imitate all or most of the American way of life, social, political, economic. If he wishes to help the world (as many do), he will have to learn to help it in un-American ways, to learn un-American qualities such as patience and the willingness to wait a long time for results. If what he wants is allies against Communism, he will find in nationalism the most, perhaps the only effective force against international Communism, even when that nationalism is unwilling to stand up and be counted. For the great battles will probably be fought in the hearts of men, not on material beaches where marines can land, but in a world now effectually united for the first time in history by material means and divided by passion and envy. One may regret the old imperial days, but the awkward and often unprogressive nationalist world is that in which we all must now live.

Further reading:

Brogan, D. W.: THE PRICE OF REVOLUTION. New York: Harper and Brothers; 1952.

Atiyah, Edward: THE ARABS. Baltimore: Penguin Books; 1955.

Guillaume, Alfred: ISLAM. Baltimore: Penguin Books.

Hancock, W. Keith: WEALTH OF COLONIES. New York: Cambridge University Press; 1950.

Jennings, Sir Ivor: THE APPROACH TO SELF-GOVERNMENT. New York: Cambridge University Press; 1956.

Nuseibeh, Hazem Zaki: THE IDEAS OF ARAB NATIONALISM. Ithaca, N. Y.: Cornell University Press; 1957.

Richmond, Anthony: THE COLOR PROBLEM. Baltimore: Penguin Books; 1955.

Staley, Eugene: THE FUTURE OF UNDERDEVELOPED COUNTRIES. New York: Harper and Brothers; 1954.

What Makes

Basic Research Basic?

BY

HANS SELYE

With the discovery—popularly expounded in his book
The Stress of Life—*that the human organism has innate
defenses against fatigue, pain, and disease, Dr. Hans Selye
influenced the entire course of modern medicine. His findings have been ranked beside those of Pasteur, Koch, and
Ehrlich. A Viennese by birth and a naturalized Canadian
subject, Dr. Selye now directs the Institute of Experimental Medicine and Surgery at the University of Mont-
real.*

Until recently most of us engaged in basic research saw
no reason to explain our work or our motives to the
public. We felt there was something vulgar in discussing our
peculiar problems with people not fully prepared to appreciate
all the fine technical points and that it would be an immodest
bid for attention. We felt that the singular world of basic research could be understood only by those who live in it. To
attempt to explain it in lay language seemed hopeless and even

childish—as futile and naïve as to expound the current problems of the American automobile industry to an African chieftain who had never seen either America or an automobile. Now, however, as Bertrand Russell puts it, "Not only will men of science have to grapple with the sciences that deal with man but—and this is a far more difficult matter—they will have to persuade the world to listen to what they have discovered. If they cannot succeed in this difficult enterprise, man will destroy himself by his halfway cleverness."

The basic research of today produces both the lifesaving drugs and the destructive weapons of tomorrow. Its outcome will affect everybody, and in a democracy whose people decide how wealth shall be distributed everybody shares the responsibility of developing the nation's scientific potential. But how can anybody vote intelligently without some grasp of the problems bearing upon that development?

Bridging the gap between the scientist and the general public will not be easy. The former will have to learn to translate his problems into a language meaningful to the layman; the latter will have to realize that, however simplified, the essence of basic research cannot be assimilated without mental effort.

What is basic research? Charles E. Wilson, the former Secretary of Defense, defined it as what you do "when you don't know what you're doing," a sarcasm presumably intended to justify the inadequacy of financial support for basic research. More commonly, basic research is thought of as the opposite of "practical" research, the kind that can be immediately applied. This suggests its disassociation from man's everyday problems. The development of weapons, television sets or vaccines is obviously practical. Studies of the inner temperature of distant stars, of the habits of infinitely small living beings, of the laws governing the inheritable coloration of flowers, all seemed eminently impractical—at least when first undertaken. They were viewed as sophisticated pastimes, pursued by intelligent but somewhat eccentric, maladjusted people, whose otherwise excellent minds had been sidetracked by a queer interest in the farfetched and useless.

I remember my own reaction in school when I was taught how to estimate the inner temperature of distant stars. Cunning, I thought, but why should anybody want to know? When Louis Pasteur reported that germs might transmit diseases, he was ridiculed. Fancy a grown man worrying about being attacked by bugs so small no one could see them! When the Austrian monk, Gregor Johann Mendel, amused himself by observing the results of crossbreeding red with white-flowering peas in the monastery garden, even his most farsighted contemporaries failed to imagine the momentous implications.

Yet, without basic knowledge of the behavior of distant stars, we would not be placing satellites in orbits today; without knowledge about bacteria, there would be no vaccines and antibiotics; and without those observations on the inheritance of color in peas, modern genetics—with its importance to agriculture and medicine—could never have developed.

Such considerations must arouse public interest in basic research. They are bound to make people realize that the more manifestly sensible and practical a research project, the closer it is to the commonplace we already know. Thus, paradoxically, knowledge about the seemingly most farfetched, impractical phenomena may prove the likeliest to yield novel basic information, and lead us to new heights of discovery.

Some insist that basic research must proceed in the same spirit as "art for art's sake," and should not be appraised by its practical applicability. Yet, in defending this view they usually argue that even the most abstruse research may eventually yield practical results. It is odd that the study of the impractical should have to be justified by its potential usefulness.

Others maintain that not even potential usefulness should enter into our assessment of important basic research. It was the eminent English chemist and physicist, Michael Faraday, who, more than a century ago, made the remark so often quoted by these ultra-purists—"What is the use of a newborn baby?" But not everything important to us need be useful in the accepted sense of the word. At the same time, utility is inseparable from man's assessment of what is important. Perhaps in this still unprejudiced, pliable core of a human being we sense a possible future helpful friend. In any case, a baby is useful because we can lavish our love on it—and without love there can be no happiness. Pure art—a great painting, a piece of music—is useful, since it lifts us beyond the preoccupations of everyday life, bringing us peace and serenity. Bearing these facts in mind, I am inclined to define basic research as the study of natural laws for their own sake, irrespective of immediate practical applicability —with emphasis on the qualification "immediate."

But, to me, the need is not so much to define basic research as to distinguish between greater and lesser basic-research projects. This distinction is of immense importance, both to the investigator who requires a standard by which to choose his subject and to the public who pays for his work in the hope of profiting by it. The future welfare of humanity depends largely upon the recognition of first-rate basic research in its earliest stages, when it lacks practical applicability. No nation can afford to subsidize every kind of research, and many a fertile, creative thought has had to be buried stillborn because no one wanted to risk money on it until its value was proved.

Let me emphasize that only the kind of research usually designated as "basic" is true *discovery*. What follows is *development*. The former kind is basic, or fundamental, precisely because every other kind of research develops from it. It strikes us as impractical and the work involved as haphazard, because wholly original observations cannot be planned in advance. To do so the observation would have to be anticipated on the basis of previously known facts, and hence could not be wholly original. That is why most of the completely new leads are accidental discoveries made by men with the rare talent of noticing the totally unexpected. These form the basis of all premeditated research projects—the kind I call development.

It may be argued that any attempt at early recognition must be foredoomed, since the unexpected cannot be anticipated. To some extent this is true. Of course, there is no reliable yardstick with which to compare the relative importance of basic-research projects, but I believe it possible to formulate certain principles which can serve as general directives. Think of them not as rigid measurements, but rather as a kind of course in science appreciation, helping us to recognize and enjoy creative scientific thought.

To my mind, it is characteristic of great basic discoveries that they possess, to a high degree and simultaneously, three qualities: they are true not merely as facts but also in the way they are interpreted, they are generalizable and they are surprising in the light of what was known at the time of the discovery.

It may seem redundant to say that the newly discovered facts must be true, but by this I mean they must be both correct and seen in proper perspective. Otherwise the finding may be misleading because of the inferences drawn from it.

Not long ago a chemist tried to make a compound that would diminish appetite and cause loss of weight. After years of study, he succeeded in producing a drug that conformed to his theories concerning the structure this kind of substance should have. He then tested the compound on rats, cats, dogs and monkeys. As he expected, all the animals ate very little and lost weight. In a paper describing his findings, he explained why he thought a drug of such chemical structure would act in this manner. In the conventional sense, his findings were true. In my sense they were false. We know that almost any damaging substance will diminish appetite, and his substance was damaging. The author neither admitted nor denied this. He did not recommend his drug for human use. Still, his paper implied applicability. Hence, his finding was untrue by implication. Had he realized that his compound decreased appetite only because of its damaging effects, he would not have bothered to write a paper about it. Few scientists knowingly publish untruths, but many scientific papers contain such untruths by implication.

Yet, even if a finding is true by all standards, it may not be important. I recently read a paper describing the mean weights of the internal organs of laboratory rats. The author's facts were correct; he had killed hundreds of animals to build up a highly significant series. But the resulting information was of limited importance, being neither generalizable nor surprising. It is not generalizable, because we can deduce no general laws from it; it does not necessarily apply even to rats of a different strain. Indeed, in the researcher's own stock, the organ weights probably would have varied had he changed the diet or the temperature of the laboratory. Nor is the information surprising, because it was evident at the start that the mean weights could be determined by measurement. This sort of work not only fails to qualify as "basic research" but it has not even been practically applied to anything.

The best you can say for it is that it might be applicable by somebody needing these figures as a standard of comparison for original investigation, but then his would be the basic research. Scientific literature abounds in such reports. The authors customarily protect themselves by stating self-righteously that they draw no conclusions from their observations. But this is not good enough. Facts from which no conclusions can be drawn are hardly worth knowing.

This sort of finding may be made accidentally, but usually it results from what we call "screening," and, hence, falls into the class of development rather than of discovery. Such screening might be used by the clinician testing a number of cortisone derivatives, more or less at random, on patients with rheumatic diseases. Cortisone itself is a hormone that has been found effective in such cases and the clinician merely wants to screen related compounds to see whether one of them might prove more effective. Again, all this is development of previously known facts, not original, creative research.

We are guided in such work by so-called "deductive reasoning," which helps us foretell certain things about an individual case from a previously established generalization. If most cortisonelike compounds are effective against rheumatism, any newly prepared member of this group looks promising. But the deduction itself cannot be generalized. The work may be of immediate practical importance, leading us perhaps to the ideal antirheumatic compound, but, in the highest sense, it is sterile, because the observation is complete in itself, offering little likelihood of further discoveries.

Unfortunately, this drab kind of research is the easiest to finance, because of its immediate applicability to practical problems which can be precisely described in a routine application for funds.

Other observations lend themselves to "inductive reasoning," the formulation of general laws from individual observations. But this feature does not suffice either. To illustrate, it was shown that the first ten hormones, the products of endocrine glands, that could be prepared in pure form were all white. From this, we could generalize. We could foretell, with a high degree of probability, that the next five hormones to be synthesized would also be white. So they were. But what of it? Who cares what color future hormone preparations will be? The appearance of the substances is irrelevant.

Here, then, was an observation both true and generalizable, but lacking the third essential quality of important basic research, the quality of surprise; that is, the unexpectedness of the discovery at the time of making it. Most body constituents are white when purified; hence, it is not surprising that hormones should be white.

I recall my astonishment on learning in medical school that certain pathological growths in the human ovary, the so-called "dermoids," may contain teeth and hair. A medical curiosity, but not generalizable—at least not at present. All we can say now is that occasionally, even without fertilization, an egg in the human ovary may develop into a monster consisting mainly of hair and teeth. This much has been known ever since the seventeenth-century German physician, Scultetus, gave the first complete description of what he called *"morbus pilaris mirabilis,"* the astonishing hair malady. Martin Luther referred to it as the "Offspring of the Devil."

For centuries, physicians and laymen alike have been fascinated by the anomaly. But it opened up no new vistas of research. The reason is, I think, that the observation was made too early. Even today we are not equipped to evaluate it. It is like a strange island remote from the charted areas of human knowledge. Perhaps, later—when we know more about fertilization, about reproduction without fertilization and about the "organizers" that direct the formation of human structures—the

"Offspring of the Devil" will become an angel guiding us to the solution of Nature's mysteries. But merely being aware of the oddity avails us nothing. Scultetus saw, but he did not discover.

Laymen rarely appreciate the fundamental difference between seeing and discovering. America was not discovered for mankind by the Indians, nor by the Vikings who came in the tenth century, but by Christopher Columbus, who established a permanent bridge between the new and the old worlds. It is the process of unifying, the "creative synthesis," be it even of long-known facts, that alone can promote true understanding and progress.

As Hans Zinsser, the great American bacteriologist, put it: "So often, in the history of medicine, scientific discovery has merely served to clarify and subject to purposeful control, facts that had long been empirically observed and practically utilized. The principles of contagion were clearly outlined and invisible micro-organisms postulated by Fracastorius about a hundred years before the most primitive microscopes were invented; and the pre-Pasteurian century is rich with clinical observations that now seem a sort of gestation period leading to the birth of a new science."

This essential distinction between seeing and discovering is illustrated by the development of insulin, the pancreatic hormone with which we treat diabetes. In 1889, the German physiologist, Minkowski, and his associate, Von Mering, surgically removed the pancreas in dogs and thereby produced diabetes. They did not, however, realize that the disease resulted from a lack of pancreatic insulin, and their finding did not stimulate much progress until 1922, when the Canadian, Frederick Banting, and his co-workers extracted insulin from the pancreas, and showed that this hormone can actually abolish not only the Minkowski type of experimental diabetes but also spontaneous kinds.

It subsequently turned out that, some seventeen years earlier, the French physiologist, Marcel Eugène Emile Gley, had performed experiments similar to Banting's. He had even described them in a private communication deposited in a sealed envelope with the Société de Biologie. Only in 1922, after Banting's publication, did Gley permit his letter to be opened. It fully supported his claim to have first found insulin. But he received little credit. As Minkowski remarked during an international symposium on diabetes, after Gley violently protested against the injustice of it all, "I know just how you feel. I could also have kicked myself for not having discovered insulin, when I realize how close I came to it."

Obviously, Gley did not recognize the importance of what he saw. He failed to generalize from it, to tie it in with clinical medicine; otherwise he would not have been satisfied to deposit his findings under seal. In fact, it would have been criminal to do so, had he realized that he thereby signed the death warrant of the thousands who succumbed from diabetes for want of insulin. None of Gley's work was comparable in importance to the discovery of insulin. Why did he put it aside, if not because he failed to understand its significance? It is easy to deposit private communications about things we are not sure of, and unseal them when somebody else proves that we were on the right track. To my mind, Gley not only failed to discover insulin but he also proved that he could not do so. By chance he saw it, but he did not discover it.

The element of chance in basic research is overrated. Chance is a lady who smiles only upon those few who know how to make her smile.

Let us consider a really great achievement of basic research: The observation by Alexander Fleming that penicillin can kill varieties of disease-producing microbes, at dose levels tolerated by man. This is true both in the fact itself and in the obvious inference that penicillin can protect against infections. It is also a generalizable observation. It has enabled other investigators to discover many useful drugs derived, like penicillin, from molds. And, finally, it was surprising to find that molds, which we regarded as contaminators, can have a curative value. Only a highly creative, original mind, one that can completely free itself from established ways of observation, can make such a discovery. Many bacteriologists had seen that cultures of microbes are spoiled when exposed to molds, but all they concluded was that molds must be kept out of such cultures. It took a stroke of genius to see the medicinal promise of the basic observation.

Basic research must, of course, penetrate deep into the unknown without losing contact with known realities. To accomplish this, the scientist must have a peculiar kind of intuition. Perhaps his most important characteristic is a negative one. He must lack prejudice to a degree where he can look at the most "self-evident" facts or concepts without necessarily accepting them, and, conversely, allow his imagination to play with the most unlikely possibilities. In the process he requires serendipity, the gift of finding unsought treasures. (The word was coined by Horace Walpole, in allusion to the fairy tale of The Three Princes of Serendip, who were always discovering, by chance or by sagacity, things they were not seeking.) He must have the power of abstract thinking. Planned steps into the unknown must first be made in the mind, without the concrete support of experience.

The basic researcher must also be able to dream and have faith in his dreams. To make a great dream come true, the first requirement is a great capacity to dream; the second is persistence—a faith in the dream. As for intellect, I repeat what I said in The Stress of Life, "Pure intellect is largely a quality of the middle-class mind. The lowliest hooligan and the greatest creator in the field of human endeavor are motivated mainly by imponderable instincts and emotions, especially faith. Curiously, even scientific research—the most intellectual creative effort of which man is capable—represents no exception in this respect. That is why the objective, detached form of an original scientific publication or of a textbook falls so ludicrously short of really conveying the spirit of an investigation."

Finally, the basic scientist must have all these qualities in the proper proportion. Too great a propensity for abstract thinking may turn him into a bookworm addicted to sterile ratiocination. Too much faith in his dreams can hinder the verification of concepts by experiment. That is why the line of demarcation between the rare genius and the eccentric inventor is often seemingly so indistinct. To the uninitiated, there is much in common between crack brains and cracked brains. Yet it is important to recognize the promising basic scientist early, when he needs support for the development of his singular gifts. The nation's culture, health and strength depend primarily upon its creative basic scientists—the "eggheads."

What is really meant by this now-so-popular term? To my mind, an egghead's main endeavor is to search for the kind of truth that can be verified by experience. The researcher employed by industry may be excellent at his particular job, but usually he does it for a living; rarely is it his main purpose in life. (Of course, if it is, he qualifies as an egghead.) An intellectual may accept a fact unquestioningly on the authority of books or scholars, without feeling the urge to verify it by experience. The theologians who must accept dogma on faith, the teachers who try to disseminate knowledge, the lawyers, engineers or physicians, who apply truths, are all intellectuals and may be very valuable people. But they are not eggheads.

We can no longer afford to allow scientific genius to remain idle for want of money. Nor can we afford to concentrate all our attention upon the physical sciences because of Sputnik. Nuclear war may or may not come, but the war against disease and death from "natural causes" is on now.

The problem, however, goes beyond the mere provision of financial aid to our scientific elite. To adapt ourselves to the spirit of this century we must reassess our whole philosophy and our sense of values. Just as the Stone Age, the Bronze Age and the Iron Age were characterized by the use of stone, bronze and iron, so our era will undoubtedly go down in history as the Age of Basic Research. Man has gained unprecedented power through investigation of natural laws. This power can lead us to the brightest chapter in human history—or the final chapter.

We must ask ourselves one supreme question, and act according to our answer. Shall we fight each other or shall we fight Nature? Men attack men in bitter competition for profit. Nations attempt to exterminate other nations in the struggle for dominance. The real enemy is Nature. Yet we can make Nature our servant. Let man measure his strength against an adversary worthy of the strongest contender, an adversary at once powerful enough to challenge us all and rich enough to provide us all with priceless treasure as long as the universe endures.

There are those who create wealth and those who fight over it. The former are undoubtedly the happier. Wealth is the by-product of their passion. The scientist loves research. The great industrialist does not create jobs for his workers and products for his customers merely to enrich himself, nor does the artist paint chiefly for fame. To these creators the pursuit is not tedious toil, nor are the rewards the ultimate aim of existence. To them wealth and recognition are largely the unexpected, though gratifying, secondary result of what they do for its own sake.

Nature seems to have so arranged matters that her essential objectives are camouflaged, as it were, so that they impress us as the unplanned consequences of something we enjoy doing. (Few people enter the nuptial chamber with the production of a child as their main preoccupation.) That is why the public at large, and often the scientists themselves, do not feel that honors or material rewards are called for. Yet, the man of creative mind must be accorded a privileged position, not as payment, nor because he needs encouragement, nor even to help him in his work, but as the most effective means we have to demonstrate our appreciation of human values to the next generation.

We must educate our children to understand that from now on man's great wars will not be fought with muscle. His battles will not be won by the glorious, intoxicating, momentary courage to face danger and die for a cause. Our children must learn that the great victories in peace and war will be won by warriors of a different stamp, men of intellectual vigor, and by the sober, persistent dedication of their entire lives. They will have to learn that it is far more difficult to live than to die for a cause.

Further reading:

Selye, Hans: THE STRESS OF LIFE. New York: McGraw-Hill Book Company; 1956.

Burtt, E. A.: THE METAPHYSICAL FOUNDATIONS OF MODERN PHYSICAL SCIENCE. New York: Humanities Press; 1952.

Conant, James B.: MODERN SCIENCE AND MODERN MAN. New York: Columbia University Press; 1952.

———: ON UNDERSTANDING SCIENCE. Mentor Books. New York: New American Library; 1952.

Whitehead, A. N.: SCIENCE AND THE MODERN WORLD. New York: The Macmillan Company; 1925.

Art and Life

BY

SIR HERBERT READ

Sir Herbert Read, essayist, editor, critic, and poet, has devoted the last twenty-five years to what he calls the administration of the arts. After serving as an infantry officer of the Yorkshire Regiment in the First World War, Sir Herbert joined the staff of the Victoria and Albert Museum in London and later became Professor of Fine Arts at Edinburgh University. A frequent visitor to the United States, Sir Herbert has in recent years taught at Harvard and lectured at the National Gallery of Art in Washington.

There is an early story of Tolstoi's which has always seemed to me to have a fundamental bearing on the relation of the creative activities we call "art" to the destructive forces we call "crime." Tolstoi describes a walk he took with three boys from the school on his estate. Their imaginations had been excited by a classroom reading of a violent story by Gogol. It was a moonless winter night with snow on the ground and clouds in the sky. In a spirit of daring the boys wanted to go into the woods where wolves roamed, but, being too afraid, they skirted round them, and began to talk about Caucasian robbers. Tolstoi told them tales about the Cossack braves he had known when he was a soldier; of one who, surrounded by his enemies, broke out into song and threw himself on his dagger.

The children were struck by the idea of a man singing in the face of death. But their appetite for horrors was not satisfied. So Tolstoi went on to recount the gruesome murder of his aunt, whose throat was cut by robbers. Fedka, a boy of ten "with a tender, receptive, poetic yet daring nature," suddenly asked: "Why does one learn singing? I often think, why does one?"

Tolstoi comments: "What made him jump from the terror of the murder to this question, heaven only knows; yet by the tone of his voice, the seriousness with which he demanded an answer, and the attentive silence of the other two, one felt there was some vital and legitimate connection between this question and our preceding talk. Whether the connection lay in some response to my suggestion that crime might be explained by lack of education (I had spoken of that), or whether he was testing himself—transferring himself into the mind of the murderer and remembering his own favorite occupation (he has a wonderful voice and immense musical talent), or whether the connection lay in the fact that he felt that now was the time for sincere conversation, and all the problems demanding solution rose in his mind—at any rate his question surprised none of us."

"And what is drawing for? And why write well?" Tolstoi asked, not knowing how to answer the child's question. "What *is* drawing for?" repeated Fedka, and Tolstoi adds: "He was really asking, What is Art for? And I could not explain."

Tolstoi thought about this question all his life, and it was not until thirty-seven years later, in his book, What Is Art?, that he attempted to explain the mysterious relationship that exists between art and life.

Tolstoi knew that the relationship was very profound, and even these children knew instinctively that there is some intimate connection between beauty and violence, between love and death. Such a connection is made by the great poets, by Homer and the Greek tragedians, by Shakespeare and by Tolstoi himself in War and Peace, but now we have lost it. Our technological civilization ignores all such values in its blind drive toward power and affluence, and pays the toll in a mass neurosis whose symptoms are fearful despair, apathy and violence for its own sake.

Recently, an outbreak of savagery occurred among young people in England. Colored immigrants from the West Indies were beaten up and their homes smashed. This outbreak had little to do with racial prejudice. Color is only an excuse to exercise an impulse which would, if necessary, find other excuses. The teen-age delinquent and at a literate level the Angry Young Man are giving vent to suppressed feelings of frustration. Something in their nature has no disciplined outlet, and in their boredom and restless urge to action, these frustrated youths seek to destroy; for destruction, as the nihilist Bakunin said, is also creation. More exactly, it is a substitute for creation.

Such violence of action is no doubt related to the violence of expression that has increasingly become a feature, not only of novels, newspapers, films, and television but also of literature universally acclaimed as of great cultural value. America is not unique in this respect; the cynical brutality of William Faulkner's novels is but an outstanding example of a phenomenon characteristic of our civilization everywhere.

Violence, of course, is not new to literature. The Iliad is full of it. So are the writings of Shakespeare and Cervantes. But those classic writers do not condone violence. They view it as just retribution for sins against the divine order, or as a sacrifice sanctioned by heroism or martyrdom. What is peculiar to the modern literature is violence for the sake of violence. Perhaps our reverence for life has been dulled by mass slaughter, though mass slaughter has not been exceptional in the history of mankind. What is exceptional is the boredom that now alternates with war. The basic emotion in peacetime has become a *horror vacui*: a fear of being alone, of having nothing to do, a neurosis whose symptoms are restlessness, an unmotivated and undirected rage, sinking at times into vapid listlessness. This neurotic syndrome is intensified by the prevailing sense of insecurity. The threat of atomic war has corrupted our faith in life itself.

This universal neurosis has developed with the progress of technology. It is the neurosis of men whose chief expenditure of energy is to pull a lever or push a button, of men who have ceased to make things with their hands. Such inactivity applies not only to muscles and nerves but to the creative processes that once engaged the mind. If one could contrast visually, by time-and-motion studies, the daily actions of an eighteenth-century chairmaker with a twentieth-century machinist, the latter would appear as a confined, repetitive clot, the former as a free and even fantastic pattern. But the most significant contrast could not be visualized—the contrast between a mind suspended aimlessly above an autonomous movement, and a mind consciously bent on the shaping of a material substance according to the persistent evidence of the senses.

Routine activities existed in other ages, but generally human beings were in direct contact with nature and dependent on *things*. Long before the Industrial Revolution, Jean Jacques Rousseau laid down as a principle of education: *Keep the child dependent on things only*. Rousseau believed that the child learns by trial and error better than by formula. This kind of pragmatic learning is essentially physical; skill develops in coping with material objects. Skill of this kind is still involved in many industrial processes; we divide labor into skilled and unskilled categories. But too often today, skill means the understanding and control of a mechanical process, rather than the manual shaping of a physical substance. It is an activity more cerebral than sensual. This is true even of agricultural operations; the farmer who formerly used the spade and the scythe has been replaced by a mechanic driving a tractor.

Such a change in the basic modes of human activity must deeply affect mental life and moral behavior. Its most obvious expression would be aimlessly aggressive. Satan finds mischief still for idle hands. Unused energies, deprived of traditional outlets, explode in violence.

The Greeks, though the source of our philosophy of art, had no word for art. They used *techne*—the equivalent of our word "skill," which is a word of Norse derivation whose original meaning implied discrimination. The root *ar* means "to fit or join." The Romans were probably responsible for the distinction that gradually developed between arts and crafts, for they personified the Arts and thought of them as refined (i.e. fine) activities. Nevertheless, during the Middle Ages the primary meaning of art remained skill—skill in making things, whether a chair, music or poetry. The liberal arts taught in schools were taught as objective skills—grammar, rhetoric, logic; arithmetic, geometry, music and astronomy. We no longer speak of the liberal arts, but of *science;* that is to say, various categories of *knowledge* expressed in verifiable language. The arts were a way of "doing," involving skill; the sciences are a way of "knowing," implying logical consistency.

The history of words is a key to the history of ideas. We have now effected a complete divorce between the originally identical concepts of *techne* and *ars.* Technique, scientific method, skilled craft—all these terms imply intellectual know-how, and are characteristic of our technological civilization. But, though moribund art schools still teach art as a skill, it is regarded more as an instinctual activity, exercised by a minority of gifted people, essentially inspirational in origin and personal in manifestation and significance. Its relevance to a technological civilization is considered marginal: an optional grace which most economies cannot afford. The controlling ideal of a technological civilization is not grace or beauty, but productive efficiency.

The Greeks did not distinguish between grace and efficiency; they considered them identical. Plato argued that statesmanship was a skill, comparable to that of the weaver (or, as we should say, an art, not a science). The state is an intuition of form in all things—not a tyrannical application of law. The modern philosopher disagrees with Plato. Politics he considers a science. We deliver ourselves into the remote hands of technical experts, who attempt to control our natural tendencies by means of scientific organizations.

To make a distinction between the art of government and the science of government may now seem an academic exercise, but it is part of the vital problem of distinguishing between an art and a science of life itself. I call it a *vital* problem with a precise intention, because I believe that the future welfare of mankind depends on a realization of the issues involved, and then upon a clear choice of alternatives. To say that we stand at a crossroad of human development may be a cliché, but it is a formidable fact.

Let us look more closely at this human faculty we call "skill." As Dr. Loren C. Eiseley made clear in his contribution to this book, it is the faculty upon which man has depended for his survival in the struggle for existence. Man has not reached his present superior status in the evolution of species by force alone, or even by adjustment to changes in his environment. He has reached it by the development of consciousness, enabling him to discriminate the *quality* of things.

The long historical process whereby man became able to impose his will on recalcitrant matter can be reconstructed only speculatively. But there is nothing speculative about the process through which the child achieves this capacity. The great Swiss pedagogue Jean Piaget, director of the International Bureau of Education, has published a series of books based on his observations of infantile behavior. In one of them he defines intelligence as a relationship between the human organism and things. It is not, he insists, a power of reflection independent of the organism's particular position in the universe; rather it is linked, from the very beginning, with the organism's reaction to its physical environment. But this is not a simple reflex action; simultaneously with the organism's assimilation of external things, there is a mental organization of the things assimilated. The infant "gropes" among its first confused experiences, becomes aware of certain relationships between the acts to be performed and an end to be attained, and *profits from experience*. Habits are formed, reactions to environment are automatically repeated, and gradually the groping becomes more continuous and consistent until it constitutes an *intention*. Intention is the essential characteristic of intelligence.

Intelligence presupposes intention. Intention is connected with the power of evoking images, and eventually with the whole process of symbolization and speech. In a series of observations of sucking reflexes in infants, Piaget shows that intentional adaptation begins as soon as the child transcends the level of simple corporal activities, and *acts upon things and uses the interrelationships of objects*. In other words, intelligence develops (as Rousseau perceived) in contact with things.

Intention implies intention *toward* something. It is motivated by what Freud called the pleasure-principle, which in terms of bodily reactions is simply a sense of balance or ease. It will be seen that an element of choice is involved—a choice between the various mental combinations that might make for mental comfort. Where there is choice there is value. Value, as Piaget says, is the expression of desirability at all levels of experience, and it is my contention that the desirable values are always aesthetic—that is to say, determined by their contribution to whatever structure of experience gives the greatest pleasure to the organism. Such an ideal of equilibrium represents the final goal of our actions, and whatever means are used to attain this goal are the "values" involved not only in life's primary processes but also in the work of art. There is a continuous link between the methods that determine the origins of intelligence in the child and the methods that determine the beauty of a work of art.

We are still left with the problem of defining the values that make for ease and stability. There is a school of psychologists, of German origin, but now active in the United States, which has concentrated on this problem—the problem of why things look the way they do. They find the solution in perception itself. Perception is a process that gives a coherent order to the jumble of images received by the senses. We *learn* to see. We learn to give these images a good layout or *Gestalt* (the German word from which the school takes its name). According to Professor Koffka, the nervous system, under the impact of the stimulations that impinge on the retina of the eyes, "produces processes of organization in such a way that the pattern produced is the best possible under the prevailing conditions . . . thus color and brightness, shape and space, figure and background, location and motion, are all *interdependent* aspects of the organized pattern which ordinary visual stimulation will produce." In other words the way the nervous system develops its organized patterns is not very different from the way the artist paints his pictures. It is by this faculty of assimilating sensuous impressions from material things and then combining them in significant relationships, that the human race found its place in the world, and it is this faculty that contemporary man utilizes less and less. Mental faculties can develop only through use. Thus, the whole structure of human intelligence is now threatened at its foundations.

An infinite distance may seem to separate the sucking reflexes of an infant from the constructive intelligence needed to build a cathedral or compose a symphony, but the same laws of perception are involved. They are involved in any process of discrimination, which we have found to be the meaning of words like craft or skill. It follows that the same laws are also involved in the appreciation of a work of art, for the appreciation is based on a play of perceptual images that re-enacts the processes underlying artistic creation. An artist works toward a unity that emerges progressively from his perception and manipulation of material quantities, whereas we who appreciate the result begin with this unity and afterward become aware of the isolated quantities which have cohered to produce it.

We enjoy works of art because they possess these values of required order and unity. But what we do not often realize is that the same formal values differentiate intelligence from sensori-motor reflexes at every stage of human mental development.

A technological civilization has a devastating effect on these discriminative processes. True, we cannot yet generalize about our whole contemporary social structure; it varies from country to country, and there are entire nations, particularly in Asia and Africa, who, though enjoying the imported products of technology, are not yet subject to its immediate impact. What I have to say, therefore, applies mainly to North America and Europe, where the majority of the population has little or no sensuous contact with the soil, with animals, with the handling of wood, clay or metal. Progressive schools make some attempt to give the child sensuous experience. But technology is a ruthless tyranny, and its processes demand from the educational system a training directed exclusively toward conceptual modes of thought. "Money, mechanization, algebra. The three monsters of contemporary civilization." So wrote Simone Weil. . . .

But these, it will be said, are the methods by which science has won its greatest victories; to logic and mathematics, to introspection rather than observation, to hypothesis rather than classification, we owe the wonders (and the terrors) of our atomic age.

All true, and I shall not try to balance these scientific achievements against the evils that have accompanied them. I am concerned here with a social problem, with the anxiety, the all-prevailing sense of insecurity which undoubtedly motivates the crime and violence of our age.

Many earnest people call for moral sanctions. Man's ethical standards, they point out, have not kept pace with his scientific knowledge. He has lost his sense of sin, and has no fear of retribution. But our moral philosophers and religious leaders fail to indicate any practical methods for imbuing a technological civilization with ethical standards. Morality is not so much a question of beliefs as of habitual behavior, of tradition. Moral habits are acquired in the home, in the school, in the social milieu. One might say they are conditioned reflexes, like those of a domesticated animal. No man is good simply because he believes in goodness, but because the way of life in which he was brought up is good. What incentives to goodness exist in the mechanized ways of a technological society? This is not a political question, a question of the relative moral values of socialism or capitalism: all contemporary political systems are technological. In this respect their aims and ideals are identical. Technical idealism dominates the world, and overwhelms all forms of moral idealism.

What we must finally recognize is the existence of two distinct modes of intelligence: one, which might be called the Cartesian intelligence since it began with Descartes, who was the first philosopher to divorce reasoning from a sensuous dependence on things (I *think*, therefore I am); and one which might be called the aesthetic intelligence since it maintains contact with the sensuous world at every stage of its reasoning (I *feel*, therefore I am: reality is a creation of my senses). To the Cartesian intelligence we owe the great structures of rational or idealistic thought; to the aesthetic intelligence the discoveries of the physical sciences and the creation of works of art. In the modern world we have never kept a sensible balance between these two modes of intelligence, and so we have reached the abyss which now separates the man of feeling from the man of thought, the geometrician from the mathematician, the practical scientist from the scientific philosopher. Higher education in the modern world aspires to an ideal of mathematical perfection in which direct sensuous experience is no longer admitted as evidence. The only truths are logical, and they are of no practical importance.

To cultivate the aesthetic intelligence would require a complete change in the direction and ideals of education. To keep the child dependent on things only, as recommended by Rousseau, would mean a considerable sacrifice of the efforts which are now made to emancipate the child from things and make it dependent on words only; that is to say, on abstract thought. While not denying the disciplinary virtues of subjects like logic and algebra, their ideals should not be confused with those of the physical or natural sciences. Scientists like Newton and Einstein have proclaimed their dependence on the vivid imagery that comes from sensuous experience, or like Darwin have lamented a life devoted to abstractions.

Whether we are scientists or artists, our aim is what Wordsworth called "joy in widest commonalty spread": a society rid of its neuroses, a civilization rid of the threat of annihilating war. This aim will never be achieved by political legislation or by any form of totalitarian coercion. The change must come about organically, and must correspond to those vital laws which from the moment of birth determine the physical and psychological equilibrium of unfolding life.

These laws are known. It remains only to magnify them to the scale of our social problem and to animate them with that faith in life which is the finis sanction of all human endeavor. Life, in its intimate recesses, is intelligence, is creative, is art. But how shall we penetrate to these recesses and insure that life's creative forces are liberated?

Tolstoi had an answer to this question and I believe that it is the true answer. Tolstoi was not an impractical visionary. He was a man who had experienced to the full the passions and tragedies of life. He had been a soldier and a landowner, a father and a schoolmaster, a sinner and a saint; he had possessed great riches and given all that he had to the poor; he wrote the greatest prose epic of our time, and he ranks with the greatest figures of world literature. In What Is Art?, a mature work of his old age, he answered the question of the schoolboy Fedka— What is art for? He answered it in three clear sentences: the evolution of feeling proceeds by means of art; art is accessible to all men; art and only art can cause violence to be set aside. "The task of art is enormous. Through the influence of real art, aided by science, guided by religion, that peaceful co-operation of man which is now maintained by external means—by our law courts, police, charitable institutions, factory inspection, and so forth—should be obtained by man's free and joyous activity."

It is not necessary to agree with everything Tolstoi said about art—he sometimes allowed moral prejudices to cloud his aesthetic judgment. But he realized as no one since Plato had so clearly realized that art is not an ornamental addition to life, "not a pleasure, a solace, or an amusement. . . . Art is an organ of human life transmitting man's reasonable perception into feeling." Not only is art a process co-equally important with science for the life and progress of mankind but it has the unique function of uniting men in love of each other and of life itself. Why does one learn singing? What is drawing for? Tolstoi could now answer these questions and we can now answer them. The cultivation of the arts is an education of the sensibilities, and if we are not given an education of this kind, if our hands remain empty and our perception of form is unexercised, then in idleness and vacancy we revert to violence and crime. When there is no will to creation the death instinct takes over and wills endless, gratuitous destruction.

An education of the sensibilities—what I have elsewhere called an education through art—is not the present concern of our schools. Something is done at the primary stage—at kindergarten and infant schools; but the child is then quickly swallowed up in a system that ignores the evolution of feeling and provides no time for the free and joyous activity of art. To know becomes the exclusive aim of education: to create is the concern of a tiny minority that evades the social pattern of our technological civilization. The growing child gradually loses all contact with things, all capacity to manipulate materials or discriminate forms. Unless we can discover a method of basing education on these primary biological processes, not only shall we fail to create a society united in love: we shall continue to sink deeper into disunity, mass neuroses and war.

The kind of curriculum required for such a method of education is not a vague ideal; it was given a convincing demonstration almost forty years ago when Walter Gropius established his Bauhaus School of Design in Germany. As Doctor Gropius wrote in his Adventures of the Mind article (The Curse of Conformity): "I shared the belief that it was essential to select talented young people before they had either surrendered to the conformity of the industrial community or withdrawn into ivory towers. We proposed to train them to bridge the gap between the rigid mentality of the businessman and technologist and the imagination of the creative artist."

It remains for us to extend and apply to all stages, the principles Doctor Gropius worked out for a postgraduate stage of education.

Further reading:

Read, Sir Herbert: EDUCATION THROUGH ART. New York: Pantheon Books; 1958.

Arnheim, Rudolf: ART AND VISUAL PERCEPTION: PSYCHOLOGY OF THE CREATIVE EYE. Berkeley: University of California Press; 1954.

Kohler, Wolfgang: GESTALT PSYCHOLOGY. New York: Liveright Publishing Corporation; 1947.

Piaget, Jean: THE ORIGIN OF INTELLIGENCE IN CHILDREN. Translated by Margaret Cook. New York: International Universities Press; 1952.

Tolstoi, Leo: WHAT IS ART? AND ESSAYS ON ART. Translated by Aylmer Maude. World's Classics. New York: Oxford University Press.

ꙮꙮꙮꙮꙮꙮꙮꙮꙮꙮꙮꙮꙮꙮꙮꙮꙮꙮꙮꙮꙮꙮ

When Time Began

BY

FRED HOYLE

Fred Hoyle, mathematician and astrophysicist, is a forty-four-year-old Yorkshireman who recently became one of Cambridge University's youngest professors. As Plumian Professor of Astronomy and Experimental Philosophy at St. John's College, Professor Hoyle divides his time between teaching at Cambridge and research at Mount Wilson and Mount Palomar observatories in California. A writer of diverse talents, Professor Hoyle has produced, in addition to his scientific papers, several popular books on cosmology and an eerie novel of science fiction, The Black Cloud. *Another novel is on the way.*

Throughout the centuries man, gazing at the night sky in wonder, has never ceased to speculate about the larger aspects of the universe around him. How and when and why did it all begin and will there be an end? I shall here describe three different theories which attempt to probe these mysteries of time and space and matter. They will be referred to as the Explosion Theory, the Expansion-Contraction Theory and the Steady-State Theory. Before we begin this cosmological exploration, however, we must understand the background common to all three theories.

Our modern ideas concerning the larger aspects of the universe are both more detailed and more consistent than those of former ages. Observations can now be made, with both radio and visual telescopes, that were impossible a decade ago. We are even beginning to overcome the handicaps imposed on us by the terrestrial atmosphere, through the use of instruments mounted in satellites. And our recent advances in particle physics now enable us to calculate accurately how matter behaves under the extremely varied conditions found throughout the universe.

Space is populated by vast galaxies of stars. The Milky Way, of which the earth is part, is such a galaxy. The galaxies tend to be distributed in groups, sometimes in big groups with as many as a thousand galaxies, sometimes in small groups of only two or three galaxies. Our galaxy belongs to a small collection known as the local group. It has only two main members, the Milky Way and the famous galaxy, M-31, which is seen through the constellation of Andromeda—a configuration of Milky Way stars. If you know exactly where to look, you can see this second galaxy with the naked eye on a dark, clear night.

About a thousand million galaxies lie within the range of the Hale 200-inch telescope on Mt. Palomar in California. They can be observed at the stupendous distance of some 30,000,-000,000,000,000,000,000 (30 sextillion) miles. Almost certainly our terrestrial telescopes do not mark the limit of the universe; the galaxies may be strewn through space without limit.

The galaxies move around within their particular group, and sometimes two of them collide at high speed. In such a collision the component stars rarely hit each other, because they are small and the distances between them great. But the galaxies also contain huge clouds of gas, and these clouds do collide.

In such an encounter the gas moves with violent turbulence, and becomes intensely hot. A colossal emission of radio waves then seems to result. A radio station on earth, with an output of 100 kilowatts, is considered fairly powerful. Two such colliding galaxies observed in the constellation of Cygnus emit some 10,-000,000,000,000,000,000,000,000,000,000,000 (10 decillion) kilowatts.

Here we come to the most crucial point. Observations indicate that the different clusters of galaxies are constantly moving apart from each other. To illustrate by a homely analogy, think of a raisin cake baking in an oven. Suppose the cake swells uniformly as it cooks, but the raisins themselves remain of the same size. Let each raisin represent a cluster of galaxies, and imagine yourself inside one of them. As the cake swells, you will observe that all the other raisins move away from you. Moreover, the farther away the raisin, the faster it will seem to move. When the cake has swollen to twice its initial dimensions, the distance between all the raisins will have doubled itself—two raisins that were initially an inch apart will now be two inches apart; two raisins that were a foot apart will have moved two feet apart. Since the entire action takes place within the same time interval, obviously the more distant raisins must move apart faster than those close at hand. So it happens with the clusters of galaxies.

The analogy brings out another important point. No matter which raisin you happen to be inside, the others will always move away from you. Hence the fact that we observe all the other clusters of galaxies to be moving away from us *does not mean that we are situated at the center of the universe.* Indeed, it seems certain that the universe has no center. A cake may be said to have a center only because it has a boundary. We must imagine the cake to extend outward without any boundary, an infinite cake, so to speak, which means that however much cake we care to consider there is always more.

This brings us to the Explosion Theory. In expansion, as we have seen, the clusters of galaxies move apart from each other. It can therefore be argued that space is becoming emptier as time goes on. The same argument suggests that space was formerly more densely occupied. Indeed, if the universe has always been in a state of expansion, space must once have been jammed tight with galaxies. Astrophysicists have calculated that the universe was apparently packed tight roughly eight or nine billion years ago.

According to an entirely different line of reasoning, the ages of stars inside our own galaxy can be determined by considering the nuclear processes within them. By this calculation the oldest stars also originated about eight or nine billion years ago. The agreement between the two methods of calculating is highly interesting. It would appear that the universe originated nearly ten billion years ago, and that our galaxy was formed about a billion years later.

The essential concept is that universal matter was originally in a state of very high density, enormously greater than the density of the galaxies today. This original matter we assume to have been explosive. The whole universe expanded rapidly, its initial state of very high density lasting only a few minutes. In time the continuing expansion produced less and less density. After almost a billion years of expansion and decreasing density, the clusters of galaxies formed. They have since continued to move apart and will go on moving apart throughout eternity.

Thus, according to the Explosion Theory, the universe was born a definite time ago. The state of dispersal caused by the explosion will never cease in this theory. The galaxies will continue to move apart from each other until, in the ultimate limit in the future, space will present a uniform, featureless emptiness. All activity inside the galaxies will ultimately cease. The stars will no longer shine. All sources of energy will be exhausted.

Until very recently, astronomers and physicists thought this theory could be supported by a further powerful argument. The 100 or so known chemical elements possess curious regularities in the abundances with which they exist in nature. These regularities indicate that some process of building from hydrogen, the simplest element, has been at work. But if complex elements have been formed from the simplest, if carbon, oxygen, iron, have been "made," the great question is how?

At first thought it seemed as if the first few minutes of universal explosion provided the ideal conditions for the creation of complex elements—that is, extreme density combined with extreme heat. In short, it looked as if the complex elements might be relics of the earliest period in the history of the universe.

Flaws in this argument soon appeared, however. In the first place, it contains hypotheses that contradict our knowledge of nuclear physics. Moreover, it would lead us to expect to find the same proportions of complex atoms in all stars. For if the process that originated complex atoms were truly universal, there should be no purely local variations of composition. Yet such local variations are marked. The oldest stars to have formed in our galaxy have been found to possess very low concentrations of the complex atoms, much lower than in middle-age stars—the sun, for example. This strongly suggests that production of the complex atoms takes place inside the stars and has nothing to do with the early history of the universe.

We must therefore turn the whole question inside out and ask why no nuclear relics remain from the early superdense state of matter, if indeed there ever was a superdense state. A satisfactory technical answer can be given, provided the early state was even hotter than we formerly thought. For we now know that a still-higher temperature, instead of promoting fusion, prevents hydrogen from fusing to produce complex elements. This realization led to a modification of the Explosion Theory. It is called the Expansion-Contraction Theory.

Some astronomers think that the original explosion of the superdense material may not have been sufficiently violent to produce a complete dispersal. They believe that the clusters of galaxies are moving apart from each other at a markedly declining rate, and that eventually expansion will cease altogether. Gravitational attraction will then cause the clusters to start moving together. This means that the universe will pass into a phase of contraction. The clusters will approach each other at ever-increasing speeds until the galaxies collide. Still further contraction will cause even the stars to collide. As a consequence of the greatly rising temperature that accompanies such a strong compression, the complex atoms will disintegrate and be transformed back into hydrogen. The stage will thereby be set for a reversal of the contraction process, and another universal expansion.

Here, then, is a very different picture—a cyclic universe, with expansion and contraction alternating. During expansion, galaxies and stars are formed. Hydrogen supplies energy inside the stars and is gradually changed into complex elements. During contraction, the galaxies and stars are disrupted, and the complex elements are broken down by the high temperature generated at the stage of greatest compression. Each cycle is similar to the previous one, and there is no limit to the number of cycles. Each cycle lasts roughly thirty billion years. The universe is now about halfway through an expansion phase.

According to the Expansion-Contraction Theory, the amount of matter in the universe is finite. Even the volume of space itself is finite, in somewhat the same way as the area of the surface of a sphere is finite. During expansion, all space swells up like an expanding balloon. During contraction, space collapses literally to a point.

The third theory—the Steady-State Theory—differs in almost all essentials both from the Explosion Theory and from the Expansion-Contraction Theory. The first two theories rest on the assumption that all matter now existing also existed in the past. The argument for a superdense state of the universe disappears if this assumption is false. It is therefore important to examine the possibility that much of the matter now in existence was not in existence in the past, and that much of the matter of the universe that will be in existence in the future is not in existence today.

What do the physicists say about this question? They consider no particle of matter permanent. One particle can be changed into another; new particles can be created. These processes take place partly through fields of force associated with the atomic-nuclear particles, partly through the electromagnetic field. These are the fields responsible for holding the atomic nuclei together, and for propagating all forms of electromagnetic disturbance, such as light, X rays and radio waves.

Such impermanence scarcely seems important in the problem of the expansion of the universe, however, for here we have to consider impermanence, not in the nuclear or electromagnetic field, but in the gravitational field—the field that brings a parachutist back to the ground, that holds the earth in its orbit around the sun. It is the main controlling field of the cosmos. But modern physicists can tell us very little about the properties of gravitation. They have been unable to gather adequate information from experimental laboratory work.

Gravitation is difficult to study in the laboratory, because in the laboratory we are limited to small quantities of matter. These small quantities suffice to produce the full impact of the nuclear and electromagnetic fields. Indeed, the nuclear field can be studied in a single atom by itself. In order to assess the full impact of gravitation, however, we would have to measure the gravitational forces of the entire universe, because all the atoms in the universe add their gravitation contributions together. Thus gravitation cannot be studied piecemeal; it must be measured in its totality. No satisfactory way of doing this has yet been found.

So, lacking adequate information from the laboratory, we have no choice but to weigh the two possibilities—first, that particles have permanence in the gravitational field; second, that they have impermanence. The Explosion Theory and the Expansion-Contraction Theory demand permanent particles because they exclude the possibility of the continuous creation of matter. The Steady-State Theory requires impermanent particles because it postulates such a continuous creation.

Einstein's general theory of relativity provides a powerful framework within which the possibility of impermanence can be tested. But if we accept that framework, we are not free to formulate the hypothesis of impermanence exactly as we might like. In return for the advantages it offers, the relativity theory imposes constraints.

These constraints can be met. As they are met, it emerges that impermanence must take the form either of a steady creation of matter or of a steady annihilation, but it cannot take the form of both together. We cannot have creation in one part of the universe and annihilation in another. The creation of matter is linked to the expansion of the universe. According to Einsteinian mathematics, space cannot accommodate more than a certain fixed average density of matter. Therefore, we cannot have a steady creation of matter without a steady expansion of the universe. Conversely, we cannot have a steady annihilation without a contraction of the universe, Obviously, expansion and contraction of space cannot take place at the same time—just as a balloon cannot be simultaneously inflated and deflated.

We are thus faced with the alternatives of creation plus expansion or of annihilation plus contraction. In theory we must weigh both these alternatives, because every physical hypothesis considers two possible ways of viewing the direction of time—the case where time runs forward into the future in the usual sense, and the case where time runs backward into the past. An analogy might be found in unrolling a strip of carpet from beginning to end—from the past through the present to the future; reverse the process and you go from the end to the beginning, or from the future to the past. In practice, when we restrict ourselves to the usual sense of past and future, the relativity theory gives us just the one possibility—that of the creation of matter allied firmly to the expansion of the universe.

The maintenance of a constant average density of matter in space leads to the Steady-State Theory, first discussed by Prof. Hermann Bondi, Prof. Thomas Gold and myself some ten years ago. Because the density remains constant, the condensation of clusters of galaxies should apply to the present and future as well as to the past. More recently, Gold and I have been exploring the possibility that the matter in space may be extremely hot, and that the formation of galaxies arises from a cooling process within localized blobs of material. The pressure inside the blobs is thereby reduced below that existing in the still-hot surrounding material. This causes strong compression of the blobs. In proceeding on this assumption we find that many of the difficulties formerly encountered in trying to understand the genesis of galaxies disappear. We also find that the cooling process may be associated with the production of cosmic radio waves and with the origin of cosmic rays. We tend to believe that such a cooling is going on at present in many of the distant radio sources observed by radio-astronomers, and that in these sources we are observing a phase in the process of formation of new galaxies.

In the Steady-State Theory the clusters of galaxies expand apart, but as they do so new galaxies are born, and at such a rate that their average density in space remains unaltered with time. The individual clusters change and evolve, but the universe itself, viewed on the large scale, does not change. Thus the old problem of the beginning and end of the universe does not arise at all in the Steady-State Theory, for the universe did not have a beginning and it will not have an end. Every cluster of galaxies, every star, every atom, had a beginning, but the universe itself did not.

The perceptive reader may here find himself pondering the destiny of the distant galaxies in an ever-expanding universe without an end. As we demonstrated in our raisin-cake analogy, the more distant the galaxy, the faster it will move away from the observer. This relationship between distance and velocity is an observable fact and is measured by the so-called "red shift," by which certain wave lengths of the light from a given star shift across the spectrum. A similar shift, in the sound spectrum, is noticed when the pitch of a train whistle decreases as the train moves away from the listener. The speed of the distant galaxy continues to increase until, presumably, it exceeds the speed of light—186,000 miles per second.* At that point the light emanating from the stars in the galaxy is being carried away at a velocity exceeding its return speed, and the galaxy as an observable fact is lost to us forever.

These, then, are the dominant hypotheses concerning the structure of the universe. The decision among them rests with observation. As an example, it would be of great interest to know whether new galaxies are being formed at the present time. If new galaxies are being formed, the Explosion Theory and the Expansion-Contraction Theory would be suspect because they do not provide for such creation. If new galaxies are not being formed, the Steady-State Theory becomes untenable.

Although many such observational tests are being actively worked on, it must be realized that cosmological observations are very difficult to make. The tests are all concerned with objects that lie very far away from us. This forces the observer to work near the limit of reliability of his instruments. In these circumstances only great persistence and care, combined with fine judgment, will separate the genuine from the spurious. A decision among the different theories, therefore, is not an issue that

* This does not contradict Einstein's statement that no material body *in our particular locality* can move faster than light; a distant body is not so limited. Ed.

can be hastened. Only the slow evolution of astronomy will enable us to reach an unambiguous decision.

In the meantime we must fall back on philosophic criteria for distinguishing between the different pictures presented by astronomical theory. Such criteria are by no means to be decried, so long as it is clearly understood that observational tests must take priority, once the appropriate observational results become available.

The Explosion Theory gives us the picutre of the universe as an explosion from a superdense state of matter. Many people are especially attracted to this hypothesis because it requires a definite moment of creation for the whole universe. According to this theory, the universe is not a self-operating concern. It has to be started, much as one might switch on a huge machine. There are many questions relating to this hypothesis that we can never hope to answer, for many of the present-day characteristics of the universe depend on the precise manner of the "switching on" process. There is also a philosophic undercurrent of an existence outside the universe that touches on religion, a feature that seems attractive to some and unappealing to others.

The Expansion-Contraction Theory and the Steady-State Theory are similar in that they both present the universe as a fully self-operating system. There is no moment of origin, time extends backward into the past as far as we care to consider it. Otherwise these two theories are very different, the one depending on permanence and the other on impermanence of particles in the gravitational field.

Space and time play very different roles in the three theories. In the Explosion Theory, space is infinite, while time is finite toward the past and infinite toward the future. In the Expansion-Contraction Theory, time is infinite in both the past and future, but space is finite. In the Steady-State Theory, space and time are both infinite. Moreover, space and time have a still deeper connection in the Steady-State Theory. This is a point of such considerable interest as to be worth a short diversion.

The concept of the equivalence of spatial observers has been used in cosmology for many years. This simply means that observers situated at widely different points of space will observe exactly the same large-scale structure of the universe—that the universe has no point of space from which things look any different than they do from other points of space. An observer in a distant galaxy would see large-scale features entirely similar to those that we ourselves observe. This important condition is satisfied in both the Explosion Theory and the Expansion-Contraction Theory provided *one crucial requirement is met*—that the observers look at the universe at the same moment of time. Equivalence is lost in these theories if this proviso is not satisfied because time is linked with nonrecurring cosmological changes. An evolving universe, in which space becomes progressively less dense with matter, must present different aspects to an observer viewing it at different moments of time. *But equivalence is still maintained in the Steady-State Theory even if observers look at the universe at different times*, for there is a continuing pattern of development. A universe which maintains its general cosmological structure through the continuous creation of matter will present the same aspect to observers at any moment of time.

This wider interpretation of equivalence provides one of the strongest aesthetic reasons for preferring the Steady-State Theory. Moreover, the whole progress of modern physics has been closely bound up with the discovery of relations that are independent of the special position of the observer. For this reason alone, I feel that it would be most surprising if the Steady-State Theory, with its compelling space-time equivalence, should turn out to be wrong.

I would like to present my own point of view on all these questions, to give my reasons for preferring the Steady-State Theory to its rivals. These reasons are for the most part philosophical in character. But first there is one purely scientific point that must be mentioned. In the Steady-State Theory all observable features of the universe must be the consequences of processes that are going on all the time: We cannot take refuge in the argument that things were different in the past, as it is possible to do in the other theories. This means that every feature of the universe must be susceptible to the principle of observational investigation. Thus the Steady-State Theory aims to place observation on a very much firmer footing than is the case in rival theories.

Considerations of elegance and economy also appear to be highly relevant. In both the Explosion Theory and the Expansion-Contraction Theory all matter is supposed to have been in a hot superdense condition. Yet, as we have seen, this condition cannot have promoted any nuclear reactions. The superdense state of matter must be designed specifically to prevent nuclear reactions from taking place. Indeed, the universe must be constructed in a way that hides from us all direct evidence of the existence of this singular state. Personally I find it difficult to place much credence in this very negative supposition. It would seem to be more natural to believe that a superdense state never existed at all.

In the Expansion-Contraction Theory we are asked to think of expansion and contraction following each other in a never-ending series. During expansion, matter becomes organized into galaxies, stars, planets, living creatures. During contraction the galaxies, stars, and so on, are entirely disintegrated in preparation for the succeeding phase of expansion. Each cycle is exactly similar to the preceding cycle. Nothing new ever happens from cycle to cycle, and it is just this that seems uninspired and inelegant. This is an aesthetic rather than a scientific objection, but it may be worth adding that scientists are more concerned with aesthetics than is commonly supposed!

What then of the Steady-State universe? This third picture might seem at first sight to contain a similar inelegance. But it turns out that there is an important sense in which this is not so. I would like to begin the explanation of this point with another diversion.

In recent years physicists have come to pose a very important question: How deep are the laws of physics? How far must one dig before nothing basically new remains to be discovered, before the level of absolute truth is revealed? Twice during the past seventy years scientists have believed themselves within sighting distance of the ultimate laws of physics. On both occasions their optimism was unfounded. The tendency is now rather to ask: Are there any ultimate final laws of physics?

Might it not be that however deep one digs, there are always still deeper levels of subtlety to be uncovered? Nowadays the trend is to answer the last question affirmatively, to believe that no end will be found to the intricacy of the laws of physics.

Such a point of view makes sense in the Steady-State Theory but not, I think, in the other theories. In the Expansion-Contraction Theory, for instance, we have a universe that is entirely finite—a finite amount of matter, finite space, a finite time of cycling. It seems to me most doubtful whether such a universe could possibly accommodate laws of an infinite complexity. The situation is better in the Explosion Theory. Here we could possibly have an infinite universe with infinite laws—but one in which only a finite fragment of the laws was discoverable. For in the Explosion Theory there is but one single generation of galaxies. The stars and the living creatures in these galaxies live only for a finite time of a few tens of billions of years. Hence any understanding gained by living creatures must always remain finite. Digging beyond a certain finite depth would manifestly be impossible.

The situation is otherwise in the Steady-State Theory. Here it is possible to accumulate knowledge indefinitely, to dig to any depth, however deep. Here we have an unending series of generations of galaxies. When a particular galaxy dies, the knowledge that has been gained by creatures in it can (in principle!) be passed to a nearby younger galaxy. This process can be repeated without end, so that in the long run knowledge can be piled up to any required degree. Here we have a universe that is infinite, not only in its obvious physical characteristics but also in its intellectual possibilities.

Further reading:

 Hoyle, Fred: FRONTIERS OF ASTRONOMY. New York: Harper and Brothers; 1955.

 Hubble, Edwin: THE REALM OF THE NEBULAE. New York: Dover Publications; 1958.

 Lyttleton, Raymond A.: A MODERN UNIVERSE. New York: Harper and Brothers; 1957.

 THE UNIVERSE. By the editors of *Scientific American*. New York: Simon and Schuster; 1957.

How War Began

BY

LEWIS MUMFORD

Lewis Mumford, writer, cultural philosopher, architectural and urban-planning critic, classifies himself as a "generalist" whose forte is "not in finding or fabricating the pieces, but in putting them together into a significant picture." An early public advocate (1935) of military resistance to the antidemocratic totalitarian powers, Mr. Mumford lost his son in World War II. Author of twenty-two books, onetime faculty member of five universities, now Ford Research Professor at the University of Pennsylvania, Mr. Mumford lives at Amenia, New York.

At the time that the first great civilizations of the ancient world were coming into existence, the human race suffered an injury from which it has not yet recovered. If I interpret the evidence correctly, that injury still plays an active part in our lives, and caps our most hopeful dreams about human improvement with nightmares of destruction and extermination.

This injury happened at a moment when primitive man's powers, like ours today, had suddenly expanded; and it was due essentially to an aberration, or a series of aberrations, which put his most beneficent inventions at the command of his neurotic anxieties. So, far from disappearing with time and being healed by the growth of law and reason, this original injury has only tightened its hold upon the collective actions of tribes and nations.

The aberration I refer to is the institution of war; and my purpose in discussing its origins is to bring into consciousness a group of events and beliefs that have long remained buried, partly through sheer neglect, partly through a repression of painful irrationalities that contradicted civilized man's belief in his own orderly and rational behavior. It is only today, after a century of prodigious research into human origins, that some of these events have come to light and been thrown open to interpretation.

That early injury had an effect upon civilized life, somewhat comparable to the kind of childhood injury that psychiatrists characterize as a trauma: an injury whose worst results may not show themselves till far on in adult life. Instead of being buried in the psyche of an individual, it became embedded in the institutional life of every succeeding city, state and empire.

In making this analysis, I shall have to start from an assumption that is unprovable; namely, that there is a parallel between the general human situation today and that faced by the individual, unable to cope with the problems of his life, unable to make rational decisions, baffled, depressed, paralyzed, because he is still the prey of infantile fantasies he is unable to escape or control. In the case of individuals, we know that such fantasies, deeply embedded in childhood, may keep on poisoning the whole system, though the wound has seemingly healed and the scar is hardly visible. Childhood misapprehensions, animosities and resentments, childhood misinterpretations of natural events, such as birth, death, separation—all account for the persistence of infantile patterns of conduct. Often, later in life, these patterns overcome the adult and leave him helpless. He still views present realities through the distorting glasses of his childhood fantasy.

That something unfortunate once happened to man at the very moment when an immense creativity was released was perhaps recognized in part in the Jewish and Christian myth of the Fall, which was anticipated by even earlier Egyptian lamentations over the perverse wickedness of man in going contrary to the gods. Many other peoples, from China to Greece, looked back to a golden age when war and strife were unknown, and when, as Lao-tse put it, one village might look at the smoke rising from the chimneys of another nearby, without envy or rivalry.

There is now enough anthropological and archaeological evidence to show that there is at least a partial basis for these wistful memories of a more peaceful past, when scarcity of food, violence, danger and death were mainly the results of natural disasters, not the deliberate products of man. If civilization's first great achievements awakened new fears and anxieties, we must understand how and why this happened; for these fears and anxieties still press on us. As long as the source of our irrational acts remains hidden, the forces that are still driving us to destruction will seem uncontrollable. The worst part about civilized man's original errors and the most threatening aspect of our present situation are that we regard some of our most self-destructive acts as normal and unavoidable.

There is a close parallel between our own age, exalted yet stunned by the seemingly limitless expansion of all its powers, and the epoch that marked the emergence of the earliest civilizations in Egypt and Mesopotamia. In his pride over his present accomplishments, it is perhaps natural for modern man to think that such a vast release of physical energy and human potentiality had never taken place before. But on examination this proves a too flattering illusion: the two ages of power, modern and ancient, are bound together by many similar characteristics, both good and evil, which set them apart from other phases of human history.

Just as the prelude to the nuclear age came with the large-scale introduction of water, wind and steam power, so the first steps toward civilization were taken in the neolithic domestication of plants and animals. This agricultural revolution gave man food, energy, security and surplus manpower on a scale no earlier culture had known. Among the achievements that mark this transformation from barbarism to civilization were the beginnings of astronomy and mathematics, the first astronomical calendar, the sailboat, the plow, the potter's wheel, the loom, the irrigation canal, the man-powered machine. Civilized man's emotional and intellectual potentialities were raised further through the invention of writing, the elaboration of the permanent record in painting, sculpture and monuments, and the building of walled cities.

This great leap forward came to a climax about 5000 years ago. A like mobilization and magnification of power did not again take place until our own era. For most of recorded history, mankind has lived on the usufruct of that early advance, making many piecemeal additions and widening the province held by civilization, but never essentially changing the original pattern.

There was probably an important religious side to this whole transformation. With the priestly observations that produced the measured months and years, people became conscious, as never before, of human dependence upon the cosmic forces, the sun, the moon, the planets, on whose operations all life depended. Planetary movement of "clockwork" regularity gave man his first glimpse of an orderly, repetitive, impersonal world, utterly reliable, but benignly productive only within the frame of its inflexible laws.

With this new cosmic theology there came a sudden fusion of sacred and secular power, in the person of the all-powerful king, standing at the apex of the social pyramid. The king was both a secular ruler and the chief priest or even, in the case of the Egyptians, a living god. He no longer needed to follow village tradition and customs, like the village council of elders. His will was law. Kingship by divine right claimed magic powers and evoked magic collective responses.

What kingly power could not do solely by intimidation, and what magical rites and orderly astronomical observation could not do alone by successful prediction, the two in combination actually did accomplish. Large assemblages of men moved and acted as if they were one, obedient to the royal command, fulfilling the will of the gods and rulers. People were driven to heroic physical efforts and sacrifices beyond all precedent. Throughout history, the major public works—canals, embankments, roads, walls, "pyramids" in every form—have been built with forced labor, either conscripted for part of the year or permanently enslaved. The enduring symbol of this vast expansion and regimentation of power is, of course, the Great Pyramid of Cheops, built without wheeled vehicles or iron tools, by relays of 100,000 men working over many years.

Should we be surprised that the achievements of our own age of nuclear power appeared first at this period as myths and fantasies associated with the gods? Absolute power, power to create and annihilate, became the attribute of a succession of deities. Out of his own substance the Egyptian sun god, Atum, created the universe. Instantaneous communication, remote control, the collective incineration of whole cities (Sodom and Gomorrah), and germ warfare (one of the plagues of Egypt) were freely practiced by a succession of inhumane deities in order to insure that their commands would be obeyed. Human rulers, who still lacked the facilities to carry out these dreams on a great scale, nevertheless sought to counterfeit them. With the growth of an efficient bureaucracy, a trained army, systematic taxation and forced labor, this early totalitarian system showed all the depressing features that similar governments show in our own day.

An overconcentration on power as an end in itself is always suspect to the psychologist. He reads in it attempts to conceal inferiority, anxiety and impotence. Perhaps early civilized man was justifiably frightened by the forces he himself had brought into existence, in the way that many people are frightened now by nuclear power. In neither case was the extension of physical power and political command accompanied by a complementary development of moral direction and humane control.

There were further grounds for doubt and fear among men of that early civilization. Though they had achieved a hitherto unattainable security and wealth, the very growth of population and the extension of trade made their whole economy more subject to conditions and forces they could not control.

Our age knows how difficult it is to achieve equilibrium and security in an economy of abundance. But the early fabric of civilization was far more precariously balanced, since the welfare of the whole was based on the magical identification of the king and the community in the beliefs and rites of their religion. The

king personified the community; he was the indispensable con-
necting link between ordinary men and the cosmic powers they
must propitiate and obey. While the king assumed full responsibility for the life and welfare of his subjects, the community,
in turn, waxed and waned with the life of its ruler.

The magical identification produced a further occasion for
anxiety, far deeper than any threat of actual floods or bad crops;
for despite their claims to divine favor and immortality, kings too
were subject to mortal accidents and misfortunes. So constant
was this anxiety that the Egyptian Pharaoh's name could not be
uttered without interjecting the prayer, "Life! Prosperity!
Health!" This identification of the king's life with the community's fate produced an even more sinister perversion. To
avert the wrath of the gods, indicated by any natural mischance,
the king himself must be slain as a sacrifice. At this early stage,
dream and fact, myth and hallucination, religion and science
formed a confused welter. One lucky change in weather after a
ritual sacrifice might give sanction to a long-repeated chain of
ritualistic slaughters.

To save the king from this discouraging fate, which might
lessen the attractions of the office, a further trick of religious
magic came into play. A stand-in would be chosen and temporarily treated with all the honors and privileges of a king, in order to perform the final role of sacrificial victim on the altar. As
the demand for such victims increased in times of trouble, these
substitutes were sought outside the community, by violent capture. And what began as a one-sided raid for captives in time
brought about the collective reprisals and counterraids that became institutionalized as war. Back of war lay this barbarous religious sanction: only by human sacrifice can the community be
saved.

War, then, was a specific product of civilization—the outcome
of an organized effort to obtain captives for a magical blood sacrifice. In time, armed might itself took on a seemingly independent existence, and the extension of power became an end in itself, a manifestation of the "health" of the state. But underneath
the heavy overlayers of rationalization, war remained colored by
the original infantile misconception that communal life and

prosperity could be preserved only by sacrificial expiation. Civilized man's later efforts to impute the origin of war to some primal animal instinct toward murderous aggression against his own kind are empty rationalizing. Here the words of the anthropologist, Bronislaw Malinowski, are decisive, "If we insist that war is a fight between two independent and politically organized groups, war does not occur at a primitive level."

What is most remarkable about the spread of war as a permanent institution is that the collective anxiety that originally brought about the ritual of human sacrifice seems to have deepened with material progress. And as anxiety increased, it could no longer be appeased by a mere symbolic sacrifice at the altar, for the ritual itself produced hatred, fear and a natural desire for revenge among the peoples victimized. In time ever greater numbers, with more effective weapons, were drawn into the brutal ceremony, so that what was at first a preliminary, one-sided raid before the sacrifice became the essential sacrifice itself. The alternative to permitting the mass slaughter of one's own people was the destruction of the enemy's city and temple and the enslavement of the population. These acts periodically eased anxiety and enhanced power. War provided a kind of self-justification in displacing neurotic anticipations by actual dangers—that return to reality seems to restore human equipoise. Psychiatrists observed during the blitz in London that the need for facing real dangers often removed a patient's load of neurotic anxiety. But war performs this service at a ghastly price. Psychologically healthy people have no need to court dismemberment and death.

The growth of law and orderly behavior and morals, which improved the relation of men in cities, was not transferred to the collective relations of communities; for the ability to produce disorder, violence and destruction itself remained a symbol of royal power. From the relatively peaceful Egyptians to the bloodthirsty Assyrians and Mongolians, one monument after another boasts of kings humiliated, prisoners killed, cities ruined. The solemn association of kingship, sacred power, human sacrifice and military effectiveness formed a dominant complex that governed human behavior everywhere. But in time the search for sacrificial captives took on a utilitarian disguise—if spared as slaves, they added to the labor force. So the secondary products of military effort—slaves, booty, land, tribute—supplanted and concealed the original anxiety motive. Since a general expansion of productive power and culture had accompanied kingship and human sacrifice, people were conditioned to accept the evil as the only way of securing the good. The repeated death of civilizations from internal disintegration and outward assault underscores the fact that the evil elements in this amalgam largely canceled the goods and blessings.

This perception is not a discovery of modern historians. After the eighth century B.C. the working principles of a power-centered civilization were boldly challenged by a long series of religious prophets, from Amos and Isaiah to Lao-tse and Mo Ti. Whatever their differences the exponents of these new ideas scorned the notion of a mere increase of power and material wealth as the central purpose of life. In the name of peace and love they rejected irrational human sacrifice in every form—on the altar or on the battlefield. Christianity went even further. Alone among the religions, instead of sacrificing human beings to appease the divine wrath, its God sacrificed himself, renouncing His power in behalf of love, in order to save mankind by cleansing the sinner of anxiety and guilt.

But the power complex, embedded in the routines of civilization, was not dislodged by even this challenge. Ironically, Christianity itself supplanted its pagan rivals by seizing the power of the state under Constantine (A.D. 313) and utilizing all its engines of compulsion. As in the times of Moloch and Bel, the bloodiest collective sacrifices in history were those made in wars to establish the supremacy of a state religion.

How are we to explain the persistence of war, with its victories that turn out as disastrous as its defeats, its just causes that produce unjust or contradictory consequences, and its heroic martyrdoms sullied and betrayed by the base, selfish conduct of the survivors? There seem to me two general answers. One is that the original pattern of civilization, as it took form in the walled city and in turn produced the "walled" state, has remained unaltered until modern times. War was an integral part of the constellation of civilized institutions, held in tension within the city, on the basis of a division of classes, slavery and forced labor, and religious uniformity. To remove any part of this fabric seemed, to the rulers of men, a threat to every other part. They exalted the sacrifices of war because they wanted to maintain their own power.

There was an additional mitigating factor: until recent times, only a small part of the world's population accepted the terms of civilized life and its constant involvement with war; moreover, the amount of damage any army could inflict was limited. In Christian nations the human cost of war had been further reduced by the acceptance of a military code that limited violence to armed soldiers and generally exempted civilians and even their property from capture or deliberate destruction. Finally, the greater part of the world's population, living in rural communities, immune by their feebleness and poverty from the rapacious temptations of urbanized power, constituted a reservoir of vitality and sanity.

These mitigations and compensations progressively reduced the evils of total war as practiced by the early empires; but neither the needs of commerce, nor the admonitions of religion, nor the bitter experience of bereavement and enslavement altered the basic pattern. By any reasonable standard, war should early have been classed with individual murder, as an unqualified collective crime or an insane act, but those who held power never permitted any subversive judgment on the irrationality of the method, even if applied to rational ends. The fact that war has persisted and now threatens, at the very peak of our advances in science and technology, to become all-enveloping and all-destructive, points to the deep irrationality that first brought it into existence. This irrationality springs not only from the original aberration but from the unconscious depths of man, plagued with repressed guilt and anxiety over the godlike powers he presumptuously has learned to wield.

Western culture during the last four centuries has produced an explosive release of human potentialities and powers. Unfortunately the irrationalities of the past have been subjected to a similar projection and magnification.

The most formidable threat we confront, perhaps, is the fact that the fantasies that governed the ancient founders of civilization have now become fully realizable. Our most decisive recent inventions, the atom bomb and the planetary rocket, came about through a fusion of secular and "sacred" power, similar to their ancient union. Without the physical resources of an all-powerful state and the intellectual resources of an all-knowing corps of scientsts, that sudden command of cosmic energy and interplanetary space would not have been possible. Powers of total destruction that ancient man dared impute only to his gods, any mere Russian or American air-force general can now command. So wide and varied are the means of extermination by blast and radiation burns, by slow contamination from radioactive food and water, to say nothing of lethal bacteria and genetic deformities, that the remotest hamlet is in as great peril as a metropolis. The old factor of safety has vanished.

As our agents of destruction have reached cosmic dimensions, both our tangible fears and our neurotic apprehensions have increased until they are so terrifying to live with that they are involuntarily repressed. This repression is particularly notable in America, where it is marked by the virtual absence of any discussion or critical challenge of either our nuclear weapons or our ultimate aims. This is perhaps an indication of the unconscious guilt we feel for developing and actually using the atom bomb. Along with an unwillingness to face our own conduct or search for alternative courses, our behavior presents an even more dangerous symptom—an almost pathological sense of compulsion to pyramid our errors. This drives us to invest ever-increasing quantities of intelligence and energy in the building of ever more dangerous absolute weapons, while devoting but an insignificant fraction of this same energy and intelligence to the development of indispensable political and moral controls. We are in fact using our new knowledge and our new powers to reenforce ancient errors and prolong the life of obsolete institutions that should long ago have been liquidated.

What is more disturbing than our official reversion to the lowest level of barbarism in war is the fact that even after the last war only a minority of our countrymen seems to have reflected on the moral implications of this practice of total extermination as a normal and acceptable means of overcoming an enemy's resistance. There is nothing in our own code now to distinguish us from moral monsters like Genghis Khan. If we are willing to kill 100,000 people with one blow by random genocide, as at Hiroshima, there is nothing to keep us from killing 100,000,000 —except the thought that our own countrymen may be massacred in equally large numbers.

During the last dozen years every responsible head of government has confessed openly that with our present readiness to use methods of atomic, bacterial and chemical extermination, we might bring an end to civilization and permanently deform, if not destroy, the whole human race. Our failure to act on this warning, as an animal would act in the face of a comparable danger, gives the measure of our neurotic compulsions. So even the prudent thought of our own retributory, collective death offers no guarantee against the misuse of our powers so long as the engines of total annihilation remain available and the neurosis itself persists.

The two principal nuclear powers have been acting as if each was all-powerful and could dictate the terms of existence to the rest of the planet. In the name of absolute sovereignty they have actually achieved impotence. What has been called the "stalemate of terror" is in fact a deliberate checkmate of those humane gifts and adroit moves that might save us. This precarious stalemate may be ended at any moment by a careless gesture, which could upset the board itself and sweep away all the pieces. It can be effectively ended only by both sides acknowledging their paralyzing inability to move and agreeing to start a new game.

To conceive this new game, which can no longer be played under the old rules with the old pieces, both powers must take their eyes off each other and address themselves to the common task of saving the world from the threatened catastrophe they have impetuously brought within range. Instead, these governments with the connivance of their allies have been seeking to normalize their neurosis and have made participation in their infantile plans and infantile fantasies a test of political sanity. By now, a respected official in charge of Civil Defense finds it easier to envisage a whole nation of 180,000,000 people living permanently underground than to conceive of any means of delivering the world of its diabolical hatreds and collective paranoias. Strangely, such a national burial is put forward as an ingenious method for combating possible Russian blackmail. This failure to recognize when the remedy is worse than the disease is one of the score of current symptoms of mental disorder in apparently orderly minds.

If no great changes were yet visible in the general pattern of civilization, this picture would be extremely dismal; for as long as the old institutions remain operative, war will continue an integral expression of the anxieties and tensions they produce. Fortunately, this original structure has undergone a profound change during the past four centuries; and a large part of it is no longer acceptable. The old urban container has in fact exploded, leaving behind only a few citadels of absolute power on the ancient pattern, like the Kremlin and the Pentagon. What is even more important, the invisible walls between classes and castes have been breaking down steadily during the last several decades—more rapidly in the United States perhaps than in Communist countries.

What applies to the division of classes also applies to the disparity between nations. Neither knowledge nor power nor material goods can be monopolized by any privileged class or privileged country. Those Americans who fancied we had a permanent monopoly of atomic energy and technical skill recently found this out to their dismay; but the moral is not that we must "catch up with the Russians," but that we must accept the duties and demands of living in an open world among our equals. The real world of modern man has become porous and penetrable: every part of it is more closely interrelated than ever before and therefore more dependent upon the good will and sympathy and self-restraint of the rest of mankind. St. Paul's injunction to the little Christian congregations that everyone should be "members one of another," has now become a practical necessity of survival among the nations.

If so many other institutions of civilization, which held together solidly for 6000 years, have been crumbling away and are being replaced, is it likely that war will escape the same fate? The logic of history suggests it will not—if history has a logic. Our own military leaders have wryly admitted that in any large-scale war neither side can hope for a victory; indeed they have not the faintest notion of how such a war, once begun, might be ended, short of total extermination for both sides. Thus we are back at the very point at which civilization started, but at an even lower depth of savagery and irrationality. Instead of a token sacrifice to appease the gods, there would now be a total sacrifice, merely to bring an end to our neurotic anxieties.

In short, only the irrational, superstitious, magical function of war remains as a live possibility—the propitiation of gods in whom we do not believe by a sacrifice that would nullify the meaning of human history. In that surviving pocket of festering irrationality lies our chief, if not our only, enemy.

What are the possibilities of mankind's acquiring a fresh grip on reality and shedding the compulsive fantasies that are pushing us to destruction? There is little question of what measures must be taken to avoid a general nuclear catastrophe. Every intelligent observer understands the minimum precautions necessary for securing physical safety and for enabling a reconstituted United Nations to operate, not as a feeble hand brake on power politics, but as an active agent of international justice and comity. The only vital problem now is whether we can liberate ourselves from our irrational attitudes and habits, so that we may firmly take the necessary steps. It is not enough to appeal to human reason alone, as intelligent people often so earnestly do, to avert a general holocaust. We must first bring our long-buried sacrificial fantasies into the open before they erupt once more through internal pressure. Only exposure will counteract their power over us.

As with a neurotic patient, one of the conditions for resuming control and making rational decisions, free from pathological deformation, is the continued existence of large areas of conduct that are still orderly, co-operative, harmonious, life-directed. Once the patient has the courage to unburden himself of his disruptive experiences and recognize them for what they are, the sound parts of his personality can be brought into play. Fortunately, much of our life is still conducted on wholly rational and humane terms; furthermore, modern man is closer to confronting his hidden irrationalities than ever before. Scientific curiosity, which led to the discovery of the hidden structure of matter, also led to the exploration of the hidden structure of the human psyche. We now begin to understand the actual meaning of the morbid dreams, fantasies and nightmares that have repeatedly undermined the highest human achievements.

With the knowledge that the biologist and the psychologist have furnished us, we must now perceive that both the original premises of civilization and those of our own so-called Nuclear, or Space, Age are humanly obsolete—and were always false. In purely physical terms, we now have possession of absolute power of cosmic dimensions, as in a thermonuclear reaction. But "absolute power" belongs to the same magico-religious scheme as the ritual of human sacrifice itself: living organisms can use only limited amounts of power. "Too much" or "too little" is equally fatal to life. Every organism, indeed, possesses a built-in system of automatic controls which governs its intake of energy, limits its excessive growth, and maintains its equilibrium. When those controls do not operate, life itself comes to an end. When we wield power extravagantly without respect to other human goals, we actually upset the balance of the organism and threaten the pattern of the whole organic environment. Unqualified power diminishes the possibilities for life, growth, development. More than a century ago Emerson wrote, "Do not trust man, great God! with more power until he has learned to use his little power better."

The test of maturity, for nations as for individuals, is not the increase of power, but the increase of self-understanding, self-control, self-direction and self-transcendence. For in a mature society, man himself, not his machines or his organizations, is the chief work of art.

The real problem of our age is to search into the depths of the human soul, both in the present generation and in the race's history, in order to bring to light the devious impulses that have deflected man for so long from his fullest development. For the human race has always lived and flourished, not by any one-sided

exhibition of power, but by the constant sustenance and co-operation of the entire world of living beings. Not to seize power, but
to protect and cherish life is the chief end of man; and the godlike powers that the human race now commands only add to its
responsibilities for self-discipline and make more imperative a
post-magical, post-mechanical, post-nuclear ideology which shall
be centered, not on power, but on life.

Can such a new approach become operative in time to liberate man from war itself, as he was once liberated by his own
efforts from incest, cannibalism, the blood feud and slavery? It
is too early to answer this question, and it is perhaps almost too
late to ask it. Admittedly it may take an all-but-fatal shock treat-
ment, close to catastrophe, to break the hold of civilized man's
chronic neurosis. Even such a belated awakening would be a
miracle. But with the diagnosis so grave and the prognosis so un-
favorable, one must fall back on miracles—above all, the miracle
of life itself, that past master of the unexpected, the unpredict-
able, the all-but-impossible.

Further reading:

Mumford, Lewis: THE TRANSFORMATIONS OF MAN. New
York: Harper and Brothers; 1956.

Frankfort, Henri: KINGSHIP AND THE GODS: A STUDY OF
ANCIENT NEAR EASTERN RELIGION AS THE INTEGRATION
OF SOCIETY AND NATURE. Chicago: University of Chicago
Press; 1948.

Nef, John U.: WAR AND HUMAN PROGRESS. Cambridge, Mass.:
Harvard University Press; 1950.

Toynbee, A. J.: WAR AND CIVILIZATION. Edited by A. V.
Fowler. New York: Oxford University Press; 1950.

Turney-High, Harry: PRIMITIVE WAR. Columbia: University
of South Carolina Press.

The Pleasures of
Music

AARON COPLAND

*Aaron Copland has been acclaimed the "Dean of Ameri-
can Composers." Born in Brooklyn fifty-eight years ago, he
was the first American to study composition with Nadia
Boulanger, who later taught so many of his musically gifted
compatriots. Some of his best-known compositions draw
their inspiration from folk sources, notably the ballets
Rodeo, Billy the Kid, and Appalachian Spring. He is also a
compelling lecturer and writer on music. "The Pleasures of
Music" was originally presented as a lecture at the University of New Hampshire.*

That music gives pleasure is axiomatic. Because this is so,
the pleasures of music may seem a rather elementary subject for discussion. Yet the source of that pleasure, our musical
instinct, is not at all elementary, is, in fact, one of the prime
puzzles of consciousness. Why is it that sound waves, when
they strike the ear, cause, as a British critic describes it, "volleys
of nerve impulses to flow up into the brain," resulting in a
pleasurable sensation? More than that, why is it that we are

able to make sense out of these nerve signals so that we emerge from engulfment in the orderly presentation of sound stimuli as if we had lived through a simulacrum of life? And why, when safely seated and merely listening, should our hearts beat faster, our toes start tapping, our minds start racing after the music, hoping it will go one way and watching it go another, deceived and disgruntled when we are unconvinced, elated and grateful when we acquiesce?

We have a part answer, I suppose, in that the physical nature of sound has been thoroughly explored; but the phenomenon of music as an expressive, communicative agency remains as inexplicable as ever. We musicians don't ask for much. All we want is to have one investigator tell us why this young fellow seated in row A is firmly held by the musical sounds he hears while his girl friend gets little or nothing out of them, or vice versa. Think how many millions of useless practice hours might have been saved if some alert professor of genetics had developed a test for musical sensibility.

The fascination of music for some human beings was curiously illustrated for me once during a visit I made to the showrooms of a manufacturer of electronic organs. As part of my tour I was taken to see the practice room. There, to my surprise, I found not one but eight aspiring organists, all busily practicing simultaneously on eight organs. More surprising still was the fact that not a sound was audible, for all eight performers were listening through earphones to their individual instrument. It was an uncanny sight, even for a fellow musician, to watch these grown men mesmerized, as it were, by a silent and invisible genie. On that day I fully realized how mesmerized we ear-minded creatures must seem to our less musically inclined friends.

If music has impact for the mere listener, it follows that it will have much greater impact for those who sing it or play it themselves with some degree of proficiency. Any educated person in Elizabethan times was expected to be able to read musical notation and take his or her part in a madrigal-sing. Passive listeners, numbered in the millions, are a comparatively recent innovation. Even in my own youth, loving music meant that you either made it yourself, or you were forced out of the house to go hear it where it was being made, at considerable cost and some inconvenience. Nowadays all that has changed. Music has become so very accessible that it is almost impossible to avoid it. Perhaps you don't mind cashing a check at the local bank to the strains of a Brahms symphony, but I do. Actually, I think I spend as much time avoiding great works as others spend in seeking them out. The reason is simple: meaningful music demands one's undivided attention, and I can give it that only when I am in a receptive mood, and feel the need for it. The use of music as a kind of ambrosia to titillate the aural senses while one's conscious mind is otherwise occupied is the abomination of every composer who takes his work seriously.

Thus, the music I have reference to in this article is designed for your undistracted attention. It is, in fact, usually labeled 'serious' music in contradistinction to light or popular music. How this term 'serious' came into being no one seems to know, but all of us are agreed as to its inadequacy. It just doesn't cover enough cases. Very often our 'serious' music *is* serious, sometimes deadly serious, but it can also be witty, humorous, sarcastic, sardonic, grotesque and a great many other things besides. It is, indeed, the emotional range covered which makes it 'serious' and, in part, influences our judgment as to the artistic stature of any extended composition.

Everyone is aware that so-called serious music has made great strides in general public acceptance in recent years, but the term itself still connotes something forbidding and hermetic to the mass audience. They attribute to the professional musician a kind of masonic initiation into secrets that are forever hidden from the outsider. Nothing could be more misleading. We all listen to music, professionals and nonprofessionals alike, in the same sort of way, in a dumb sort of way, really, because simple or sophisticated music attracts all of us, in the first instance, on the primordial level of sheer rhythmic and sonic appeal. Musicians are flattered, no doubt, by the deferential attitude of the layman in regard to what he imagines to be our secret understanding of music. But in all honesty we musicians know that in the main we listen basically as others do, because music hits

us with an immediacy that we recognize in the reactions of the
most simple-minded of music listeners.

It is part of my thesis that music, unlike the other arts, with
the possible exception of dancing, gives pleasure simultaneously
on the lowest and highest levels of apprehension. All of us, for
example, can understand and feel the joy of being carried forward by the flow of music. Our love of music is bound up with
its forward motion; nonetheless it is precisely the creation of
that sense of flow, its interrelation with and resultant effect upon
formal structure, that calls forth high intellectual capacities of a
composer, and offers keen pleasures for listening minds. Music's
incessant movement forward exerts a double and contradictory
fascination: on the one hand it appears to be immobilizing time
itself by filling out a specific temporal space, while generating
at the same moment the sensation of flowing past us with all
the pressure and sparkle of a great river. To stop the flow of
music would be like the stopping of time itself, incredible and
inconceivable.

To the enlightened listener this time-filling forward drive has
fullest meaning only when accompanied by some conception
as to where it is heading, what musico-psychological elements are
helping to move it to its destination, and what formal architectural satisfactions will have been achieved on its arriving
there.

Musical flow is largely the result of musical rhythm, and the
rhythmic factor in music is certainly a key element that has
simultaneous attraction on more than one level. To some African tribes rhythm *is* music, they have nothing more. But what
rhythm it is! Listening to it casually, one might never get beyond the ear-splitting poundings, but actually a trained musician's ear is needed to disengage its polyrhythmic intricacies.
Minds that conceive such rhythms have their own sophistication; it seems inexact and even unfair to call them primitive.
By comparison our own instinct for rhythmic play seems only
mild in interest—needing reinvigoration from time to time.

It was because the ebb of rhythmic invention was comparatively low in late nineteenth-century European music that
Stravinsky was able to apply what I once termed "a rhythmic

hypodermic" to Western music. His shocker of 1913, The Rite of Spring, a veritable rhythmic monstrosity to its first hearers, has now become a standard item of the concert repertory. This indicates the progress that has been made in the comprehension and enjoyment of rhythmic complexities that non-plussed our grandfathers. And the end is by no means in sight. Younger composers have taken us to the very limit of what the human hand can perform and have gone even beyond what the human ear can grasp in rhythmic differentiation. Sad to say, there is a limit, dictated by what nature has supplied us with in the way of listening equipment. But within those limits there are large areas of rhythmic life still to be explored, rhythmic forms never dreamt of by composers of the march or the mazurka.

Tone color is another basic element in music that may be enjoyed on various levels of perception from the most naive to the most cultivated. Even children have no difficulty in recognizing the difference between the tonal profile of a flute and a trombone. The color of certain instruments holds an especial attraction for certain people. I myself have always had a weakness for the sound of eight French horns playing in unison. Their rich, golden, legendary sonority transports me. Some present-day European composers seem to be having a belated love affair with the vibraphone. An infinitude of possible color combinations are available when instruments are mixed, especially when combined in that wonderful contraption, the orchestra of symphonic proportions. The art of orchestration, needless to say, holds endless fascination for the practicing composer, being part science and part inspired guesswork.

As a composer I get great pleasure from cooking up tonal combinations. Over the years I have noted that no element of the composer's art mystifies the layman more than this ability to conceive mixed instrumental colors. But remember that before we mix them we hear them in terms of their component parts. If you examine an orchestral score, you will note that composers place their instruments on the page in family groups: reading from top to bottom it is customary to list the woodwinds, the brass, the percussion and the strings, in that order. Modern orchestral practice often juxtaposes these families one against the other so that their personalities, as families, remain recognizable and distinct. This principle may also be applied to the voice of the single instrument, whose pure color sonority thereby remains clearly identifiable as such. Orchestral know-how consists in keeping the instruments out of each other's way, so spacing them that they avoid repeating what some other instrument is already doing, at least in the same register, thereby exploiting to the fullest extent the specific color value contributed by each separate instrument or grouped instrumental family.

In modern orchestration, clarity and definition of sonorous image is usually the goal. There exists, however, another kind of orchestral magic dependent on a certain ambiguity of effect. Not to be able to identify immediately how a particular color combination is arrived at adds to its attractiveness. I like to be intrigued by unusual sounds which force me to exclaim: Now I wonder how the composer does that?

From what I have said about the art of orchestration, you may have gained the notion that it is nothing more than a delightful game, played for the amusement of the composer. That is, of course, not true. Color in music, as in painting, is meaningful only when it serves the expressive idea; it is the expressive idea that dictates to the composer the choice of his orchestral scheme.

Part of the pleasure in being sensitive to the use of color in music is to note in what way a composer's personality traits are revealed through his tonal color schemes. During the period of French impressionism, for example, the composers Debussy and Ravel were thought to be very similar in personality. An examination of their orchestral scores would have shown that Debussy, at his most characteristic, sought for a spraylike iridescence, a delicate and sensuous sonority such as had never before been heard, while Ravel, using a similar palette, sought a refinement and precision, a gemlike brilliance that reflects the more objective nature of his musical personality.

Color ideals change for composers as their personalities change. A striking example is again Igor Stravinsky who, beginning with the stabbing reds and purples of his early ballet scores, has in the past decade arrived at an ascetic grayness of tone that positively chills the listener by its austerity. For contrast we may turn to a Richard Strauss orchestral score, masterfully handled in its own way, but overrich in the piling-on of sonorities, like a German meal that is too filling for comfort. The natural and easy handling of orchestral forces by a whole school of contemporary American composers would indicate some inborn affinity between American personality traits and symphonic language. No layman can hope to penetrate all the subtleties that go into an orchestral page of any complexity, but here again it is not necessary to be able to analyze the color spectrum of a score in order to bask in its effulgence.

Thus far I have been dealing with the generalities of musical pleasure. Now I wish to concentrate on the music of a few composers in order to show how musical values are differentiated. The late Serge Koussevitzky, conductor of the Boston Symphony, never tired of telling performers that if it weren't for composers they would literally have nothing to play or sing. He was stressing what is too often taken for granted and, therefore, lost sight of, namely, that in our Western world music speaks with a composer's voice and half the pleasure we get comes from the fact that we are listening to a particular voice making an individual statement at a specific moment in history. Unless you take off from there you are certain to miss one of the principal attractions of musical art, namely, contact with a strong and absorbing personality.

It matters greatly, therefore, who it is we are about to listen to in the concert hall or opera house. And yet I get the impression that, to the lay music lover, music is music and musical events are attended with little or no concern as to what musical fare is to be offered. Not so with the professional, to whom it matters a great deal whether he is about to listen to the music of Monteverdi or Massenet, to J. S. or to J. C. Bach. Isn't it true that everything we, as listeners, know about a particular composer and his music prepares us in some measure to empathize with his special mentality. To me Chopin is one thing, Scarlatti quite another. I could never confuse them, could you? Well, whether you could or not, my point remains the same: there are as many ways for music to be enjoyable as there are composers.

One can even get a certain perverse pleasure out of hating

the work of a particular composer. I, for instance, happen to be rubbed the wrong way by one of today's composer idols, Serge Rachmaninoff. The prospect of having to sit through one of his extended symphonies or piano concertos tends, quite frankly, to depress me. All those notes, think I, and to what end? To me, Rachmaninoff's characteristic tone is one of self-pity and self-indulgence tinged with a definite melancholia. As a fellow human being I can sympathize with an artist whose distempers produced such music, but as a listener my stomach won't take it. I grant you his technical adroitness, but even here the technique adopted by the composer was old fashioned in his own day. I also grant his ability to write long and singing melodic lines, but when these are embroidered with figuration, the musical substance is watered down, emptied of significance. Well, as Andre Gidé used to say, "I didn't have to tell you this, and I know it will not make you happy to hear it." Actually, it should be of little concern to you whether I find Rachmaninoff digestible or not. All I am trying to say is that music strikes us in as many different ways as there are composers, and anything less than a strong reaction, pro or con, is not worth bothering about.

By contrast, let me point to that perennially popular favorite among composers, Giuseppe Verdi. Quite apart from his music, I get pleasure merely thinking about the man himself. If honesty and forthrightness ever sparked an artist, then Verdi is a prime example. What a pleasure it is to take contact with him through his letters, to knock against the hard core of his peasant personality. One comes away refreshed, and with renewed confidence in the sturdy, nonneurotic character of at least one musical master.

When I was a student it was considered bad form to mention Verdi's name in symphonic company, and quite out of the question to name Verdi in the same sentence with that formidable dragon of the opera house, Richard Wagner. What the musical elite found difficult to forgive in Verdi's case was his triteness, his ordinariness. Yes, Verdi is trite and ordinary at times, just as Wagner is long-winded and boring at times. There is a lesson to be learned here: the way in which we are gradually able to accommodate our minds to the obvious weaknesses in a creative artist's output. Musical history teaches us that at first contact the academicisms of Brahms, the *longeurs* of Schubert, the portentousness of Mahler were considered insupportable by their early listeners, but in all such cases later generations have managed to put up with the failings of men of genius for the sake of other qualities that outweigh them.

Verdi can be commonplace at times, as everyone knows, but his saving grace is a burning sincerity that carries all before it. There is no bluff here, no guile. On whatever level he composed a no-nonsense quality comes across; all is directly stated, cleanly written with no notes wasted, and marvelously effective. In the end we willingly concede that Verdi's musical materials need not be especially choice in order to be acceptable. And, naturally enough, when the musical materials *are* choice and inspired they profit doubly from being set off against the homely virtues of his more workaday pages.

If one were asked to name one musician who came closest to composing without human flaw, I suppose general consensus would choose Johann Sebastian Bach. Only a very few musical giants have earned the universal admiration that surrounds the figure of the eighteenth-century German master. What is it that makes his finest scores so profoundly moving? I have puzzled over that question for a very long time, but have come to doubt whether it is possible for anyone to reach a completely satisfactory answer. One thing is certain: we will never explain Bach's supremacy by the singling out of any one element in his work. Rather it was a combination of perfections, each of which was applied to the common practice of his day; added together they produced the mature perfection of the completed *oeuvre*.

Bach's genius cannot possibly be deduced from the circumstances of his routine musical existence. All his life long he wrote music for the requirements of the jobs he held. His melodies were often borrowed from liturgical sources, his orchestral textures limited by the forces at his disposal, and his forms, in the main, were similar to those of other composers of his time, whose works, incidentally, he had closely studied. None of these oft-repeated facts explain the universal hold his best music has come to have on later generations.

What strikes me most markedly about Bach's work is the marvellous rightness of it. It is the rightness not merely of a single individual but of a whole musical epoch. Bach came at the peak point of a long historical development; his was the heritage of many generations of composing artisans. Never since that time has music so successfully fused contrapuntal skill with harmonic logic. This amalgam of melodies and chords, of independent lines conceived linear-fashion within a mold of basic harmonies conceived vertically provided Bach with the necessary framework for his massive edifice. Within that edifice is the summation of an entire period, with all the grandeur, nobility and inner depth that one creative soul could bring to it. It is hopeless, I fear, to attempt to probe further into why his music creates the impression of spiritual wholeness, the sense of his communing with the deepest vision. We would only find ourselves groping for words, words that can never hope to encompass the intangible greatness of music, least of all the intangible in Bach's greatness.

Those who are interested in studying the interrelationship between a composer and his work would do better to turn to the century that followed Bach's, and especially to the life and work of Ludwig von Beethoven. The English critic, Wilfrid Mellers, had this to say about Beethoven recently: "It is the essence of the personality of Beethoven, both as man and as artist, that he should invite discussion in other than musical terms." Mellers meant that such a discussion would involve us, with no trouble at all, in a consideration of the rights of man, free will, Napoleon and the French Revolution, and other allied subjects. We shall never know in exactly what way the ferment of historical events affected Beethoven's thinking, but it is certain that music such as his would have been inconceivable in the early nineteenth century without serious concern for the revolutionary temper of his time and the ability to translate that concern into the original and unprecedented musical thought of his own work.

Beethoven brought three startling innovations to music: first, he altered our very conception of the art by emphasizing the psychological element implicit in the language of sounds. Because of him, music lost a certain innocence, but gained instead a new dimension in psychological depth. Secondly, his own stormy and explosive temperament was, in part, responsible for a "dramatization of the whole art of music." The rumbling bass tremolandos, the sudden accents in unexpected places, the hitherto unheard-of rhythmic insistence and sharp dynamic contrasts, all these were externalizations of an inner drama that gave his music theatrical impact.

Both these elements, the psychological orientation and the instinct for drama are inextricably linked in my mind with his third and possibly most original achievement: the creation of musical forms dynamically conceived on a scale never before attempted and of an inevitability that is irresistible. Especially the sense of inevitability is remarkable in Beethoven. Notes are not words, they are not under the control of verifiable logic, and because of that, composers in every age have struggled to overcome that handicap by producing a directional effect convincing to the listener. No composer has ever solved the problem more brilliantly than Beethoven; nothing quite so inevitable had ever before been created in the language of sounds.

One doesn't need much historical perspective to realize what a shocking experience Beethoven's music must have been for his first listeners. Even today, given the nature of his music, there are times when I simply do not understand how this man's art was 'sold' to the big musical public. Obviously, he must be saying something that everyone wants to hear. And yet if one listens freshly and closely the odds against acceptance are equally obvious. As sheer sound there is little that is luscious about his music—it gives off a comparatively 'dry' sonority. He never seems to flatter an audience, never to know or care what they might like. His themes are not particularly lovely or memorable; they are more likely to be expressively apt than beautifully contoured. His general manner is gruff and unceremonious, as if the matter under discussion were much too important to be broached in urbane or diplomatic terms. He adopts a peremptory and hortatory tone, the assumption being, especially in his most forceful work, that you have no choice but to listen. And that is precisely what happens: you listen.

Above and beyond every other consideration Beethoven has one quality to a remarkable degree: he is enormously compelling. What is it he is so compelling about? How can one not be compelled and not be moved by the moral fervor and conviction of such a man. His finest works are the enactment of a triumph, a triumph of affirmation in the face of the human condition. Beethoven is one of the great yea-sayers among creative artists; it is exhilarating to share his clear-eyed contemplation of the tragic sum of life. His music summons forth our better nature; in purely musical terms Beethoven seems to be exhorting us to Be Noble, Be Strong, Be Great in Heart, yes, and Be Compassionate. These ethical precepts we subsume from the music, but it is the music itself—the nine symphonies, the sixteen string quartets, the thirty-two piano sonatas—that holds us, and holds us in much the same way each time we return to it. The core of Beethoven's music seems indestructible; the ephemera of sound seems to have little to do with its strangely immutable substance.

My concern here with composers of the first rank like Bach and Beethoven is not meant to suggest that only the greatest names and the greatest masterpieces are worth your attention. Musical art, as we hear it in our day, suffers if anything from an overdose of masterworks, an obsessive fixation on the glories of the past. This narrows the range of our musical experience and tends to suffocate interest in the present. It blots out many an excellent composer whose work was less than perfect. It may be carping to say so, but the fact is that we tire of everything, even of perfection. It would be truer to point out, it seems to me, that the forerunners of Bach have an awkward charm and simple grace that not even he could match, just because of his mature perfection. The artist, Delacroix, had something of my idea when he complained about the playwright, Racine, "that perfection and the absence of breaks and incongruities deprive him of the spice one finds in works full of beauties and defects at the same time."

Part of the pleasure of involving oneself with the arts is the excitement of venturing out among its contemporary manifestations. But a strange thing happens in this connection in the field of music. The same people who find it quite natural that modern books, plays, or paintings are likely to be controversial seem to want to escape being challenged and troubled when they turn to music. In the musical field there appears to be an unquenchable thirst for the familiar, and very little curiosity as to what the newer composers are up to. Such music lovers, as I see it, simply don't love music enough, for if they did their minds would not be closed to an area that holds the promise of fresh and unusual musical experience. Charles Ives used to say that people who couldn't put up with dissonance in music had "sissy ears." Fortunately, there are in all countries today some braver souls who mind not at all having to dig a bit for their musical pleasure, who actually enjoy being confronted with the creative artist who is problematical.

These adventurous listeners refuse to be frightened off too easily. I myself, when I encounter a piece of music whose import escapes me immediately, think: "I'm not getting this, I shall have to come back to it for a second or third try." I don't at all mind actively disliking a piece of contemporary music, but in order to feel happy about it, I must consciously understand why I dislike it. Otherwise it remains in my mind as unfinished business.

This doesn't resolve the problem of the music lover of good will who says: I'd like to like this modern stuff, but what do I do? Well, the unvarnished truth is that there are no magic formulas, no short cuts for making the unfamiliar seem comfortably familiar. There is no advice one can give other than to say: relax —that's of first importance, and then listen to the same pieces enough times to really matter. Fortunately not all new music must be rated as difficult to comprehend. I once had occasion to divide contemporary composers into categories of relative difficulty, from very easy to very tough, and a surprising number of composers fitted into the first group.

One of the attractions of concerning oneself with the new in music is the possible discovery of important work by the younger generation of composers. The French critic, Sainte-Beuve, had this to say about discovering young talent: "I know of no pleasure more satisfying for the critic than to understand and describe a young talent in all its freshness, its open and primitive quality, before it is glossed over later by whatever is acquired and perhaps manufactured."

The young composers of today upset their elders in the traditional way by positing a new ideal for music. This time they called for a music that was to be thoroughly controlled in its every particular. What they produced, admirably logical on paper, often makes a rather haphazard and samelike impression in actual performance. After a first hearing of some of their works, I jotted down these observations: "One gets the notion that these boys are starting again from the beginning, with the separate tone and the separate sonority. Notes are strewn about like membra disjecta; there is an end to continuity in the old sense and an end of thematic relationships. In this music one waits to hear what will happen next without the slightest idea of what *will* happen, or why what happened did happen once it has happened. Perhaps one can say modern painting of the Paul Klee school has invaded the new music. The so-to-speak disrelation of unrelated tones is the way I might describe it. No one really knows where it will go, and neither do I. One thing is sure, however, whatever the listener may think of it, it is without doubt the most frustrating music ever put on a performer's music-stand."

Some of the younger European composers have branched off into the first tentative experiments with electronically produced music. No performers, no musical instruments, no microphones are needed. But one must be able to record on tape and be able to feed into it electromagnetic vibrations. Listening to the results, one feels that in this case we shall have to broaden our conception of what is to be included under the heading of musical pleasure. We will have to take into account areas of sound hitherto excluded from the musical scheme of things. And why not? With so many other of man's assumptions subject to review how could one expect music to remain the same? Whatever we may think of their efforts, these young experimenters obviously need more time; it is pointless to attempt evaluations before they have more fully explored the new terrain.

No discussion of musical pleasures can be concluded without mentioning that ritualistic word, jazz. But, someone is sure to ask, is jazz music serious? I'm afraid it is too late to bother with the question, since jazz, serious or not, is very much here, and it obviously provides pleasure. The confusion comes, I believe, from attempting to make the jazz idiom cover broader expressive areas than naturally belong to it. Jazz does *not* do what serious music does either in its range of emotional expression or in its depth of feeling, or in its universality of language. (It does have universality of appeal, which is not the same thing.) On the other hand, jazz does do what serious music cannot do, namely, suggest a colloquialism of musical speech that is indigenously delightful, a kind of here-and-now feeling, less enduring than classical music, perhaps, but with an immediacy and vibrancy that audiences throughout the world find exhilarating.

Personally, I like my jazz free and untrammeled, as far removed from the regular commercial product as possible. Fortunately, the more progressive jazz men seem to be less and less restrained by the conventionalities of their idiom, so little restrained that they appear in fact to be headed our way. By that I mean that harmonic and structural freedoms of recent serious music have had so considerable an influence on the younger jazz composers that it becomes increasingly difficult to keep the categories of jazz and nonjazz clearly divided. A new kind of cross-fertilization of our two worlds is developing that promises an unusual synthesis for the future.

Thus, the varieties of musical pleasure that await the attentive listener are broadly inclusive. The art of music, without specific subject matter and little specific meaning, is nonetheless a balm for the human spirit; not a refuge or escape from the realities of existence, but a haven wherein one takes contact with the essence of human experience. It is an inexhaustible font from which all of us can be replenished.

Further reading:

Copland, Aaron: Music and Imagination. Cambridge, Mass.: Harvard University Press; 1952.

——: Our New Music. New York: McGraw-Hill Book Company; 1941.

——: What to Listen For in Music. Revised edition. New York: McGraw-Hill Book Company; 1957.

Dent, Edward J.: Opera. Baltimore: Penguin Books; 1949.

Einstein, Alfred: A Short History of Music. New York: Alfred A. Knopf; 1947.

Hodeir, André: Jazz: Its Evolution and Essence. New York: Grove Press; 1956.

Sullivan, J. W. N.: Beethoven: His Spiritual Development. New York: Alfred A. Knopf; 1927.

Tovey, Donald Francis: The Forms of Music: Musical Articles from the Encyclopaedia Britannica. New York: Oxford University Press; 1944.

Turner, W. J.: Mozart: The Man and His Works. Anchor Books. New York: Doubleday and Company; 1954.

The Varieties of
Human Love

MARTIN CYRIL D'ARCY, S.J.

*For many years the Rev. Martin Cyril D'Arcy lectured at
Oxford University on philosophy, and from 1932 to 1945
was master of Campion Hall. After World War II he was
Provincial (that is, the head) of the Jesuits in Great Brit-
ain. He also was Catholic representative to the British
Broadcasting Corporation. A frequent visitor to the United
States, he has taught at Fordham, Notre Dame, the Insti-
tute for Advanced Study at Princeton, and at Georgetown
University. His voluminous writings include* The Nature of
Belief, *the recent* Communism and Christianity, *and the
forthcoming* The Meaning and Matter of History: A Chris-
tian View.

Carved on the gates of Harvard University are the words:
". . . Dreading to leave an illiterate Ministry to the
Churches when our present Ministers shall lie in the Dust."
These words show the intention of the founders to educate
students in "knowledge and godliness." Until recent times, culture and religion went hand in hand. In early societies, kings
were usually high priests and the wise men were seers and

prophets. Western culture had its beginning in the schools of the Benedictines and the bishops; in the middle ages the scholars were tonsured clerics. "The Lord is my Light" is Oxford University's motto, and to this day we can see the influence on the democratic institutions in the west of the Christian philosophy and outlook. The contrast is striking today when we behold in one large part of the world a violently atheist system, and in the other a secular culture which may be neutral or friendly or hostile to religion.

Religion, then, has obviously lost its former place in culture. Owing to their having held prescriptive rights in so many fields of learning, Christian theologians were slow in relinquishing some of the positions they held, and clashed with scientists on disputable points. Hence religion and science have been taken to be chronic adversaries. Science, however, is by now secure in its rights, and the more pertinent question at the moment is whether a new alliance is not due. The democracies need a unifying and invigorating philosophy of life, and human beings without belief are subject to bad dreams. If only the Christian religion could bring out from its stores what is new as well as what is old, and adapt its treasures to our modern predicaments, there would be hope of a new and vigorous culture.

Growth in religious and philosophic ideas follows a different rule from that of science. Scientists do not as yet agree as to the methods which they pursue in their studies of a physical nature. There is still dispute both as to the relation of their discoveries to nature and as to the function of the hypotheses upon which these discoveries are based. But what is clear is that the scientist holds to hypotheses so long as they serve to unify the data and predict the future. As soon as new data appear which do not conform with these hypotheses, new ones must be sought.

Now in religion and philosophy, hypothesis does not play the same part. Here, knowledge grows by a form of speculation which consists in poring over an often well-known truth, discovering further horizons to it as well as hitherto unsuspected connections with other truths. It is as if the obvious were continually taking one by surprise, and at times an analytical thinker, like George Edward Moore, of Cambridge, will show us how carelessly we have been thinking about such a simple idea as "goodness"; or a metaphysician, like the late Alfred North Whitehead, will bring together in one synthesis ideas and objects which we had assumed to be quite unconnected. Philosophy deals principally with what is immemorially true, and religion has for its field such subjects as God and man, conscience, doctrine and experience, providence and the afterlife.

The human mind, like human sensibility, has its fashions, and grows bored with one aspect of an idea. It is a mark of genius not to throw away the idea and put in its place something new or artificial, but to show a new aspect of the *same* idea and to associate with it what no one so far had suspected. Platitude, then, which the positivists rejected, is the cornerstone of his philosophy! Truth, like beauty, therefore, should be "ever ancient and ever fresh," and it is quite possible for a lover to use, for example, only the one word "love" and never to repeat himself.

Any genuine philosophical or religious idea would serve to exemplify this; we have but to think of this word "love" or of "human personality" to see how in the course of centuries, their meaning, though ever the same, has grown clearer and fuller. The Christian religion claims to teach revealed truth, and therefore Christian doctrine, in a manner all its own, is said to develop without revealed or external contradiction.

Today this claim is better understood by the educated public, with the result that the quarrel between science and the Christian religion has abated. Much of the former bickering was based on a misunderstanding, on the belief that the subject matter of science and religion was necessarily the same. Both sides erred here. The scientist was not sufficiently aware of the limitation imposed upon his subject matter by the yardstick he used, and the Christian did not notice that the formal object or specific aspect of his faith depended upon a special kind of insight. What this means can be seen easily if we think with what different eyes a farmer, a scientist and a painter look at an acre of farmland, or how the sound issuing from a violin can be described as the rubbing of the hair of a dead horse over the intestines of a dead cat or as a concerto by Beethoven. The crowds round the foot of the Cross, as Saint Augustine said, saw a condemned man dying; the Christian sees in the same scene a God redeeming. What are common in the two interpretations are the facts, and for a justifiable interpretation the facts must reinforce each other and point in one direction, just as stray evidence can turn into clues in a law court or in a detective story.

For an understanding of the relations between science and religion, it is essential to understand this diversity in method and outlook. The scientist relies upon observation and experiment, and for his purpose measurement by highly developed techniques is all-important. Though employing such measurements he did not, until recent times, discard some of the old common-sense philosophical notions of nature as uniform in its causes. Now, however, the scientist has purified his science of all that does not belong to it. Instead of the language of cause he deals with mathematical equations, and his predictions are of the nature of mathematical probability. The successes of this method have been beyond belief, but they have been bought at a price; for if asked what they are talking about, many distinguished scientists would answer that they do not know. Most would admit to an "animal faith" in the presence of things and their awareness of them, but once "things" have been broken down and then reconstituted as measurable quantities, very different worlds begin to appear.

Nor should we expect a mathematical world to be a complete representation of the infinitely variegated world of quality we live in, any more than we should expect the information given by a weighing machine to cover all our manhood. Every science uses a yardstick, and the results tell us nothing beyond the yardstick's capacity. What has beguiled and helped philosophers from early times has been the far-reaching applicability of the mathematical or measurable, the power it provides for dealing with almost everything that is human. Whether living matter be radically different from the inorganic or not, we can treat them both by the scientific methods. The quality of music has its own value and its own criterion, but it can be translated into quantitative mathematical terms. Similarly in economics and sociology, and to some extent in experimental psychology, it has become the habit to use statistical methods. Attempt has even been made by philosophers of science and some schools of positivists to reduce mind to some form of behaviorism.

Throughout this procedure what is distinct in its own right is transformed into a mathematical or measurable substitute. Time is describable in terms of distance. We speak of light as waves.

"Light itself," writes Bertrand Russell, "the thing which seeing people experience and blind people do not, is not supposed by science to form any part of the world that is independent of us and our senses." Scientists treat organic growth in terms of physical aggregates, and learn much, but they have to ignore the fact that physical aggregates do not grow. The atomic particles that make up the aggregate remain what they are all the time, whereas in the growth of living matter what was there at the beginning is still there at the end, but in a completer form of itself; the ugly duckling *becomes* the handsome swan. If then the quantitative and the qualitative, the inorganic and the organic can be treated for some purposes as one, and nevertheless also be different, it would appear that there are different ways of approaching the real world, and one explanation need not contradict the other, as a triangle includes an angle, and a square with a diagonal includes both.

This possibility brings us back to the varying standpoints and insights of the scientist and the religious philosopher. Now not only do they approach the same objects with different yardsticks and different interests; their very attitude to certainty and truth may differ. The modern scientist, as already pointed out, has given up the dogmatism of his predecessors; he does not pretend to reveal to us the nature of reality. His subject matter is at least one remove from the real, and all he claims is to be consistent with his initial postulates. Modern science is pragmatic, hoisting hypotheses on high, and later replacing them by other flags. On the other hand, it has been a characteristic of philosophy and theology to keep their gaze fixed on basic or ultimate truths and to concern themselves with the origin and destiny of man, the nature of goodness and freedom, and the relation of man to nature and to God. Christian theologians are particularly interested in providing a coherent and adequate setting for the doctrines contained in the Creeds. Here, they would say, is to be found an air in which man can breathe and grow, a true and a more abundant life.

The Christian philosopher, therefore, supports humanism against any attempt to rob man of his rights, his freedom and his personal responsibilities. This being so, in the long drawn-out crisis of the twentieth century, when many of the old forms of civilization are in danger, and its high codes threatened; when, too, a large proportion of the human race is being conditioned to accept a subhuman status, the religious thinker is anxious not so much to defend his position as to make a positive contribution to truth, which will serve his fellow men.

Christianity, if it be a live religion, must ever grow, and do so by keeping its identity, and at the same time enlivening itself with all that is best in the modern world. As we still live upon the ground of a Christian culture, there is no antecedent reason why the church should not bring an intellectual concord into society, as it did in the dark ages, but now with a much more complicated and rich material to work upon.

Another function of philosophy is to discover an order in reality, one based on the principles which govern the whole of reality in so far as it is known to us. This interest of the mind can be called synthetic. It unifies, and is comparable with what the artist or writer or musician tries to do in any composition. In the past we notice how the metaphysicians differ from one another, Aristotle from Plato, Marx from Hegel. Aristotle believed that in his distinction of matter and form, of potency and act, he had discovered characteristics of the real order which permitted him to make a scale running from prime matter to pure thought. Hegel found the vital clue in a form of dialectic, in the clash of apparent opposites which brought as a result a richer unity in the synthesis of these opposites. The scientific philosopher, on the other hand, is inclined to rely upon a general form of evolution to provide a framework of order.

To judge from the religious ideas now current, and the boldness of some of them, a new synthesis, or an old synthesis with a new look, is being premeditated. What else can explain the

fearless effort of the late Père Teilhard de Chardin to rope together evolution and the Christian religion? Other writers have
offered ingenious solutions of the fall of man, and of nature too,
in terms of evolution, but Père Teilhard goes much further and
argues that man is still developing, and, under the direction of
Christianity, is evolving into a higher species.

As a scientist of high repute, one of those responsible for the
verdict on the Peking man, and at the same time a distinguished
priest of the Catholic Church, Père Teilhard was in the happy
position of being able to speak with some authority as a scientist
and as a Christian. He was convinced that the secret of the
universe lay in evolution, which he regarded as "regular, continuous and total." There is, he reasoned, a continuous, upward
process from matter to the organic, and from the organic to
Homo sapiens and still higher. Man is the end product, so far,
of nature, and able, therefore, to reflect and discover the truth
about nature and himself. Mankind is one, but is not invariant.
Owing to the power of reflection, man is in the process of evolving into a new superorganism or species, which will individually
and collectively mirror reality in its mind. It will be coconscious
and one in truth and affection. To use Père Teilhard's own
words, "There will be only one science, one ethic and one passion, that is to say, one mystique." The present time may seem
to be a melting pot; but, "man is in process of re-emerging
. . . as the head of nature. The reason is that by being in this
way cast into the general current of a convergent Cosmogenesis,
he acquires the power and the quality of forming, in the very
heart of Time and Space, a central and singular gathering-
point of the whole stuff of the universe." This cosmos of affection and thought must in turn be centered around One, who
is the Word by and in whom all things were made and have
their meaning.

That scientists of many countries should have willingly supported the publication of Père Teilhard's ideas shows the general respect for these ideas. Few probably would entirely concur
with them. The Catholic theologians, on their side, are also
critical; not so much, I think, because of any distaste for the
theme as for the defects in the argument. I believe that more

work has still to be done by both philosophers and scientists before evolution can pass from a working hypothesis to a general philosophical theory.

The obscurities of the evolutionary hypothesis are apparent in Père Teilhard's gallant work. He goes beyond the territory of the biologists and extends the hypothesis to mind and inorganic matter as well as to living organisms. As a result he finds himself forced to attribute some form of mind to the simplest material elements. It is a desperate measure. It cannot be verified; it is based on no empirical evidence, and it runs counter to common sense, making meaningless the distinctions on which human intercourse depends. If the rocket to be fired to the moon, or the table at which I write or the dust collecting on the window has some form of consciousness, meaning is taken out of what we call consciousness, and we are as illogical as the Oriental who drinks water filled with micro-organisms though he refuses to destroy any form of living thing.

Yet to make the general theory of evolution coherent, there is need to introduce consciousness at the earliest possible stage; otherwise there is no continuity, no one thing which evolves. When John Tyndall, an advocate of Darwin's views, said that he discerned "Plato, Shakespeare, Newton and Raphael potential in the fires of the sun," he was emphasizing this necessary continuity between mind and matter. If evolution be extended to everything, there must be something implicit in undeveloped matter or organisms, which will later be revealed. On the other hand, any talk about mind, as about vitalism, is abhorred by the strict biologist as a *deus ex machina*. He prefers to keep the physical and chemical laws, and assumes that there is a continuing physical thing, or aggregate of physical things, throughout the uninterrupted generation of germ cells. But there is no material unit which persists as the subject of the process, whether we take the growth of an individual from a fertilized egg cell, or an individual from a remote ancestor of different form. An electron may continue unchanged in all kinds of combinations; if so, it has no development. So far as the history of the germ plasm is concerned, nothing physical continues throughout all the generations. At this crucial point the biologist falls back on metaphor and writes, for example, of "molecules carrying genetic information from one generation to the next." One might as well call a rain cloud a continual development, because the aggregate which composes it is forever changing, and then, to add to the fun, ask with Bertrand Russell whether it is raining between the drops.

Nevertheless, Père Teilhard surely strikes a rich vein in insisting on the new world of communication and unity opened up by the advent of mind. In far-off times, tribe was separated from tribe; the stranger was an enemy. Then slowly came the development of communication by speech and writing, and also the facility to travel. Now there is no distance which cannot be covered easily, and instead of human beings living in little worlds apart, we have one in which all men can share knowledge. Père Teilhard did not greatly exaggerate when he said that mankind has developed what is almost a new form of life and may be moving into a new phase of coconsciousness.

He saw, too, that the most vital problem of the future is that of society or the state and the freedom and development of the individual. Here, in presenting a picture of man reaching full consciousness and forming a spiritual hive, utterly unlike the classless society envisaged by Marx, he followed the trend of Christian theology today. That trend is toward personal freedom and love.

If we are to believe certain anthropologists, the individual members of primitive tribes behaved and thought coconsciously and collectively. Like sheep moving through a gate, the tribe, almost somnambulistically, carried out the routine of its daily life. The coming of a full, independent will and consciousness must be gradual, and, even when freedom of will is realized, the mind works with the general and the universal in order to arrive at truths. Even in Greek philosophical literature there was no proper conception of the individual nor any satisfactory account of the will as freely choosing. The Greek was interested in the universal and the necessary, and only with the advent of Christianity did the value of the individual come to full recognition.

The Christian belongs to a community, a holy people. Nevertheless, so sacred is each member that he has to be regarded as an individual, free and with the highest obligations, and commanded to love his neighbor as himself. A primitive coconsciousness, therefore, has been succeeded by the splendor and dangers of individual and independent life. Furthermore, to complete the story of man, a new and higher form of coconsciousness is promised, and is said to be already inaugurated in the sacred community. This new form is to combine the unity of the human race with the complete freedom of the individual, and the image of this unity is a body with human members and with Christ as its head.

Such union, however, though it be initiated in this life, belongs for the full experience to life after death. On this point, what the theologians say fits in very well with the ideal of a new species, because they teach that as Christ was God and man, so through our incorporation into his life we shall be able to share finitely in the supreme life of divinity.

Consider how we evolve from conception to death. There is a rhythm of self-renewal. At first the embryo, grafted in the womb upon another life, exercises the movements necessary to its birth. Birth breaks the primitive symbiosis and provides the first stage of liberty and selfhood. There remains, however, a total dependence for food, for language and race on what is not itself. New freedoms are acquired at puberty and manhood, new struggles of spirit and body at marriage and companionship, and slowly, where there is a good will, the body and soul form a harmony and the body assists the movements of the spirit to be unimpeded, preparing it for the new birth, the *dies natalis* of death, when, in a last great option, the self will pass from a chrysalis stage to a new selfhood and be coconscious with a new humanity in Christ.

This new form of existence is in process of development here and now. We know what it is to think with another person and, better still, to experience another person thinking with us and being at one with us. Where there is the marriage of true minds, one and one do not make two, but infinity. Such infinity does not, however, take us out of ourselves into a nonhuman state; it increases our humanity. It is along these lines that Christian philosophers are now thinking. They are only too aware that the growth of large states and corporations, of vast and complicated machinery, has made personal and full life more difficult. As science develops, those who think in its terms tend to regard human beings as numbers, commodities and things. This habit lies behind the sharp distinction which the theologians, Martin Buber and Gabriel Marcel, made between what they call the I-It and the I-Thou relation. The scientist, the doctor, the employer and the economist must treat many people as if they had no individuality. This is the I-It relation. But when I "face" another person as I-Thou, I meet the other person, and in the meeting I become an "I" for the first time. Marcel also dwells on the extraordinary force of love as between persons, where I do not seek to possess the other, but wish to be present with him and with an open heart.

What with the dialectical materialism of Marx and the evidence produced by Freud that even spiritual love belonged to the libido, it seemed as if there would be no breathing space for the old true love. But that is not so. The French philosopher Jean Guitton tells us that for a while he found something scandalous in the close association of the ideals of love and the mechanism of reproduction. Even to the biologist this is disconcerting, as it does not fit in with the neat, laborsaving development demanded by evolution. Parthenogenesis would have been so much simpler, mating restricted to certain phases and seasons.

Nevertheless, the closer one looks at the various manifestations of human love the more one is conscious of a congruity between spiritual love and sex. Guitton argues that these various manifestations are not haphazard; they disclose a sequence as unified and progressive as a symphony of music by a great master. It is as if some presiding genius of the species were watching over the expressions of love and regulating the human lottery. Sex proves to be the surest means of arousing and sustaining love. The permanence of the species is assured, and at the same time the greatest variety of the individual encouraged. The vital energies allow themselves to be transformed into something spiritual. What was begun in carnality ends in heaven; what seemed to be mere animal breeding partakes of spirituality, and what appears at first to be just a bodily function acquires a value of its own above even that of knowledge. So it comes about that the vital energies can be enlisted in the service of the soul, and the highest spiritual experiences await those who are faithful to the institutes of nature. The art of loving is not in the least what the libertine tradition would have us believe. It is rather the science of making the fleeting loves of youth endure and multiply in fresh waves of experience throughout the course of a long human life. Love is no episode, it imposes itself like a divinity, regulating, inspiring, and offering the promise of an undreamed-of perfection.

Lastly, there is the philosophy of the two loves, encompassing all life, eternity and time, heaven and hell. Saint Augustine wrote of the two loves, which make two cities, the city of God and the city of unregenerate man. In this philosophy the relation between libido and the highest personal love can be traced. At the same time, it prepares the way for a reconciliation between the religious love and the noblest ambitions of man capable of realization in the life of family or society. According to this view, two loves rule every individual in different measures. In theological language, the first is called Agape, the second, Eros. Psychologically they represent the masculine and feminine elements which are present in every human being. Eros is possessive and self-assertive, its end that of self-realization, its virtues those of honor, independence and self-respect. Agape is submissive, and, disregarding the measures imposed by reason and propriety, would lose itself in the emotion of a herd or the ecstasy of religious faith, in wooing death and darkness, or in a total self-surrender for love's sake.

These two loves make up the warp and woof of life lived in common. They have their dark descents, and they are in harmony; they are in the gentle relation of love between individuals, where each can give and receive the other's love. But in everything human there is imperfection, a coming to be and a passing away, and a chamber of loneliness which cannot be entered. This very incompleteness points to something beyond it, giving a glimpse of a love without misunderstanding, where each lives by the life of the other. This would be the supreme Agape. But the divine Agape is not an image or shadow. It is the rainbow in the sky and the sunlight in the heart.

Further reading:

D'Arcy, M. C.: THE MIND AND HEART OF LOVE. New York: Henry Holt and Company; 1947.

Aquinas, Saint Thomas: SELECTED WRITINGS. Everyman Library. New York: E. P. Dutton and Company; 1939.

Buber, Martin: SELECTED WRITINGS. Edited by Will Herbert. Gloucester, Mass.: Peter Smith; 1958.

Mascall, E. L.: CHRISTIAN THEOLOGY AND NATURAL SCIENCE. New York: The Ronald Press Company; 1957.

Einstein's Great Idea

BY

JAMES R. NEWMAN

*James R. Newman has achieved equal distinction as a law-
yer and as a writer on mathematics. In the former capacity
he taught at Yale Law School, served as adviser to the
White House on scientific legislation, and as counsel to
the Senate Special Committee on Atomic Energy. His
books include* Mathematics and the Imagination (*written
with Edward Kasner*), The Control of Atomic Energy
(*with Byron Milner*), *and recently the monumental four-
volume* World of Mathematics. *He is currently at work
on a biography of Michael Faraday.*

> *To the eyes of the man of imagination,
> nature is imagination itself.*
>
> —WILLIAM BLAKE

E instein died four years ago. Fifty years earlier, when
he was twenty-six, he put forward an idea which
changed the world. His idea revolutionized our conception of
the physical universe; its consequences have shaken human society. Since the rise of science in the seventeenth century, only
two other men, Newton and Darwin, have produced a comparable upheaval in thought.

Einstein, as everyone knows, did something remarkable, but

219

what exactly did he do? Even among educated men and women, few can answer. We are resigned to the importance of his theory, but we do not comprehend it. It is this circumstance which is largely responsible for the isolation of modern science. This is bad for us and bad for science; therefore more than curiosity is at stake in the desire to understand Einstein.

Relativity is a hard concept, prickly with mathematics. There are many popular accounts of it, a small number of which are good, but it is a mistake to expect they will carry the reader along—like a prince stretched on his palanquin. One must tramp one's own road. Nevertheless, relativity is in some respects simpler than the theory it supplanted. It makes the model of the physical world more susceptible to proof by experiment; it replaces a grandiose scheme of space and time with a more practical scheme. Newton's majestic system was worthy of the gods; Einstein's system is better suited to creatures like ourselves, with limited intelligence and weak eyes.

But relativity is radically new. It forces us to change deeply rooted habits of thought. It requires that we free ourselves from a provincial perspective. It demands that we relinquish convictions so long held that they are synonymous with common sense, that we abandon a picture of the world which seems as natural and as obvious as that the stars are overhead. It may be that in time Einstein's ideas will seem easy; but our generation as the severe task of being the first to lay the old aside and try the new. Anyone who seeks to understand the world of the twentieth century must make this effort.

In 1905 while working as an examiner in the Swiss Patent Office, Einstein published in the *Annalen der Physik*, a thirty-page paper with the title On the Electrodynamics of Moving Bodies. The paper embodied a vision. Poets and prophets are not alone in their visions; a young scientist—it happens mostly to the young—may in a flash glimpse a distant peak which no one else has seen. He may never see it again, but the landscape is forever changed. The single flash suffices; he will spend his life describing what he saw, interpreting and elaborating his vision, giving new directions to other explorers.

At the heart of the theory of relativity are questions connected with the velocity of light. The young Einstein began to brood about these while still a high-school student. Suppose, he asked himself, a person could run as fast as a beam of light, how would things look to him? Imagine that he could ride astride the beam, holding a mirror just in front of him. Then, like a fictional vampire, he would cause no image; for since the light and the mirror are traveling in the same direction at the same velocity, and the mirror is a little ahead, the light can never catch up to the mirror and there can be no reflection.

But this applies only to *his* mirror. Imagine a stationary observer, also equipped with a mirror, who watches the rider flashing by. Obviously the observer's mirror will catch the rider's image. In other words, the optical phenomena surrounding this event are purely relative. They exist for the observer; they do not exist for the rider. This was a troublesome paradox, which flatly contradicted the accepted views of optical phenomena. We shall have to see why.

The speed of light had long engaged the attention of physicists and astronomers. In the seventeenth century the Danish astronomer Römer discovered that light needed time for its propagation. Thereafter, increasingly accurate measurements of its velocity were made and by the end of the nineteenth century the established opinion was that light always travels in space at a certain constant rate, about 186,000 miles a second.

But now a new problem arose. In the mechanics of Galileo and Newton, rest and uniform motion (*i.e.*, constant velocity) are regarded as indistinguishable. Of two bodies, A and B, it can only be said that one is in motion *relative* to the other. The train glides by the platform; or the platform glides by the train. The earth approaches the fixed stars; or they approach it. There is no way of deciding which of these alternatives is true. And in the science of mechanics it makes no difference.

One of the questions, therefore, was whether, in respect to motion, light itself was like a physical body; that is, whether its motion was relativistic in the Newtonian sense, or absolute.

The wave theory of light appeared to answer this question. A wave is a progressive motion in some kind of medium; a sound wave, for example, is a movement of air particles. Light waves, it was supposed, move in an all-pervasive medium called the ether. The ether was assumed to be a subtle jelly with marvelous properties. It was colorless, odorless, without detectable features of any kind. It could penetrate all matter. It quivered in transmitting light. Also, the body of the ether as a whole was held to be stationary. To the physicist this was its most important property, for being absolutely at rest the ether offered a unique frame of reference for determining the velocity of light. Thus while it was hopeless to attempt to determine the absolute motion of a physical body because one could find no absolutely stationary frame of reference against which to measure it, the attempt was not hopeless for light; the ether, it was thought, met the need.

The ether, however, did not meet the need. Its marvelous properties made it a terror for experimentalists. How could motion be measured against an ectoplasm, a substance with no more substantiality than an idea? Finally, in 1887, two American physicists, A. A. Michelson and E. W. Morley, rigged up a beautifully precise instrument, called an interferometer, with which they hoped to discover some evidence of the relationship between light and the hypothetical ether. If the earth moves through the ether, a beam of light traveling in the direction of the earth's motion should move faster through the ether than a beam traveling in the opposite direction. Moreover, just as one can swim across a river and back more quickly than one can swim the same distance up and down stream, it might be expected that a beam of light taking analogous paths through the ether would complete the to-and-fro leg of the journey more quickly than the up-and-down leg.

This reasoning was the basis of the Michelson-Morley experiment. They carried out a number of trials in which they compared the velocity of a beam of light moving through the ether in the direction of the earth's motion, and another beam traveling at right angles to this motion. There was every reason to believe that these velocities would be different. Yet no difference was observed. The light beam seemed to move at the same velocity in either direction. The possibility that the earth dragged the ether with it having been ruled out, the inquiry had come to a dead end. Perhaps there was no difference; perhaps there was no ether. The Michelson-Morley findings were a major paradox.

Various ideas were advanced to resolve it. The most imaginative of these, and also the most fantastic, was put forward by the Irish physicist, G. F. Fitzgerald. He suggested that since matter is electrical in essence and held together by electrical forces, it may contract in the direction of its motion as it moves through the ether. The contraction would be very small; nevertheless in the direction of motion the unit of length would be shorter. This hypothesis would explain the Michelson-Morley result. The arms of their interferometer might contract as the earth rotated; this would shorten the unit of length and cancel out the added velocity imparted to the light by the rotation of the earth. The velocities of the two beams—in the direction of the earth's motion and at right angles to it—would appear equal. Fitzgerald's idea was elaborated by the famous Dutch physicist, H. A. Lorentz. He put it in mathematical form and connected the contraction caused by motion with the velocity of light. According to his arithmetic, the contraction was just enough to account for the negative results of the Michelson-Morley experiment. There the subject rested until Einstein took it up anew.

He knew of the Michelson-Morley findings. He knew also of other inconsistencies in the contemporary model of the physical world. One was the slight but persistent misbehavior (by classical standards) of the planet Mercury as it moved in its orbit; it was losing time (at a trifling rate, to be sure—forty-three seconds of arc per century), but Newton's theory of its motion was exact and there was no way of accounting for the discrepancy. Another was the bizarre antics of electrons, which, as W. Kaufmann and J. J. Thomson discovered, increased in mass as they went faster. The question was, could these inconsistencies be overcome by patching and mending classical theories? Or had the time come for a Copernican renovation?

Making his own way, Einstein turned to another aspect of the velocity problem. Velocity measurements involve time measurements, and time measurements, as he perceived, involve the concept of simultaneity. Is this concept simple and intuitively clear? No one doubted that it was; but Einstein demanded proof.

I enter my study in the morning as the clock on the wall begins to strike. Obviously these events are simultaneous. Assume, however, that on entering the study I hear the first stroke of the town-hall clock, half a mile away. It took time for the sound to reach me; therefore while the sound wave fell on my ears at the moment I entered the study, the event that produced the wave was not simultaneous with my entry.

Consider another kind of signal. I see the light from a distant star. An astronomer tells me that the image I see is not of the star as it is today, but of the star as it was the year Brutus killed Caesar. What does simultaneity mean in this case? Is my *here-now* simultaneous with the star's *there-then*? Can I speak meaningfully of the star as it was the day Joan of Arc was burned, even though ten generations will have to pass before the light emitted by the star on that day reaches the earth? How can I be sure it will ever get here? In short, is the concept of simultaneity for different places exactly equivalent to the concept for one and the same place?

Einstein soon convinced himself that the answer is no. Simultaneity, as he realized, depends on signals; the speed of light (or other signal) must therefore enter into the meaning of the concept. Not only does the separation of events in *space* becloud the issue of simultaneity in *time*, but relative motion may do so. A pair of events which one observer pronounces simultaneous may appear to another observer, in motion with respect to the first, to have happened at different times. In his own popular account of relativity (see pages 225–6), Einstein gave a convincing and easy example, which showed that *any* measurement of time is a measurement with respect to a given observer. A measurement valid for one observer may not be valid for another. Indeed, the measurement is certain not to be valid if one attempts to extend it from the system where the measurement was made to a system in motion relative to the first.

Einstein was now aware of these facts. Measuring the speed of light requires a time measurement. This involves a judgment of simultaneity. Simultaneity is not an absolute fact, the same

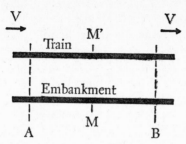

Einstein's Own Example of the Relativity of Time

The diagram shows a long railroad train traveling along the rails with velocity V, in the direction toward the right of the page. The bottom line denotes the embankment running parallel to the rails. The letters A and B mark two places on the rails, and the letter M marks a point on the embankment directly midway between A and B. At M stands an observer equipped with a pair of mirrors which are joined in a V and inclined at 90°. By means of this device he can observe both places, A and B, at the same time. We imagine two events at A and B, say two flashes of lightning, which the observer perceives in his mirror device at the same time. These he pronounces to be *simultaneous*, by which he means that the rays of light emitted at A and B by the lightning bolts meet at the midpoint M of the length A → B along the embankment. Now consider the moving train, and imagine a passenger seated in it. As the train proceeds along the rails, the passenger will arrive at a point M^I, which is directly opposite M, and therefore exactly midway between the length A → B along the rails. Assume further that the passenger arrives at M^I just when the flashes of lightning occur. We have seen that the observer at M correctly pronounces the lightning bolts as simultaneous; the question is, will the train passenger at M^1 make the same pronouncement? It is easily shown that he will not. Obviously if the point M^1 were stationary with respect to M, the passenger would have the same impression of simultaneity of the lightning flashes as the observer on the embankment. But M^1 is not stationary; it is moving toward the right with the velocity V of the train. Therefore (considered with reference to the embankment) the passenger is moving toward the beam of light coming from B, and away from the beam coming from A. It seems clear then that he will see the beam emitted by the flash at B sooner than the beam emitted by the flash at A. Accordingly he will pronounce the flash at B as *earlier in time* than the flash at A.

Which of the two pronouncements is correct, the observer's or the passenger's? The answer is that each is right in its own system. The observer is right with respect to the embankment, the passenger with respect to the train. The observer may say that he alone is right because he is at rest while the passenger is moving and his impressions are therefore distorted. To this the passenger can reply that motion does not distort the signals, and that, in any case, there is no more reason to believe that he was moving and the observer at rest than that the passenger was at rest and the observer moving.

There is nothing to choose between these views, and they can be logically reconciled only by accepting the principle that simultaneity of events is meaningful only with respect to a particular reference system; moreover, that every such system has its own particular time, and unless, as Einstein says, we are told the reference system to which the statement of time refers, a bare statement of the time of an event is meaningless.

for all observers. The individual observer's judgment depends on relative motion.

But the sequence does not end here. A further inference suggests itself, namely, that simultaneity may also be involved in measuring distances. A passenger on a moving train who wants to measure the length of his car has no difficulty. With a yardstick he can do the job as easily as if he were measuring his room at home. Not so for a stationary observer watching the train go by. The car is moving and he cannot measure it simply by laying a yardstick end on end. He must use light signals, which will tell him when the ends of the car coincide with certain arbitrary points. Therefore, problems of time arise. Suppose the thing to be measured is an electron, which is in continual motion at high speed. Light signals will enter the experiment, judgments of simultaneity will have to be made, and once again it is obvious that observers of the electron who are in motion relative to each other will get different results. The whole comfortable picture of reality begins to disintegrate: neither space nor time is what it seems.

The clarification of the concept of simultaneity thrust upon Einstein the task of challenging two assumptions, assumptions hedged with the divinity of Isaac Newton. "Absolute, true, and mathematical time, of itself and from its own nature, flows equably without relation to anything external. . . ." This was Newton's sonorous definition in his great book, *Principia Mathematica*. To this definition he added the equally majestic, "Absolute space, in its own nature, without relation to anything external, remains always similar and immovable." These assumptions, as Einstein saw, were magnificent but untenable. They were at the bottom of the paradoxes of contemporary physics. They had to be discarded. Absolute time and absolute space were concepts which belonged to an outworn metaphysic. They went beyond observation and experiment; indeed, they were refuted by the nasty facts. Physicists had to live with these facts.

To live with them meant nothing less than to accept the Michelson-Morley paradox, to incorporate it into physics rather than try to explain it away. From the point of view of common sense the results were extraordinary, yet they had been verified.

It was not the first time that science had had to overrule common sense. The evidence showed that the speed of light measured by *any* observer, whether at rest or in motion relative to the light source, is the same. Einstein embodied this fact in a principle from which a satisfactory theory of the interaction between the motion of bodies and the propagation of light could be derived. This principle, or first postulate, of his Special Theory of Relativity states that *the velocity of light in space is a constant of nature, unaffected by the motion of the observer or of the source of the light.*

The hypothesis of the ether thus became unnecessary. One did not have to try to measure the velocity of light against an imaginary frame of reference, for the plain reason that whenever light is measured against *any* frame of reference its velocity is the same. Why then conjure up ethereal jellies? The ether simply lost its reason for being.

A second postulate was needed. Newtonian relativity applied to the motion of material bodies; but light waves, as I mentioned earlier, were thought not to be governed by this principle. Einstein pierced the dilemma in a stroke. He simply extended Newtonian relativity to include optical phenomena. The second postulate says: *In any experiment involving mechanical or optical phenomena it makes no difference whether the laboratory where the experiment is being performed is at rest or in uniform motion; the results of the experiments will be the same.* More generally, one cannot by any method distinguish between rest and uniform motion, except in relation to each other.

Is that all there is to the special theory of relativity? The postulates are deceptively simple. Moreover, to the sharp-eyed reader they may appear to contradict each other. The contradictions, however, are illusory, and the consequences are revolutionary.

Consider the first point. From the postulates one may infer that on the one hand light has the velocity c, and, on the other hand, even when according to our traditional way of calculating it should have the velocity $c + q$ (where q is the velocity of the source), its velocity is still c. Concretely, light from a source in motion with respect to a given frame of reference has the same velocity as light from a source at rest with respect to the same frame. (As one physicist suggested, this is as if we were to say that a man walking up a moving stairway does not get to the top any sooner than a man standing still on the moving stairway.) This seems absurd. But the reason it seems absurd is that we take it for granted that the velocity of the moving source must be added to the normal velocity of light to give the correct velocity of the beam emitted by the source. Suppose we abandon this assumption. We have already seen, after all, that motion has a queer effect on space and time measurements. It follows that the established notions of velocity must be reconsidered. The postulates were not inherently contradictory; the trouble lay with the classical laws of physics. They had to be changed. Einstein did not hesitate. To preserve his postulates he consigned the old system to the flames. In them were consumed the most cherished notions of space, time and matter.

One of the clichés about Einstein's theory is that it shows that everything is relative. The statement that everything is relative is as meaningful as the statement that everything is bigger. As Bertrand Russell pointed out, if everything were relative there would be nothing for it to be relative to. The name relativity is misleading. Einstein was in fact concerned with finding something that is *not* relative, something that mathematicians call an invariant. With this as a fixed point, it might be possible to formulate physical laws which would incorporate the "objective residue" of an observer's experience; that is, that part of the space and time characteristics of a physical event which, though perceived by him, are independent of the observer and might therefore be expected to appear the same to all observers. The constancy principle of the velocity of light provided Einstein with the invariant he needed. It could be maintained, however, only at the expense of the traditional notion of time. And even this offering was not enough. Space and time are intertwined. They are part of the same reality. Tinkering with the measure of time unavoidably affects the measure of space.

Einstein, you will notice, arrived at the same conclusion as Fitzgerald and Lorentz without adopting their electrical hypotheses. It was a consequence of his postulates that clocks and yardsticks yield different measurements in relative motion than at rest. Is this due to an actual physical change in the instruments? The question may be regarded as irrelevant. The physicist is concerned only with the difference in measurements. If clock springs and yardsticks contract, why is it not possible to detect the change? Because any scales used to measure it would suffer the same contraction. What is at issue is nothing less than the foundations of rational belief.

Earlier I mentioned Kaufmann's and Thomson's discovery that a moving electron increases in mass as it goes faster. Relativity explains this astonishing fact. The first postulate sets an upper limit to the velocity of light, and permits of the deduction that no material body can exceed this speed limit. In Newton's system there were no such limits; moreover, the mass of a body—which he defined as its "quantity of matter"—was held to be the same whether the body was at rest or in motion. But just as his laws of motion have been shown not to be universally true, his concept of the constancy of mass turns out to be flawed. According to Einstein's Special Theory, the resistance of a body to changes in velocity increases with velocity. Thus, for example, more force is required to increase a body's velocity from 50,000 to 50,001 miles per hour than from 100 to 101 miles per hour. The scientific name for this resistance is *inertia*, and the measure of inertia is mass. (This jibes with the intuitive notion that the amount of force needed to accelerate a body depends on its "quantity of matter.") The ideas fall neatly into place: with increased speed, inertia increases; increased inertia evinces itself as increased mass. The increase in mass is, to be sure, very small at ordinary speeds, and therefore undetectable, which explains why Newton and his successors, though a brilliant company, did not discover it. This circumstance also explains why Newton's laws are perfectly valid for all ordinary instances of matter in motion: even a rocket moving at 10,000 miles an hour is a tortoise compared to a beam of light at 186,000 miles a second. But the increase in mass becomes a major factor where high-speed nuclear particles are concerned; for example, the electrons in a hospital X-ray tube are speeded up to a point where their normal mass is doubled, and in an ordinary TV-picture tube the electrons have 5 per cent extra mass due to their energy of motion. And at the speed of light the push of even an unlimited accelerating force against a body is completely frustrated, because the mass of the body, in effect, becomes infinite.

It is only a step now to Einstein's fateful mass-energy equation.

The quantity of additional mass, multiplied by an enormous number—namely, the square of the speed of light—is equivalent to the energy which was turned into mass. But is this equivalence of mass and energy a special circumstance attendant upon motion? What about a body at rest? Does its mass also represent energy? Einstein boldly concluded that it does. "The mass of a body is a measure of its energy content," he wrote in 1905, and gave his now-famous formula, $E = mc^2$, where E is energy content, m is mass (which varies according to speed) and c is the velocity of light.

"It is not impossible," Einstein said in this same paper, "that with bodies whose energy content is variable to a high degree (*e.g.*, with radium salts) the theory may be successfully put to the test." In the 1930's many physicists were making this test, measuring atomic masses and the energy of products of many nuclear reactions. All the results verified his idea. A distinguished physicist, Dr. E. U. Condon, tells a charming story of Einstein's reaction to this triumph: "One of my most vivid memories is of a seminar at Princeton (1934) when a graduate student was reporting on researches of this kind and Einstein was in the audience. Einstein had been so preoccupied with other studies that he had not realized that such confirmation of his early theories had become an everyday affair in the physical laboratory. He grinned like a small boy and kept saying over and over, '*Ist das wirklich so?*' Is it really true?—as more and more specific evidence of his $E = mc^2$ relation was being presented."

For ten years after he formulated the Special Theory, Einstein grappled with the task of generalizing relativity to include accelerated motion. This article cannot carry the weight of the details, but I shall describe the matter briefly.

While it is impossible to distinguish between rest and uniform motion by observations made within a system, it seems quite possible, under the same circumstances, to determine *changes* in velocity or direction, *i.e.*, acceleration. In a train moving smoothly in a straight line, at constant velocity, one feels no motion. But if the train speeds up, slows down or takes a curve, the change is felt immediately. One has to make an effort to keep from falling, to prevent the soup from sloshing out of the plate, and so on. These effects are ascribed to what are called *inertial forces*, producing acceleration—the name is intended to convey the fact that the forces arise from the inertia of a mass, *i.e.*, its resistance to changes in its state. It would seem then that any one of several simple experiments should furnish evidence of such acceleration, and distinguish it from uniform motion or rest. Moreover, it should even be possible to determine the effect of acceleration on a beam of light. For example, if a beam were set parallel to the floor of a laboratory at rest or in uniform motion, and the laboratory were accelerated upward or downward, the light would no longer be parallel to the floor, and by measuring the deflection one could compute the acceleration.

When Einstein turned these points over in his mind, he perceived a loose end in the reasoning, which others had not noticed. How is it possible in either a mechanical or an optical experiment to distinguish between the effects of gravity, and of acceleration produced by inertial forces? Take the light-beam experiment. At one point the beam is parallel to the floor of the laboratory; then suddenly it is deflected. The observer ascribes the deflection to acceleration caused by inertial forces, but how can he be sure? He must make his determination entirely on the basis of what he sees *within* the laboratory, and he is therefore unable to tell whether inertial forces are at work—as in the moving train—or whether the observed effects are produced by a large (though unseen) gravitating mass.

Here then, Einstein realized, was the clue to the problem of generalizing relativity. As rest and uniform motion are indistinguishable, so are acceleration and the effects of gravitation. Neither mechanical nor optical experiments conducted within a laboratory can decide whether the system is accelerated or in uniform motion and subjected to a gravitational field. (The poor wretch in tomorrow's space ship, suddenly thrown to the floor, will be unable to tell whether his vehicle is starting its rocket motors or a huge gravitational mass has suddenly appeared to bedevil it.) Einstein formulated his conclusion in 1911 in his "principle of equivalence of gravitational forces and inertial forces."

His ideas invariably had startling consequences. From the principle of equivalence he deduced, among others, that gravity must affect the path of a ray of light. This follows from the fact that acceleration would affect the ray, and gravity is indistinguishable from acceleration. Einstein predicted that this gravity effect would be noticeable in the deflection of the light from the fixed stars whose rays pass close to the huge mass of the sun. He realized, of course, that it would not be easy to observe the bending because under ordinary conditions the sun's brilliant light washes out the light of the stars. But during a total eclipse the stars near the sun would be visible, and circumstances would be favorable to checking his prediction. "It would be extremely desirable," Einstein wrote in his paper enunciating the equivalence principle, "if astronomers would look into the problem presented here, even though the consideration developed above may appear insufficiently founded or even bizarre." Eight years later, in 1919, a British eclipse expedition headed by the famous astronomer Arthur Eddington, confirmed Einstein's astounding prediction.

In 1916 Einstein announced his General Theory of Relativity, a higher synthesis incorporating both the Special Theory and the principle of equivalence. Two profound ideas are developed in the General Theory: the union of time and space into a four-dimensional continuum (a consequence of the Special Theory), and the curvature of space.

It was to one of his former professors at Zurich, the Russian-born mathematician, Hermann Minkowski, that Einstein owed the idea of the union of space and time. "From henceforth," Minkowski had said in 1908, "space in itself and time in itself sink to mere shadows, and only a kind of union of the two preserves an independent existence." To the three familiar dimensions of space, a fourth, of time, had to be added, and thus a single new medium, space-time, replaced the orthodox frame of absolute space and absolute time. An event within this medium—one may, for example, think of a moving object as an "event"—is identified not only by three spatial co-ordinates denoting *where* it is, but by a time coordinate denoting *when* the event is there. *Where* and *when* are, as we have seen, judgments made by an observer, depending on certain interchanges of light signals. It is for this reason that the time coordinate includes as one of its elements the number for the velocity of light.

With absolute space and time discarded, the old picture of the universe proceeding moment by moment from the past through the present into the future must also be discarded. In the new world of Minkowski and Einstein, there is neither absolute past nor absolute future; nor is there an absolute present dividing past from future and "stretching everywhere at the same moment through space." The motion of an object is represented by a line in space-time, called a "world-line." The event makes its own history. The signals it emits take time to reach the observer; since he can record only what he sees, an event present for one observer may be past for another, future for a third. In Eddington's words, the absolute "here-now" of former beliefs has become a merely relative "seen-now."

But this must not be taken to mean that every observer can portray only his own world, and that in place of Newtonian order we have Einsteinian anarchy. Just as it was possible in the older sense to fix precisely the distance between two points in three-dimensional space, so it is possible in the four-dimensional continuum of space-time to define and measure distance between events. This distance is called an "interval" and has a "true, absolute value," the same for all who measure it. Thus, after all, "we have found something firm in a shifting world."

How is the concept of curved space related to this picture? The concept itself sticks in the craw. A vase, a pretzel, a line can be curved. But how can empty space be curved? Once again we must think not in terms of metaphysical abstractions, but of testable concepts.

Light rays in empty space move in straight lines. Yet in some circumstances (*e.g.*, where the ray is close to the sun) the path of motion is seen to be curved. A choice of explanations offers itself. We may, for example, say that a gravitational mass in the neighborhood of the ray has bent it; or we may say that this gravitational mass has curved the space through which the ray is traveling. There is no logical reason to prefer one explanation to the other. Gravitational fields are no less an imaginary concept than space-time. The only concrete evidence comes from measuring the path of the light itself—not the field or space-time. It turns out to be more fruitful to explain the curved path of the light ray as an effect of curved space-time, rather than as an effect of the direct action of gravity on light.

Let me suggest an analogy. A thin sheet of rubber is stretched over a large drum-kettle. I take a very light marble and permit it to roll over the sheet. I observe that the path of its motion is a straight line. I now take several lead weights and place them at different points on the rubber sheet. Their weight dimples it, forming small slopes and hollows. Suppose I release the marble on this surface. The path of motion will no longer be straight, but will curve toward the slopes and eventually fall into one of the hollows. Now think of space-time as corresponding to the sheet of rubber, and large gravitational masses to the lead weights; think also of any "event"—a moving particle, a beam of light, a planet—as the counterpart of the marble rolling on the membrane. Where there are no masses, space-time is "flat" and paths of motion are straight lines. But in the neighborhood of large masses space-time is distorted into "slopes" and "hollows," which affect the path of any object entering upon them.

This is what used to be called the attraction of gravitation. But gravitation in Einstein's theory is merely an aspect of space-time. The starlight bent toward the sun "dips" into the "slope" around it, but has enough energy not to be trapped in the "hollow"; the earth circling the sun is riding on the "rim" of its "hollow" like a cyclist racing round a velodrome; a planet which gets too deep into the "hollow" may fall to the bottom. (This is one of the hypotheses astronomers make about collisions which may have formed new planets in our universe.) There are slopes and hollows wherever there is matter; and since astronomical evidence seems to favor the hypothesis that matter is on average uniformly distributed throughout the universe, and finite—though not necessarily constant—Einstein suggested the possibility that the whole of space-time is gently curved, finite, but unbounded. It is not inconsistent with this hypothesis that the universe is expanding, in which case the density of matter would decrease. A finite but unbounded universe is roughly analogous—though it is of higher dimension—to the two-dimensional curved surface of the earth. The area is finite without boundaries, and if one travels in a "straight line" in a given direction one must, after a time, return to the original point of departure.

Einstein's achievement is one of the glories of man. Two points about his work are worth making. The first is that his model of the world was not a machine with man outside it as observer and interpreter. The observer is part of the reality he observes; therefore by observation he shapes it.

The second point is that his theory did much more than answer questions. As a living theory it forced new questions upon us. Einstein challenged unchallengeable writs; he would have been the last to claim that his own writs were beyond challenge. He broadened the human mind.

Further reading:

Condon, E. U.: "What Is Physics?" in James R. Newman (ed.): What Is Science? New York: Simon and Schuster; 1955.

Dampier, Sir William: A History of Science. Fourth edition. New York: Cambridge University Press; 1948.

Eddington, Sir Arthur: The Nature of the Physical World. New York: Cambridge University Press; 1932.

Frank, Philipp: Einstein: His Life and Times. New York: Alfred A. Knopf; 1953.

Russell, Bertrand: The ABC of Relativity. Revised Edition. New York: Mentor Books; 1959.

Whitehead, Alfred North: Science and the Modern World. New York: The Macmillan Company; 1925.

How Words Change
Our Lives

BY

S. I. HAYAKAWA

*S. I. (Samuel Ichiye) Hayakawa was born in Vancouver
and was graduated from the University of Manitoba, Mc-
Gill University, and the University of Wisconsin. Dr. Hayakawa has taught and lectured at a number of American
universities, and since 1955 has been professor of Language Arts at San Francisco State College. Founder and
editor of ETC.: A Review of General Semantics, Dr. Hayakawa is author of several books on language. His Language in Action was written as a textbook and chosen as
a Book-of-the-Month Club selection in 1941. Dr. Hayakawa is married to the former Margedant Peters; they have
three children. His extracurricular interests are art, fishing,
and jazz.*

The end product of education, yours and mine and everybody's, is the total pattern of reactions and possible reactions we have inside ourselves. If you did not have within
you at this moment the pattern of reactions which we call "the
ability to read English," you would see here only meaningless
black marks on paper. Because of the trained patterns of re-

sponse, you are (or are not) stirred to patriotism by martial music, your feelings of reverence are aroused by the symbols of your religion, you listen more respectfully to the health advice of someone who has "M.D." after his name than to that of someone who hasn't. What I call here a "pattern of reactions," then, is the sum total of the ways we act in response to events, to words and to symbols.

Our reaction patterns—our semantic habits, as we may call them—are the internal and most important residue of whatever years of education or miseducation we may have received from our parents' conduct toward us in childhood as well as their teachings, from the formal education we may have had, from all the sermons and lectures we have listened to, from the radio programs and the movies and television shows we have experienced, from all the books and newspapers and comic strips we have read, from the conversations we have had with friends and associates, and from all our experiences. If, as the result of all these influences that make us what we are, our semantic habits are reasonably similar to those of most people around us, we are regarded as "well-adjusted," or "normal," and perhaps "dull." If our semantic habits are noticeably different from those of others, we are regarded as "individualistic" or "original," or, if the differences are disapproved of or viewed with alarm, as "screwball" or "crazy."

Semantics is sometimes defined in dictionaries as "the science of the meaning of words"—which would not be a bad definition if people didn't assume that the search for the meanings of words begins and ends with looking them up in a dictionary.

If one stops to think for a moment, it is clear that to define a word, as a dictionary does, is simply to explain the word with more words. To be thorough about defining, we should next have to define the words used in the definition, then define the words used in defining the words used in the definition . . . and so on. Defining words with more words, in short, gets us at once into what mathematicians call an "infinite regress." Alternatively, it can get us into the kind of run-around we sometimes encounter when we look up "impertinence" and find it defined as "impudence," so we look up "impudence" and find it defined as "impertinence." Yet—and here we come to another common reaction pattern—people often act as if words can be explained fully with more words. To a person who asked for a definition of jazz, Louis Armstrong is said to have replied, "Man, when you got to ask what it is, you'll never get to know," proving himself to be an intuitive semanticist as well as a great trumpet player.

Semantics, then, does not deal with the "meaning of words" as that expression is commonly understood. P. W. Bridgman, the Nobel Prize winner and physicist, once wrote, "The true meaning of a term is to be found by observing what a man does with it, not by what he says about it." He made an enormous contribution to science by showing that the meaning of a scientific term lies in the operations, the things done, that establish its validity, rather than in verbal definitions.

Here is a simple, everyday kind of example of "operational" criticism. If you say, "This table measures six feet in length," you could prove it by taking a foot rule, performing the operation of laying it end to end while counting, "One . . . two . . . three . . . four . . ." But if you say—and revolutionists have started uprisings with just this statement—"Man is born free, but everywhere he is in chains!"—what operations could you perform to demonstrate its accuracy or inaccuracy?

But let us carry this suggestion of "operationalism" outside the physical sciences where Bridgman applied it, and observe what "operations" people perform as the result of both the language they use and the language other people use in communicating to them. Here is a personnel manager studying an application blank. He comes to the words "Education: Harvard University," and drops the application blank in the wastebasket (that's the "operation") because, as he would say if you asked him, "I don't like Harvard men." This is an instance of "meaning" at work—but it is not a meaning that can be found in dictionaries.

If I seem to be taking a long time to explain what semantics is about, it is because I am trying, in the course of explanation, to introduce the reader to a certain way of looking at human behavior. Semantics—especially the general semantics of Alfred Korzybski (1879–1950), Polish-American scientist and educator—pays particular attention not to words in themselves, but to semantic reactions—that is, human responses to symbols, signs and symbol-systems, including language.

I say *human* responses because, so far as we know, human beings are the only creatures that have, over and above that biological equipment which we have in common with other creatures, the additional capacity for manufacturing symbols and systems of symbols. When we react to a flag, we are not reacting simply to a piece of cloth, but to the meaning with which it has been symbolically endowed. When we react to a word, we are not reacting to a set of sounds, but to the meaning with which that set of sounds has been symbolically endowed.

A basic idea in general semantics, therefore, is that the meaning of words (or other symbols) is not in the words, but in our own semantic reactions. If I were to tell a shockingly obscene story in Arabic or Hindustani or Swahili before an audience that understood only English, no one would blush or be angry; the story would be neither shocking nor obscene—indeed, it would not even be a story. Likewise, the value of a dollar bill is not in the bill, but in our social agreement to accept it as a symbol of value. If that agreement were to break down through the collapse of our Government, the dollar bill would become only a scrap of paper. We do not understand a dollar bill by staring at it long and hard. We understand it by observing how people act with respect to it. We understand it by understanding the social mechanisms and the loyalties that keep it meaningful. Semantics is therefore a social study, basic to all other social studies.

It is often remarked that words are tricky—and that we are all prone to be deceived by "fast talkers," such as high-pressure salesmen, skillful propagandists, politicians or lawyers. Since few of us are aware of the degree to which we use words to deceive ourselves, the sin of "using words in a tricky way" is one that is always attributed to the other fellow. When the Russians use the word "democracy" to mean something quite different from what we mean by it, we at once accuse them of "propaganda," of "corrupting the meanings of words." But when we use the word "democracy" in the United States to mean something quite different from what the Russians mean by it, they are equally quick to accuse us of "hypocrisy." We all tend to believe that the way we use words is the correct way, and that people who use the same words in other ways are either ignorant or dishonest.

Leaving aside for a moment such abstract and difficult terms as "democracy," let us examine a common, everyday word like "frog." Surely there is no problem about what "frog" means! Here are some sample sentences:

"If we're going fishing, we'll have to catch some frogs first." (This is easy.)

"I have a frog in my throat." (You can hear it croaking.)

"She wore a loose, silk jacket fastened with braided frogs."

"The blacksmith pared down the frog and the hoof before shoeing the horse."

"In Hamilton, Ohio, there is a firm by the name of American Frog and Switch Company."

In addition to these "frogs," there is the frog in which a sword is carried, the frog at the bottom of a bowl or vase that is used in flower arrangement, and the frog which is part of a violin bow. The reader can no doubt think of other "frogs."

Or take another common word such as "order." There is the *order* that the salesman tries to get, which is quite different from the *order* which a captain gives to his crew. Some people enter holy *orders*. There is the *order* in the house when mother has finished tidying up; there is the batting *order* of the home team; there is an *order* of ham and eggs. It is surprising that with so many meanings to the word, people don't misunderstand one another oftener than they do.

The foregoing are only striking examples of a principle to which we are all so well accustomed that we rarely think of it; namely, that most words have more meanings than dictionaries can keep track of. And when we consider further that each of us has different experiences, different memories, different likes and dislikes, it is clear that all words evoke different responses in all of us. We may agree as to what the term "Mississippi River" stands for, but you and I recall different parts of the river; you and I have had different experiences with it; one of us has read more about it than the other; one of us may have happy memories of it, while the other may recall chiefly tragic events connected with it. Hence your "Mississippi River" can never be identical with my "Mississippi River." The fact that we can communicate with each other about the "Mississippi River" often conceals the fact that we are talking about two different sets of memories and experiences.

Words being as varied in their meanings as they are, no one can tell us what the correct interpretation of a word should be in advance of our next encounter with that word. The reader may have been taught always to revere the word "mother." But what is he going to do the next time he encounters this word, when it occurs in the sentence "Mother began to form in the bottle"? If it is impossible to determine what a single word will mean on next encounter, is it possible to say in advance what is the correct evaluation of such events as these: (1) next summer, an individual who calls himself a socialist will announce his candidacy for the office of register of deeds in your city; (2) next autumn, there will be a strike at one of your local department stores; (3) next week, your wife will announce that she is going to change her style of hairdo; (4) tomorrow, your little boy will come home with a bleeding nose?

A reasonably sane individual will react to each of these events in his own way, according to time, place and the entire surrounding set of circumstances; and included among those circumstances will be his own stock of experiences, wishes, hopes and fears. But there are people whose pattern of reactions is such that some of them can be completely predicted in advance. Mr. A will never vote for anyone called "socialist," no matter how incompetent or crooked the alternative candidates may be. Mr. B-1 always disapproves of strikes and strikers, without bothering to inquire whether or not this strike has its justifications; Mr. B-2 always sympathizes with the strikers because he hates all bosses. Mr. C belongs to the "stay sweet as you are" school of thought, so that his wife hasn't been able to change her hairdo since she left high school. Mr. D always faints at the sight of blood.

Such fixed and unalterable patterns of reaction—in their more obvious forms we call them prejudices—are almost inevitably organized around words. Mr. E distrusts and fears all people to whom the term "Catholic" is applicable, while Mr. F, who is Catholic, distrusts and fears all non-Catholics. Mr. G is so rabid a Republican that he reacts with equal dislike to all Democrats, all Democratic proposals, all opposite proposals if they are also made by Democrats. Back in the days when Franklin D. Roosevelt was President, Mr. G disliked not only the Democratic President but also his wife, children and dog. His office was on Roosevelt Road in Chicago (it had been named after Theodore Roosevelt), but he had his address changed to his back door on 11th Street, so that he would not have to print the hated name on his stationery. Mr. H, on the other hand, is an equally rabid Democrat, who hates himself for continuing to play golf, since golf is Mr. Eisenhower's favorite game. People suffering from such prejudices seem to have in their brains an uninsulated spot which, when touched by such words as "capitalist," "boss," "striker," "scab," "Democrat," "Republican," "socialized medicine," and other such loaded terms, results in an immediate short circuit, often with a blowing of fuses.

Alfred Korzybski, the founder of general semantics, called such short-circuited responses "identification reactions." He used the word "identification" in a special sense; he meant that persons given to such fixed patterns of response identify (that is, treat as identical) all occurrences of a given word or symbol; they identify all the different cases that fall under the same name. Thus, if one has hostile identification reactions to "women drivers," then all women who drive cars are "identical" in their incompetence.

Korzybski believed that the term "identification reaction" could be generally used to describe the majority of cases of semantic malfunctioning. Identification is something that goes on in the human nervous system. "Out there" there are no absolute identities. No two Harvard men, no two Ford cars, no two mothers-in-law, no two politicians, no two leaves from the same tree, are identical with each other in all respects. If, how-

243

ever, we treat all cases that fall under the same class label as one at times when the differences are important, then there is something wrong with our semantic habits.

We are now ready, then, for another definition of general semantics. It is a comparative study of the kinds of responses people make to the symbols and signs around them; we may compare the semantic habits common among the prejudiced, the foolish and the mentally ill with those found among people who are able to solve their problems successfully, so that, if we care to, we may revise our own semantic habits for the better. In other words, general semantics is, if we wish to make it so, the study of how not to be a damn fool.

Identification reactions run all the way through nature. The capacity for seeing similarities is necessary to the survival of all animals. The pickerel, I suppose, identifies all shiny, fluttery things going through the water as minnows, and goes after them all in pretty much the same way. Under natural conditions, life is made possible for the pickerel by this capacity. Once in a while, however, the shiny, fluttery thing in the water may happen to be not a minnow but an artificial lure on the end of a line. In such a case, one would say that the identification response, so useful for survival, under somewhat more complex conditions that require differentiation between two sorts of shiny and fluttery objects, proves to be fatal.

To go back to our discussion of human behavior, we see at once that the problem of adequate differentiation is immeasurably more complex for men than it is for pickerel. The signs we respond to, and the symbols we create and train ourselves to respond to, are infinitely greater in number and immeasurably more abstract than the signs in a pickerel's environment. Lower animals have to deal only with certain brute facts in their physical environment. But think, only for a moment, of what constitutes a human environment. Think of the items that call for adequate responses that no animal ever has to think about: our days are named and numbered, so that we have birthdays, anniversaries, holidays, centennials, and so on, all calling for specifically human responses; we have history, which no animal has to worry about; we have verbally codified patterns of behavior which we call law, religion and ethics. We have to respond not only to events in our immediate environment, but to reported events in Washington, Paris, Tokyo, Moscow, Beirut. We have literature, comic strips, confession magazines, market quotations, detective stories, journals of abnormal psychology, bookkeeping systems to interpret. We have money, credit, banking, stocks, bonds, checks, bills. We have the complex symbolisms of moving pictures, paintings, drama, music, architecture and dress. In short, we live in a vast human dimension of which the lower animals have no inkling, and we have to have a capacity for differentiation adequate to the complexity of our extra environment.

The next question, then, is why human beings do not always have an adequate capacity for differentiation. Why are we not constantly on the lookout for differences as well as similarities instead of feeling, as so many do, that the Chinese (or Mexicans, or ballplayers, or women drivers) are "all alike"? Why do some people react to words as if they were the things they stand for? Why do certain patterns of reaction, both in individuals and in larger groups such as nations, persist long after the usefulness has expired?

Part of our identification reactions are simply protective mechanisms inherited from the necessities of survival under earlier and more primitive conditions of life. I was once beaten up and robbed by two men on a dark street. Months later, I was again on a dark street with two men, good friends of mine, but involuntarily I found myself in a panic and insisted on our hurrying to a well-lighted drugstore to have a soda so that I would stop being jittery. In other words, my whole body reacted with an identification reaction of fear of these two men, in spite of the fact that "I knew" that I was in no danger. Fortunately, with the passage of time, this reaction has died away. But the hurtful experiences of early childhood do not fade so readily. There is no doubt that many identification reactions are traceable to childhood traumas, as psychiatrists have shown.

Further identification reactions are caused by communal patterns of behavior which were necessary or thought necessary at one stage or another in the development of a tribe or nation.

General directives such as "Kill all snakes," "Never kill cows, which are sacred animals," "Shoot all strangers on sight," "Fall down flat on your face before all members of the aristocracy," or, to come to more modern instances, "Never vote for a Republican," "Oppose all government regulation of business," "Never associate with Negroes on terms of equality," are an enormous factor in the creation of identification reactions.

Some human beings—possibly in their private feelings a majority—can accept these directives in a *human* way: that is, it will not be impossible for them under a sufficiently changed set of circumstances to kill a cow, or not to bow down before an aristocrat, to vote for a Republican, or to accept a Negro as a classmate. Others, however, get these directives so deeply ground into their nervous systems that they become incapable of changing their responses no matter how greatly the circumstances may have changed. Still others, although capable of changing their responses, dare not do so for fear of public opinion. Social progress usually requires the breaking up of these absolute identifications, which often make necessary changes impossible. Society must obviously have patterns of behavior; human beings must obviously have habits. But when those patterns become inflexible, so that a tribe has only one way to meet a famine, namely, to throw more infants as sacrifices to the crocodiles, or a nation has only one way to meet a threat to its security, namely, to increase its armaments, then such a tribe or such a nation is headed for trouble. There is insufficient capacity for differentiated behavior.

Furthermore—and here one must touch upon the role of newspapers, radio and television—if agencies of mass communication hammer away incessantly at the production of, let us say, a hostile set of reactions at such words as "Communists," "bureaucrats," "Wall Street," "international bankers," "labor leaders," and so on, no matter how useful an immediate job they may perform in correcting a given abuse at a given time and place, they can in the long run produce in thousands of readers and listeners identification reactions to the words—reactions that will make intelligent public discussion impossible. Modern means of mass communication and propaganda certainly have an important part to play in the creation of identification reactions.

In addition to the foregoing, there is still another source of identification reactions; namely, the language we use in our daily thought and speech. Unlike the languages of the sciences, which are carefully constructed, tailor-made, special-purpose languages, the language of everyday life is one directly inherited and haphazardly developed from those of our prescientific ancestors: Anglo-Saxons, primitive Germanic tribes, primitive Indo-Europeans. With their scant knowledge of the world, they formulated descriptions of the world before them in statements such as "The sun rises." We do not today believe that the sun "rises." Nevertheless, we still continue to use the expression, without believing what we say.

But there are other expressions, quite as primitive as the idea of "sunrise," which we use uncritically, fully believing in the implications of our terms. Having observed (or heard) that *some* Negroes are lazy, an individual may say, making a huge jump beyond the known facts, "Negroes are lazy." Without arguing for the moment the truth or falsity of this statement, let us examine the implications of the statement as it is ordinarily constructed: "Negroes are lazy." The statement implies, as common sense or any textbook on traditional logic will tell us, that "laziness" is a "quality" that is "inherent" in Negroes.

What are the facts? Under conditions of slavery, under which Negroes were not paid for working, there wasn't any point in being an industrious and responsible worker. The distinguished French abstract artist Jean Hélion once told the story of his life as a prisoner of war in a German camp, where, during the Second World War, he was compelled to do forced labor. He told how he loafed on the job, how he thought of device after device for avoiding work and producing as little as possible—and, since his prison camp was a farm, how he stole chickens at every opportunity. He also described how he put on an expression of good-natured imbecility whenever approached by his Nazi overseers. Without intending to do so, in describing his own actions, he gave an almost perfect picture of the literary type of the Southern Negro of slavery days. Jean Hélion, confronted with the fact of forced labor, reacted as intelligently as Southern Negro slaves, and the slaves reacted as intelligently as Jean Hélion. "Laziness," then, is not an "inherent quality" of Negroes or of any other group of people. It is a *response* to a work situation in which there are no rewards for working, and in which one hates his taskmasters.

Statements implying inherent qualities, such as "Negroes are lazy" or "There's something terribly wrong with young people today," are therefore the crudest kind of unscientific observation, based on an out-of-date way of saying things, like "The sun rises." The tragedy is not simply the fact that people make such statements; the graver fact is that they believe themselves.

Some individuals are admired for their "realism" because, as the saying goes, they "call a spade a spade." Suppose we were to to raise the question "Why should anyone call it a spade?" The reply would obviously be, "Because that's what it is!" This reply appeals so strongly to the common sense of most people that they feel that at this point discussion can be closed. I should like to ask the reader, however, to consider a point which may appear at first to him a mere quibble.

Here, let us say, is an implement for digging made of steel, with a wooden handle. Here, on the other hand, is a succession of sounds made with the tongue, lips and vocal cords: "spade." If you want a digging implement of the kind we are talking about, you would ask for it by making the succession of sounds "spade" if you are addressing an English-speaking person. But suppose you were addressing a speaker of Dutch, French, Hungarian, Chinese, Tagalog? Would you not have to make completely different sounds? It is apparent, then, that the common-sense opinion of most people, "We call a spade a spade because that's what it is," is completely and utterly wrong. We call it a "spade" because we are English-speaking people, conforming, in this instance, to majority usage in naming this particular object. The steel-and-iron digging implement is simply an object standing there against the garage door; "spade" is what we *call* it—"spade" is a *name*.

And here we come to another source of identification reactions—an unconscious assumption about language epitomized in the expression "a spade is a spade," or even more elegantly in the famous remark "Pigs are called pigs because they are such dirty animals." The assumption is that everything has a "right name" and that the "right name" names the "essence" of that which is named.

If this assumption is at work in our reaction patterns, we are likely to be given to premature and often extremely inappropriate responses. We are likely to react to names as if they gave complete insight into the persons, things or situations named. If we are told that a given individual is a "Jew," some of us are likely to respond, "That's all I need to know." For, if names give the essence of that which is named, obviously, every "Jew" has the essential attribute of "Jewishness." Or, to put it the other way around, it is because he possesses "Jewishness" that we call him a "Jew"! A further example of the operation of this assumption is that, in spite of the fact that my entire education has been in Canada and the United States and I am unable to read and write Japanese, I am sometimes credited, or accused, of having an "Oriental mind." Now, since Buddha, Confucius, General Tojo, Mao Tse-tung, Syngman Rhee, Pandit Nehru and the proprietor of the Golden Pheasant Chop Suey House all have "Oriental minds," it is hard to imagine what is meant. The "Oriental mind," like the attribute of "Jewishness," is purely and simply a fiction. Nevertheless, I used to note with alarm that newspaper columnists got paid for articles that purported to account for Stalin's behavior by pointing out that since he came from Georgia, which is next to Turkey and Azerbaijan and therefore "more a part of Asia than of Europe," he too had an "Oriental mind."

Our everyday habits of speech and our unconscious assumptions about the relations between words and things lead, then, to an identification reaction in which it is felt that all things that have the same name are entitled to the same response. From this point of view, all "insurance men," or "college boys," or "politicians," or "lawyers," or "Texans" are alike. Once we recognize the absurdity of these identification reactions based on identities of name, we can begin to think more clearly and more adequately. No "Texan" is exactly like any other "Texan." No "college boy" is exactly like any other "college boy." Most of the time "Texans" or "college boys" may be what you think they are: but often they are not. To realize fully the difference between words and what they stand for is to be ready for differences as well as similarities in the world. This readiness is mandatory to scientific thinking, as well as to sane thinking.

Korzybski's simple but powerful suggestion to those wishing to improve their semantic habits is to add "index numbers" to all terms, according to the formula: A_1 is not A_2. Translated into everyday language we can state the formula in such terms as these: Cow_1 is not cow_2; cow_2 is not cow_3; $Texan_1$ is not $Texan_2$; $politician_1$ is not $politician_2$; ham and eggs (Plaza Hotel) are not ham and eggs (Smitty's Café); socialism (Russia) is not socialism (England); private enterprise (Joe's Shoe Repair Shop) is not private enterprise (A.T.&T.). The formula means that instead of simply thinking about "cows" or "politicians" or "private enterprise," we should think as factually as possible about the differences between one cow and another, one politician and another, one privately owned enterprise and another.

This device of "indexing" will not automatically make us wiser and better, but it's a start. When we talk or write, the habit of indexing our general terms will reduce our tendency to wild and woolly gneralization. It will compel us to think before we speak—think in terms of concrete objects and events and situations, rather than in terms of verbal associations. When we read or listen, the habit of indexing will help us visualize more concretely, and therefore understand better, what is being said. And if nothing is being said except deceptive windbaggery, the habit of indexing may—at least part of the time—save us from snapping, like the pickerel, at phony minnows. Another way of summing up is to remember, as Wendell Johnson said, that "To a mouse, cheese is cheese—that's why mousetraps work."

Further reading:

Hayakawa, S. I.: LANGUAGE IN THOUGHT AND ACTION. New York: Harcourt, Brace, and Company; 1949.

Bois, J. Samuel: EXPLORATIONS IN AWARENESS. New York: Harper and Brothers; 1957.

Chase, Stuart: POWER OF WORDS. New York: Harcourt, Brace, and Company; 1954.

Johnson, Wendell: PEOPLE IN QUANDARIES: THE SEMANTICS OF PERSONAL ADJUSTMENT. New York: Harper and Brothers; 1946.

Korzybski, Alfred: SCIENCE AND SANITY. Fourth edition. Lakeville, Conn.: Institute of General Semantics; 1948.

Lee, Irving: LANGUAGE HABITS IN HUMAN AFFAIRS: AN INTRODUCTION TO GENERAL SEMANTICS. New York: Harper and Brothers; 1941.

Rapoport, Anatol: OPERATIONAL PHILOSOPHY: AN ANALYSIS OF NEW TRENDS IN THINKING. New York: Harper and Brothers; 1953.

The Case for
Abstract Art

BY

CLEMENT GREENBERG

Modern art has few defenders more eloquent than Clement Greenberg. A painter himself and a critic, he has written voluminously on art for the Nation, *the* Partisan Review, *and* Commentary, *and has served on the editorial staffs of all three periodicals. At present he acts as consultant on contemporary art to the New York art and antique firm of French Co. In 1958–9 he conducted a seminar in art criticism at Princeton. The author of books on Miró and Matisse, he is currently at work on a study of the late American abstract expressionist Jackson Pollock.*

Many people say that the kind of art our age produces is one of the major symptoms of what's wrong with the age. The disintegration and, finally, the disappearance of recognizable images in painting and sculpture, like the obscurity in advanced literature, are supposed to reflect a disintegration of values in society itself. Some people go further and say that abstract, nonrepresentational art is pathological art, crazy art, and that those who practice it and those who admire and buy it are either sick or silly. The kindest critics are those who say it's all a joke, a hoax, and a fad, and that modernist art in general, or abstract art in particular, will soon pass. This sort of thing is heard or read pretty constantly, but in some years more often than others.

There seems to be a certain rhythm in the advance in popularity of modernist art, and a certain rhythm in the counterattacks which try to stem it. More or less the same works or arguments are used in all the polemics, but the targets usually change. Once it was the impressionists who were a scandal, next it was Van Gogh and Cézanne, then it was Matisse, then it was cubism and Picasso, after that Mondrian, and now it is Jackson Pollock. The fact that Pollock was an American shows, in a backhanded way, how important American art has lately become.

Some of the same people who attack modernist art in general, or abstract art in particular, happen also to complain that our age has lost those habits of disinterested contemplation, and that capacity for enjoying things as ends in themselves and for their own sake, which former ages are supposed to have cultivated. This idea has been advanced often enough to convert it into a cliché. I hate to give assent to a cliché, for it is almost always an oversimplification, but I have to make an exception in this case. While I strongly doubt that disinterested contemplation was as unalloyed or as popular in ages past as is supposed, I do tend to agree that we could do with more of it in this time, and especially in this country.

I think a poor life is lived by any one who doesn't regularly take time out to stand and gaze, or sit and listen, or touch, or smell, or brood, without any further end in mind, simply for the satisfaction gotten from that which is gazed at, listened to, touched, smelled or brooded upon. We all know, however, that the climate of Western life, and particularly of American life, is not conducive to this kind of thing; we are all too busy making a living. This is another cliché, of course. And still a third cliché says that we should learn from Oriental society how to give more of ourselves to the life of the spirit, to contemplation and meditation, and to the appreciation of what is satisfying or beautiful in its own sole right. This last is not only a cliché, but a fallacy, since most Orientals are even more preoccupied than we are with making a living. I hope that I myself am not making a gross and reductive simplification when I say that so much of Oriental contemplative and aesthetic discipline strikes me as a technique for keeping one's eyes averted from ugliness and misery.

Every civilization and every tradition of culture seem to possess capacities for self-cure and self-correction that go into operation automatically, unbidden. If the given tradition goes too far in one direction it will usually try to right itself by going equally far in the opposite one. There is no question but that our Western civilization, especially in its American variant, devotes more mental energy than any other to the production of material things and services; and that, more than any other, it puts stress on interested, purposeful activity in general. This is reflected in our art, which, as has been frequently observed, puts such great emphasis on movement and development and resolution, on beginnings, middles, and endings—that is, on dynamics. Compare Western music with any other kind, or look at Western literature, for that matter, with its relatively great concern with plot and over-all structure and its relatively small concern with tropes and figures and ornamental elaborations; think of how slow-moving Chinese and Japanese poetry is by comparison with ours, and how much it delights in static situations; and how uncertain the narrational logic of non-Western fiction tends to be. Think of how encrusted and convoluted Arabic poetry is by contrast even with our most euphuistic lyrical verse. And as for non-Western music, does it not almost always, and literally, strike us as more monotonous than ours?

Well, how does Western art compensate for, correct, or at least qualify its emphasis on the dynamic—an emphasis that may or may not be excessive? And how does Western life itself compensate for, correct, or at least qualify its obsession with material production and purposeful activity? I shall not here attempt to answer the latter question. But in the realm of art an answer is beginning to emerge of its own accord, and the shape of part of that answer is abstract art.

Abstract decoration is almost universal, and Chinese and Japanese calligraphy is quasi-abstract—abstract to the extent that few occidentals can read the characters of Chinese or Japanese writing. But only in the West, and only in the last fifty years, have such things as abstract pictures and free-standing pieces of abstract sculpture appeared. What makes the big difference between these and abstract decoration is that they are, exactly, pictures and free-standing sculpture—solo works of art meant to be looked at for their own sake and with full attention, and not as the adjuncts, incidental aspects, or settings of things other than themselves. These abstract pictures and pieces of sculpture challenge our capacity for disinterested contemplation in a way that is more concentrated and, I daresay, more conscious than anything else I know of in art. Music is an essentially abstract art, but even at its most rarefied and abstract, and whether it's Bach's or the middle-period Schoenberg's music, it does not offer this challenge in quite the same way or degree. Music tends from a beginning through a middle toward an ending. We wait to see how it "comes out"—which is what we also do with literature. Of course, the *total* experience of literature and music is completely disinterested, but it becomes that only at a further remove. While undergoing the experience we are caught up and expectant as well as detached—disinterested and at the same time interested in a way resembling that in which we are interested in how things turn out in real life. I exaggerate to make my point—aesthetic experience *has* to be disinterested, and when it is genuine it always is, even when bad works of art are involved—but the distinctions I've made and those I've still to make are valid nevertheless.

With representational painting it is something like what it is with literature. This has been said before, many times before, but usually in order to criticize representational painting in what I think is a wrong-headed when not downright silly way. What I mean when I say, in this context, that representational painting is like literature, is that it tends to involve us in the interested as well as the disinterested by presenting us with the images of things that are inconceivable outside time and action. This goes even for landscapes and flower pieces and still lifes. It is not simply that we sometimes tend to confuse the attractiveness of the things represented in a picture with the quality of the picture itself. And it is not only that attractiveness as such has nothing to do with the abiding success of a work of art. What is more fundamental is that the meaning—as distinct from the attractiveness—of what is represented becomes truly inseparable from the representation itself. That Rembrandt confined impasto—thick paint, that is—to his highlights, and that in his later portraits especially these coincide with the ridges of the noses of his subjects is important to the artistic effect of these portraits. And that the effectiveness of the impasto, as impasto— as an abstract element of technique—coincides with its effectiveness as a means of showing just how a nose looks under a certain kind of light is also genuinely important. And that the lifelike delineation of the nose contributes to the evocation of the personality of the individual to whom the nose belongs is likewise important. And the manner and degree of insight into that individual's personality which Rembrandt exhibits in his portrait is important too. None of these factors can be, or ought to be, separated from the legitimate effect of the portrait as a picture pure and simple.

But once we have to do with personalities and lifelikeness we have to do with things from which we cannot keep as secure a distance for the sake of disinterestedness as we can, say, from abstract decoration. As it happens, the whole tendency of our Western painting, up until the later stages of impressionism, was to make distance and detachment on the part of the spectator as insecure as possible. It laid more of a stress than any other tradition on creating a sculpture-like, or photographic, illusion of the third dimension, on thrusting images at the eye with a lifelikeness that brought them as close as possible to their originals. Because of their sculptural vividness, Western paintings tend to be far less quiet, far more agitated and active—in short, far more explicitly dynamic—than most non-Western paintings do. And they involve the spectator to a much greater extent in the practical and actual aspects of the things they depict and represent.

We begin to wonder what we think of the people shown in Rembrandt's portraits, *as* people; whether or not we would like to walk through the terrain shown in a Corot landscape; about the life stories of the burghers we see in a Steen painting; we react in a less than disinterested way to the attractiveness of the models, real or ideal, of the personages in a Renaissance painting. And once we begin to do this we begin to participate in the work of art in a so-to-speak practical way. In itself this participation may not be improper, but it does become so when it begins to shut out all other factors. This it has done and does, all too often. Even though the connoisseurs have usually been able in the long run to prefer the picture of a dwarf by Velasquez to that of a pretty girl by Howard Chandler Christy, the enjoyment of pictorial and sculptural art in our society has tended, on every other level than that of professional connoisseurship, to be excessively "literary," and to center too much on merely technical feats of copying.

But, as I've said, every tradition of culture tends to try to correct one extreme by going to its opposite. And when our Western tradition of painting came up at last with reservations about its forthright naturalism, these quickly took the form of an equally forthright antinaturalism. These reservations started with late impressionism, and have now culminated in abstract art. I don't at all wish to be understood as saying that it all happened because some artist or artists decided it was time to curb the excesses of realistic painting, and that the main historical significance of abstract art lies in its function as an antidote to these. Nor do I wish to be understood as assuming that realistic or naturalistic art inherently needs, or ever needed, such a thing as an antidote. The motivations, conscious and unconscious, of the first modernist artists, and of present modernists as well, were and are quite different. Impressionism itself started as an effort to push naturalism further than ever before. And all through the history of art—not only in recent times—consequences have escaped intentions.

It is on a different, and more impersonal and far more general level of meaning and history that our culture has generated abstract art as an antidote. On that level this seemingly new kind of art has emerged as an epitome of almost everything that disinterested contemplation requires, and as both a challenge and a reproof to a society that exaggerates, not the necessity, but the intrinsic value of purposeful and interested activity. Abstract art comes, on this level, as a relief, an arch-example of something that does not have to mean, or be useful for, anything other than itself. And it seems fitting, too, that abstract art should at present flourish most in this country. If American society is indeed given over as no other society has been to purposeful activity and material production, then it is right that it should be reminded, in extreme terms, of the essential nature of disinterested activity.

Abstract art does this in very literal and also in very imaginative ways. First, it does not exhibit the illusion or semblance of things we are already familiar with in real life; it gives us no imaginary space through which to walk with the mind's eye; no imaginary objects to desire or not desire; no imaginary people to like or dislike. We are left alone with shapes and colors. These may or may not remind us of real things; but if they do, they usually do so incidentally or accidentally—on our own responsibility as it were; and the genuine enjoyment of an abstract picture does not ordinarily depend on such resemblances.

Second, pictorial art in its highest definition is static; it tries to overcome movement in space or time. This is not to say that the eye does not wander over a painted surface, and thus travel in both space and time. When a picture presents us with an illusion of real space, there is all the more inducement for the eye to do such wandering. But ideally the whole of a picture should be taken in at a glance; its unity should be immediately evident, and the supreme quality of a picture, the highest measure of its power to move and control the visual imagination, should reside in its unity. And this is something to be grasped only in an indivisible instant of time. No expectancy is involved in the true and pertinent experience of a painting; a picture, I repeat, does not "come out" the way a story, or a poem, or a piece of music does. It's all there at once, like a sudden revelation. This "at-onceness" an abstract picture usually drives home to us with greater singleness and clarity than a representational painting does. And to apprehend this "at-onceness" demands a freedom of mind and untrammeledness of eye that constitute "at-onceness" in their own right. Those who have grown capable of experiencing this know what I mean. You are summoned and gathered into one point in the continuum of duration. The picture does this to you, willy-nilly, regardless of whatever else is on your mind; a mere glance at it creates the attitude required for its appreciation, like a stimulus that elicits an automatic response. You become all attention, which means that you become, for the moment, selfless and in a sense entirely identified with the object of your attention.

The "at-onceness" which a picture or a piece of sculpture enforces on you is not, however, single or isolated. It can be repeated in a succession of instants, in each one remaining an "at-onceness," an instant all by itself. For the cultivated eye, the picture repeats its instantaneous unity like a mouth repeating a single word.

This pinpointing of the attention, this complete liberation and concentration of it, offers what is largely a new experience to most people in our sort of society. And it is, I think, a hunger for this particular kind of experience that helps account for the growing popularity of abstract art in this country: for the way it is taking over in the art schools, the galleries, and the museums. The fact that fad and fashion are also involved does not invalidate what I say. I know that abstract art of the latest variety—that originating with painters like Pollock and Georges Mathieu—has gotten associated with progressive jazz and its cultists; but what of it? That Wagner's music became associated with German ultranationalism, and that Wagner was Hitler's favorite composer, still doesn't detract from its sheer quality as music. That the present vogue for folk music started, back in the 1930's, among the Communists doesn't make our liking for it any the less genuine, or take anything away from folk music itself. Nor does the fact that so much gibberish gets talked and written about abstract art compromise it, just as the gibberish in which art criticism in general abounds, and abounds increasingly, doesn't compromise art in general.

One point, however, I want to make glaringly clear. Abstract art is not a special kind of art; no hard-and-fast line separates it from representational art; it is only the latest phase in the development of Western art as a whole, and almost every "technical" device of abstract painting is already to be found in the realistic painting that preceded it. Nor is it a superior kind of art. I still know of nothing in abstract painting, aside perhaps from some of the near-abstract cubist works that Picasso, Braque and Léger executed between 1910 and 1914, which matches the highest achievements of the old masters. Abstract painting may be a purer, more quintessential form of pictorial art than the representational kind, but this does not of itself confer quality upon an abstract picture. The ratio of bad abstract painting to good is actually much greater than the ratio of bad to good representational painting. Nonetheless, the very best painting, the major painting, of our age is almost exclusively abstract. Only on the middle and lower levels of quality, on the levels below the first-rate—which is, of course, where most of the art that gets produced places itself—only there is the better painting preponderantly representational.

On the plane of culture in general, the special, unique value of abstract art, I repeat, lies in the high degree of detached contemplativeness that its appreciation requires. Contemplativeness is demanded in greater or lesser degree for the appreciation of every kind of art, but abstract art tends to present this requirement in quintessential form, at its purest, least diluted, most immediate. If abstract art—as does happen nowadays—should chance to be the first kind of pictorial art we learn to appreciate, the chances are that when we go to other kinds of pictorial art— to the old masters, say, and I hope we all do go to the old masters eventually—we shall find ourselves all the better able to enjoy them. That is, we shall be able to experience them with less intrusion of irrelevancies, therefore more fully and more intensely.

The old masters stand or fall, their pictures succeed or fail, on the same ultimate basis as do those of Mondrian or any other abstract artist. The abstract formal unity of a picture by Titian is more important to its quality than what that picture images. To return to what I said about Rembrandt's portraits, the whatness of what is imaged is not unimportant—far from it

—and cannot be separated, really, from the formal qualities that result from the way it is imaged. But it is a fact, in my experience, that representational paintings are essentially and most fully appreciated when the identities of what they represent are only secondarily present to our consciousness. Baudelaire said he could grasp the quality of a painting by Delacroix when he was still too far away from it to make out the images it contained, when it was still only a blur of colors. I think it was really on this kind of evidence that critics and connoisseurs, though they were almost always unaware of it, discriminated between the good and the bad in the past. Put to it, they more or less unconsciously dismissed from their minds the connotations of Rubens' nudes when assessing and experiencing the final worth of his art. They may have remained aware of the pinkness as a *nude* pinkness, but it was a pinkness and a nudity devoid of most of their usual associations.

Abstract paintings do not confront us with such problems. Or at least the frequenting of abstract art can train us to relegate them automatically to their proper place; and in doing this we refine our eyes for the appreciation of non-abstract art. That has been my own experience. That it is still relatively rare can be explained perhaps by the fact that most people continue to come to painting through academic art—the kind of art they see in ads and in magazines—and when and if they discover abstract art it comes as such an overwhelming experience that they tend to forget everything produced before. This is to be deplored, but it does not negate the value, actual or potential, of abstract art as an introduction to the fine arts in general, and as an introduction, too, to habits of disinterested contemplation. In this respect, the value of abstract art will, I hope, prove far greater in the future than it has yet. Not only can it confirm instead of subverting tradition; it can teach us, by example, how valuable so much in life can be made without being invested with ulterior meanings. How many people I know who have hung abstract pictures on their walls and found themselves gazing at them endlessly, and then exclaiming, "I don't know what there is in that painting, but I can't take my eyes off it."

This kind of bewilderment is salutary. It does us good not to be able to explain, either to ourselves or to others, what we enjoy or love; it expands our capacity for experience.

Further reading:

Greenberg, Clement: MATISSE. New York: Pocket Books.

Constable, W. G.: THE PAINTER'S WORKSHOP. New York: Oxford University Press; 1954.

Fry, Roger: VISION AND DESIGN. Gloucester, Mass.: Peter Smith.

Heron, Patrick: THE CHANGING FORMS OF ART. New York: The Macmillan Company; 1956.

Hess, Thomas B.: ABSTRACT PAINTING. New York: The Viking Press; 1951.

Venturi, Lionello: IMPRESSIONISTS AND SYMBOLISTS. New York: Charles Scribner's Sons; 1950.

——: MODERN PAINTERS. New York: Charles Scribner's Sons; 1947.

The Curse of Conformity

WALTER GROPIUS

Forty-one years ago in his native Germany, Dr. Walter Gropius, a successful practicing architect, founded the "Bauhaus" School of Design. Embodying the ideas of artists and designers as well as those of architects, and relating them to the needs of industry and housing, the Bauhaus has exerted enormous influence the world over. For a period of fifteen years—from 1937 to 1952 Dr. Gropius headed the Department of Architecture, Graduate School of Design, at Harvard University. Now Professor Emeritus, he continues to promulgate his ideas as an active architect and planner as the senior member of "The Architects, Collaborative," in Cambridge, Massachusetts.

From cradle to grave, this problem of running order through chaos, direction through space, discipline through freedom, unity through multiplicity, has always been, and must always be the task of education, as it is the moral of religious philosophy, science, art, politics, and economy.

THE EDUCATION OF HENRY ADAMS

Though American technique is the envy of the world, the "American Way of Life" does not command unqualified respect abroad. We have proved to all the peoples of the earth that it is possible for an energetic nation to raise its material and civic standards to undreamed-of heights. The example has been zealously studied. Other nations are eager to adopt our magic formula. Yet they are reluctant to accept the idea that the American brand of technology provides the ultimate blueprint for the good life. Indeed, we ourselves are beginning to suspect that economic abundance and civic freedom may not be enough.

Wherein have we failed?

In this attempt to analyze some of our shortcomings and to suggest remedies, I draw from my experience as an educator and practicing architect both in this country and abroad. I have had considerable opportunity to observe the impact of American culture on older countries, especially those which have recently emerged from a feudal or colonial past into the pattern of a modern industrial society. Everywhere the introduction of mechanization has produced such confusion that the problems of the conversion have been more evident than the benefits.

I have become more and more convinced that we have failed to give leadership in the right direction. We have not exported, along with our technical and scientific skills, principles of wise application—mainly because we have not formulated such principles at home. For example, our biggest man-made objects— our cities—have steadily grown more chaotic and ugly, despite brilliant individual contributions to planning and design. For all the heroic efforts of conservationists, a good deal of our loveliest countryside is being bulldozed out of existence, a sacrifice to commercial exploitation. In our smaller towns people try hard to preserve a certain regional character and community spirit—a losing struggle against the conformity imposed by mass production. Increasingly, patterns of taste dictated by purely commercial considerations win acceptance, and the natural feeling for quality and appropriateness is dissipated in the giddy tumble from novelty to novelty. The individual is so dazed by the profusion of goods which merchandising propagandists press upon him that he no longer retains much personal initiative or sales resistance.

What should be the goal of our stupendous economic progress? What do we really want to accomplish with our splendid new techniques for faster transportation and wider communication? So far, they have merely accelerated our pace without bringing us near enough to our original democratic goal. Instead, the tools of civilization have outgrown us and their multiplicity has exerted a dominance of its own, a dominance which impairs the individual's capability to seek and understand his deeper potentialities. Our subservience to our own brain child, the machine, tends to stifle individual diversity and independence of thought and action—two factors which used to be strong components of the American image. We know, after all, that *diversity in unity*, not conformity, constitutes the fabric of democracy. Unless we can reconcile diversity with unity, we may end up as robots.

I do not use the word "democracy" in the political sense. I am speaking of the modern form of life which, without political identification, is establishing itself upon the foundation of increasing industrialization, of growing communication services, and of broad admission of the masses to higher learning and universal suffrage.

To this world we have transmitted our enthusiasm for new scientific and technical invention, but we worship the machine to such a degree that we have been accused of forsaking the human standards of value in its service. Our apologia is that the rapid progress of technology and science has confounded our concepts of beauty and the good life; as a result, we are left with loose ends and a sense of helplessness in the midst of plenty.

We can overcome this defeatism only by understanding that the inertia or alertness of our brain's heart, not the machine, decides our destiny. It is not the tool, it is the mind that is at fault when things get out of hand.

Extreme specialization has dulled our faculty to bring unity to our complicated existence, and this has led to a dissolution of cultural relationships. Consequently life has become immeasurably impoverished. Man is in danger of losing his entity. The triumphal march of the practical sciences has crowded out the magic of life. The artist, the poet, the prophet have become stepchildren of the "organization man." However, our impressive organizational unity cannot conceal the lack of cultural unity. An observation of Albert Einstein throws light upon the result of this one-sided development: "Perfection of tools and confusion of aims are characteristic of our time."

There is only meager evidence that we Americans recognize the urgent task confronting us—to shift the emphasis from "bigger" to "better," from the quantitative to the qualitative, and to give significant form and beauty to our environment. An evolution of this kind would add moral authority to material abundance, would open up frontiers that we have been slow to explore.

Why have we been so hesitant to implement the ideals implicit in the development of our way of life? Why does a nation committed to the promise of free universal education take so long to provide enough schools and teachers for its children? Why have we shown so little interest in good housing? And why have we not seen to it that our cities and towns are models of sound organic planning and architectural harmony?

One probable answer is that America's Puritan colonizers, in their preoccupation with the development of an *ethical* code, paid little attention to the development of an *aesthetic* code. We are to this day largely dominated by the tenets of a bygone world. The Puritans ignored the fact that aesthetic principles may release ethical powers, and that the codes should have been developed interdependently. The consequent absence in our society of a cultivated sense of beauty has left natural talent underdeveloped and relegated the artist to an ivory tower.

Where aesthetic standards do prevail in this country, they stem mainly from a preindustrial era—*vide* our fondness for collecting antiques. But there can be no relation between the artistic inspiration of that era and the present needs of a mass audience.

These needs have not been satisfied by the material production of the eight-hour working day. We are beginning to realize that some important ingredients are missing in our brave new world—beauty and inner resourcefulness. Carrying on without them prevents us from achieving that wholeness and maturity which produce new form. This is why a visual cultural pattern such as we should have developed has thus far eluded us. Cultural problems cannot be solved only by intellectual processes. We must strike deeper chords to reawaken in every individual the ability to understand and create form.

How can such a renascence be achieved in a society almost exclusively devoted to commercial exploits and the accumulation of factual data? This may seem a strange question to ask in a country that fosters so many institutions designed to preserve art treasures and to encourage artistic activities. It is true that these institutions—the museums, art associations and foundations—perform a valuable service, but they can do no more than impart "art appreciation" to those who feel they can afford what they consider a luxury. They exert little influence on schools, where art is of secondary importance to the study of English, history and mathematics.

At one time, standards of taste were imposed from above, through power and persuasion, by an elite. Later on, in this country, the business tycoons, for better or worse, influenced others to follow their personal preferences or whims. Our generation takes its cultural guidance from groups of their fellow citizens—school boards, city councils, women's clubs—chosen by popular consent to make important cultural decisions. This is as it should be, for democratic principles not only permit but demand that each individual bring his personal conviction and insight to bear upon his surroundings.

But how have these citizens trained themselves to deserve confidence in their judgment? How have they learned to distinguish between diversity and anarchy, between organic unity and mere accumulation? We assume too much if we expect them to function properly in this role without having had a chance to develop powers of discrimination. They must first be made aware of the possibilities of promoting a stimulating environment for themselves and their community rather than resorting to clichès or pinchpenny expediency. As it is, their education rarely leads to a grasp of organic development and visual beauty. The pseudoartistic examples of design that reach them through aggressive sales techniques, with their competitive assault of chaotic shapes and colors, is apt to reduce them to a state of sensorial apathy.

267

We need to revitalize our natural creative capacities which for so long have been allowed to atrophy. It will not, of course, be easy to recapture a birthright almost completely forsaken. The effort must begin in school, during the child's formative years.

To accomplish this, our educational system, with its overemphasis on fact-finding, must cultivate attitudes which will integrate emotional experience with scientific and technical knowledge. The strong puritan bias in our national origin, mistrustful of emotional responses, has so influenced education that natural impulses have been inhibited and the artistic imagination cannot take wing. We must overcome such prejudices, and broaden our educational approach to include the recognition of emotional impulses, controlling rather than suppressing them. The development of our imaginative faculties would then generate an atmosphere in which the artist could flourish, not as an isolated phenomenon, ignored or rejected by the crowd, but as an integral part of our public life.

We already let our children in kindergarten recreate their surroundings in imaginative play. This interest, in one form or another, should be intensified and perpetuated all the way through school and college. Practical design problems in form, color and space relations should be studied and actual materials used for their representation. In such an educational concept I do not view book learning as an end in itself, but rather as a means to illuminate practical experience. It should become second nature for the student to adopt a constructive attitude towards the appearance of his own habitat so that in later life he may creatively participate in its development.

Nothing promotes an understanding of environmental planning better than active participation in it. If such a general spirit penetrates society at all levels, then the artistically gifted will respond naturally and exuberantly, giving expression to the common desire. The artist's work and message will be understood by all people, not just by one group or clique.

The modern artist is frequently accused of moving in an exclusive world of his own, a stranger to his fellow men. But a true artist is always a candid interpreter of his society. If his society has few clear aims and standards, his work will reflect that lack. Instead of condemning him for not producing soothing entertainment, we should heed and try to understand his message. The interpretation of beauty constantly changes with the development of philosophy and science, and as the artist is sensitive to the spiritual and scientific concepts of his time, he intuitively expresses them. If we cannot always follow him, the fault may lie in our complacency toward the very forces that' shape our times. There is no cause to berate the artist for deliberate mystification or frivolity when we, his audience, have lost interest in his search for a symbolic expression of contemporary phenomena. We ought instead to recognize his Apollonic work as a vital contribution to the health of a genuine democracy, because the artist bespeaks the whole man. The artist's freedom, his independence and his intuitiveness are the antidotes to the overmechanization which plagues us. Our disoriented society desperately needs his stabilizing influence to moderate the furious tempo of science and industry.

What kind of educational climate must we provide to fire the imagination of a potential artist and equip him with an infallible technique? Out of a passionate concern with this problem, realizing that the lone "visionary" had little chance to change the general education or industrial system, I took it upon myself almost forty years ago to found a pilot institute. This was the Bauhaus School of Design in Weimar and later Dessau, Germany. The faculty, whom I recruited from the ranks of the most advanced painters, sculptors and architects of the day, and I shared the belief that it was essential to select talented young people before they had either surrendered to the conformity of the industrial community or withdrawn into ivory towers. We proposed to train them to bridge the gap between the rigid mentality of the businessman and technologist and the imagination of the creative artist. We wanted our students to come to terms with the machine without sacrificing their initiative so that they might bring to mass production, to architecture and to community planning a sense of order and beauty.

To that end we combined our efforts to evolve a teachable, supraindividual language of form based on psychological and biological factors. This language was to furnish the student with an objective knowledge of visual facts. Beyond that, it was to establish a common background for spontaneous artistic creation, saving the work of the artist from arbitrariness or isolation and making it part of the development of a genuine *Zeitgeist*, away from the I-cult. Our object was not to supply a new set of recipes, but to inculcate a new set of values reflecting the thought and feeling of our time. That goal could be approached only by an unfettered search for the laws governing materials and techniques as well as those governing human psychology. Our students were first taught the psychological effects of form, color, texture, contrasts, rhythm, light and shade. They were familiarized with the rules of proportion and human scale. They were encouraged to explore the fascinating world of optical illusions, indispensable to the creation of form. The student was led through many stages of creative experience with various materials and tools to make him aware of their potentialities as well as his own talents and limitations.

After this basic course the students were trained in a specialized craft of their own choice. The instruction in craftsmanship given in the Bauhaus workshops was not an end in itself, but a means of education. The aim was to turn out designers able, by their intimate knowledge of materials and working processes, to produce models for industrial mass production which were not only designed but made at the Bauhaus. These designers had to be fully acquainted with the methods of production on an industrial scale and so, during their training, they were assigned temporarily to practical work in factories. Conversely, skilled factory workmen came to the Bauhaus to discuss the needs of industry with the staff and the students.

The Bauhaus was not concerned with producing designs of ephemeral commercial gadgets. It was rather a laboratory for basic research into design problems of all types. Staff and students succeeded in giving their work a homogeneity based not on external, stylistic features, but on a fundamental approach to design which resulted in standard products rather than novelties.

In short, the purpose of the Bauhaus was not to propagate any style, system or dogma, but to exert a revitalizing influence on design. We sought an approach to education which would promote a creative state of mind and thus help to re-establish contemporary architecture and design as a social art.

The influence of the Bauhaus on American design and design curricula has been widespread. Its lesson is particularly applicable in this country because nowhere else is the assembly-line method so firmly entrenched and, consequently, nowhere does a greater need exist for a guide to standards of excellence in mass production. A firm resolve to mass-produce goods of both technical quality and cultural significance would have far-reaching effect, because the world has learned to watch the United States for signposts to where the journey into the machine age is heading. So far, the rest of the world has been thrilled by some of the achievements of United States designers and manufacturers, but more often it has been merely snowed under by an avalanche of poorly designed gadgets, the modish fluctuations of an industry bent on attracting customers by entertainment value rather than by quality. Respect for the sound standard product, combining function with aesthetic value, is at a low ebb. Merchandising catchwords attempting to glorify every trifling industrial product have beclouded the issue. There is no sustained effort to determine which features of our vast industrial civilization represent the best and lasting values and should therefore be cultivated to form the nucleus of a new cultural tradition for the machine age. Instead of recognizing that cultural achievement stems from the selection of the essential and typical, we exalt quantity.

Selectivity is a criterion of a balanced culture. Indiscrimination leads to cultural anarchy. To achieve true standards, we must first cultivate a voluntary discipline, acknowledging that there is greater excitement and promise of beauty in purposeful limitation than in mere accumulation. Variety for variety's sake as a continuous national program will eventually surfeit even the most voracious consumer and alienate our warmest admirers abroad.

The idea of limitation has never greatly appealed to Americans. Early in their history they embarked on the ambitious plan of proving that material blessings could be shared by all. But now we must open new doors. One of the brightest prospects will be the creation of visual order out of our chaotic modern scene by co-operative efforts and co-ordinated planning.

As an architect I see the greatest challenge in applying the idea of unity in diversity to housing—to create flexible standards. Prefabrication holds enormous promise, but we got off on the wrong foot by prefabricating entire houses, each indistinguishable from its neighbor, instead of prefabricating only their components. We thereby produced monotony instead of unity. The public has shied away from prefabrication because man tends to rebel against regimentation. The present trend in prefabrication tries to satisfy the hunger for individuality by manufacturing components of houses which can be assembled in various combinations. Thus applied, prefabrication will someday bring the low-income class within reach of better cheaper and more individualized housing.

Historical precedent justifies this optimism. An artistically sophisticated system of prefabrication prevailed in Japan as early as the seventeenth century. It was, of course, based on an artisan culture. In modern Japan one can still buy all the component parts for a house of any desired size and have them quickly assembled. Each house embodies identical components, yet each looks different, and at the same time, by a common denominator of beauty and dignity, fits harmoniously into its neighborhood. What a contrast to the chaotic riot of forms, materials and colors of our Main Streets! True, the standard Japanese house could not fulfill our modern living requirements, particularly those of comfort and convenience. But its conception reflects such a remarkably mature process of selective development that we might well translate it into the terms of our own technical potentialities.

Obviously the ideas which finally crystallize into an aesthetic principle must be rooted in society as a whole, not in individual genius alone. But it is such a common background of distinct attitudes which the artist needs to relate his own contribution successfully to an established social order. In all great cultural periods unity of form has been given to the man-made environment. This, in retrospect, we call style.

To reach this goal, we must restore the influence of the artist. We must establish him in our industrial framework as a full-fledged member of the production team along with the engineer, the scientist and the businessman. Only together can they combine low cost, good technique and beautiful form in our products. Initiative in business must be balanced by initiative in cultural fields. To become fully mature a democracy must bestow the highest prestige upon the artist.

The American sophisticate roams the world today nostalgically searching for products that do not bear the stamp of mass production and sales organization. This is a sentimental journey to recover what he has lost at home. He seeks standard products whose usefulness and beauty have been patiently developed by the skill and unwavering good sense of generations of craftsmen, and which, ironically, have now become curios for connoisseurs. The thrill of acquisition grows rarer as economic pressures force other countries to remake themselves in the American image of mechanical mass production. Meanwhile, whoever turns his back on his own civilization forfeits the chance to perform a service which his heritage, his basic philosophy and present need urgently demand of him—namely, to turn the calamities of the machine age into assets by inculcating the desire for quality and beauty in the producer as well as in the consumer.

As long as our "cultured" elite insist that undiscriminating popular taste is beyond repair, that salvation lies in imposing upon an uncomprehending public an authoritative aesthetic formula, they will sidestep the particular obligation of a democratic society—to work from the ground up instead of from the top down. The dicta of the illuminati derive from an epoch when cultural matters were the concern of an elite who could enforce standards of taste, as well as of production. This cannot suffice in our present democratic system. A social organization that has conferred equal privileges on everybody must finally acknowledge its duty to prevent such privileges from being wasted through ignorance and unresponsiveness. This can be accomplished only by gradually raising the general level of perceptiveness and discrimination, not by handing out formulas from above. Aesthetic creativeness cannot survive either as the privilege and occupation of an esoteric few or as an embellishing cloak thrown over the unlovely features of the contemporary scene. It should be a primary function of all, with a solid foundation in popular custom. Unity in diversity—the symbol of culture and its sublime manifestation.

The next generation may witness such a unification of society. The role of the artist will then be to find the humanized image for society's aspirations and ideals. By virtue of his ability to give visible symbols to significant order, he may once again become society's seer and mentor, and as custodian of its conscience solve the American paradox.

The Expanding Mental Universe

BY

BERTRAND RUSSELL

Bertrand Russell, 3rd Earl Russell, Viscount Amberley, mathematician, philosopher, educator, and writer, describes himself as "a happy pessimist." A Nobel Laureate who once served a jail term for his opinions (in 1918, when he was a pacifist), Russell was characterized, during the presentation of the 1950 Nobel Prize for Literature, as "one of our time's most brilliant spokesmen of rationality and humanity and a fearless champion of free speech and free thought in the West." Now eighty-seven, Lord Russell divides his time between his home in Wales and a flat overlooking the Thames in London.

The effects of modern knowledge upon our mental life have been many and various, and seem likely, in future, to become even greater than they have been hitherto. The life of the mind is traditionally divided into three aspects: thinking, willing and feeling. There is no great scientific validity in this division, but it is convenient for purposes of discussion, and I shall, therefore, follow it.

It is obvious that the primary effect of modern knowledge is on our thinking, but it has already had important effects in the sphere of will, and should have equally important effects in the sphere of feeling, though as yet these are very imperfectly developed. I will begin with the purely intellectual effects.

The physical universe, according to a theory widely held by astronomers, is continually expanding. Everything not quite near to us is moving away from us, and the more remote it is, the faster it is receding. Those who hold this theory think that very distant parts of the universe are perpetually slipping into invisibility because they are moving away from us with a velocity greater than that of light. I do not know whether this theory of the expanding physical universe will continue to hold the field or not, but there can be no doubt about the expanding mental universe. Those who are aware of the cosmos as science has shown it to be have to stretch their imaginations both in space and in time to an extent which was unknown in former ages, and which to many in our time is bewilderingly painful.

The expansion of the world in space was begun by the Greek astronomers. Anaxagoras, whom Pericles imported into Athens to teach the Athenians philosophy, maintained that the sun is as large as the Peloponnesus, but his contemporaries thought that this must be a wild exaggeration. Before long, however, the astronomers discovered ways of calculating the distance of the sun and moon from the earth, and, although their calculations were not correct, they sufficed to show that the sun must be many times larger than the earth. Poseidonius, who was Cicero's tutor, made the best estimate of the sun's distance that was made in antiquity. His estimate was about half of the right value. Ancient astronomers after his time were further from the mark than he was, but all of them remained aware that, in comparison with the solar system, the size of the earth is insignificant.

In the Middle Ages there was an intellectual recession, and much knowledge that had been possessed by the Greeks was forgotten. The best imaginative picture of the universe as conceived in the Middle Ages is in Dante's Paradiso. In this picture there are a number of concentric spheres containing the moon, the sun, the various planets, the fixed stars, and the Empyrean. Dante, guided by Beatrice, traverses all of them in twenty-four hours. His cosmos, to a modern mind, is unbelievably small and tidy. Its relation to the universe with which we have to live is like that of a painted Dutch interior to a raging ocean in storm. His physical world contains no mysteries, no abysses, no unimaginable accumulation of uncatalogued worlds. It is comfortable and cozy and human and warm; but, to those who have lived with modern astronomy, it seems claustrophobic and with an orderliness which is more like that of a prison than that of the free air of heaven.

Ever since the early seventeenth century our conception of the universe has grown in space and time, and, until quite recent years, there has not seemed to be any limit to this growth. The distance of the sun was found to be much greater than any Greek had supposed and some of the planets were found to be very much more distant than the sun. The fixed stars, even the nearest, turned out to be vastly further off than the sun. The light of the sun takes about eight minutes to reach us, but the light of the nearest fixed star takes about four years. The stars that we can see separately with the naked eye are our immediate neighbors in a vast assemblage called "The Galaxy" or, in more popular parlance, "The Milky Way." This is one assemblage of stars which contains almost all that we can see with the naked eye, but it is only one of many millions of such assemblages. We do not know how many there may be, since increasingly powerful telescopes continually reveal increasing numbers of them.

A few figures may help the imagination. The distance of the nearest fixed star is about twenty-five million million miles. The Milky Way, which is, so to speak, our parish, contains about three hundred thousand million stars. There are many million assemblages similar to The Milky Way, and the distance from one such assemblage to the next takes about two million years for light to traverse. There is considerable amount of matter in the universe. The sun weighs about two billion billion billion tons. The Milky Way weighs about a hundred and sixty thousand million times as much as the sun, and there are many million assemblages comparable to The Milky Way. But, although there is so much matter, the immensely larger part of the universe is empty, or very nearly empty.

In regard to time, a similar stretching of our thoughts is necessary. This necessity was first shown by geology and paleontology. Fossils, sedimentary rocks and igneous rocks gave a backward history of the earth which was, of necessity, very long. Then came theories of the origin of the solar system and of the nebulae. Now, with the most powerful existing telescopes, we can see objects so distant that the light from them has taken about five hundred million years to reach us, so that what we see is not what is happening now, but what was happening in that immensely distant past.

What I have been saying so far concerns the expansion of our mental universe in the sphere of thought. I come now to the effects which this expansion has, and should have, in the realms of will and feeling.

To those who have lived entirely amid terrestrial events and who have given little thought to what is distant in space and time, there is at first something bewildering and oppressive, and perhaps even paralyzing, in the realization of the minuteness of man and all his concerns in comparison with astronomical abysses. But this effect is not rational and should not be lasting. There is no reason to worship mere size. We do not, necessarily, respect a fat man more than a thin man. Sir Isaac Newton was very much smaller than a hippopotamus, but we do not on that account value him less than the larger beast. The size of a man's mind—if such a phrase is permissible—is not to be measured by the size of a man's body. It is to be measured, in so far as it can be measured, by the size and complexity of the universe that he grasps in thought and imagination. The mind of the astronomer can grow, and should grow, step by step with the universe of which he is aware. And when I say that his mind should grow, I mean his total mind, not only its intellectual aspect. Will and feeling should keep pace with thought if man as a whole is to grow as his knowledge grows. If this cannot be achieved—if, while knowledge becomes cosmic, will and feeling remain parochial—there will be a lack of harmony producing a kind of madness of which the effects cannot but be disastrous.

We have considered knowledge, but I wish now to consider

wisdom, which is a harmony of knowledge, will and feeling, and by no means necessarily grows with the growth of knowledge.

Let us begin with will. There are things that a man can achieve and other things that he cannot achieve. The story of Canute forbidding the tide to rise was intended to show the absurdity of willing something that is beyond human power. In the past, the things that men could do were very limited. Bad men, even with the worst intentions, could do only a very finite amount of harm. Good men, with the best intentions, could do only a very limited amount of good. But with every increase in knowledge, there has been an increase in what men could achieve. In our scientific world, and presumably still more in the more scientific world of the not distant future, bad men can do more harm, and good men can do more good, than had seemed possible to our ancestors even in their wildest dreams.

Until the end of the Middle Ages, it was thought that there were only four kinds of matter, the so-called elements of earth, water, air and fire. As the inadequacy of this theory became increasingly evident the number of elements admitted by men of science increased until it was estimated at ninety-two. The modern study of the atom has made it possible to manufacture new elements which do not occur in nature. It is a regrettable fact that all these new elements are deleterious and that quite moderate quantities of them can kill large numbers of people. In this respect recent science has not been beneficent. *Per contra*, science has achieved what might almost seem like miracles in the way of combating diseases and prolonging human life.

These increases of human power remain terrestrial: we have become able, as never before, to mold life on earth, or to put an end to it if the whim should seize us. But, unless by some such whim we put an end to man, we are on the threshold of a vast extension of human power. We could now, if the expenditure were thought worth while, send a projectile to the moon, and there are those who hold that we could in time make the moon capable of supporting human life. There is no reason to suppose that Mars and Venus will long remain unconquered. Meanwhile, as Senator Johnson told the Senate, scientific power could have astonishing effects upon our own planet. It could, to quote his own words, "have the power to control the earth's weather, to cause drought and flood, to change the tides and raise the levels of the sea, to divert the Gulf Stream and change temperate climates to frigid."

When we have acquired these immense powers, to what end shall we use them? Man has survived, hitherto, by virtue of ignorance and inefficiency. He is a ferocious animal, and there have always been powerful men who did all the harm they could. But their activities were limited by the limitations of their technique. Now, these limitations are fading away. If, with our increased cleverness, we continue to pursue aims no more lofty than those pursued by tyrants in the past, we shall doom ourselves to destruction and shall vanish as the dinosaurs vanished. They, too, were once the lords of creation. They developed innumerable horns to give them victory in the contests of their day. But, though no other dinosaur could conquer them, they became extinct and left the world to smaller creatures such as rats and mice.

We shall court a similar fate if we develop cleverness without wisdom. I foresee rival projectiles landing simultaneously on the moon, each equipped with H-bombs and each successfully engaged in exterminating the other. I can feel no exultation in the thought of such a prospect. Until we have set our own house in order, I, for my part, think that we had better leave the moon in peace. As yet, our follies have been only terrestrial; it would seem a doubtful victory to make them cosmic.

If the increased power which science has conferred upon human volitions is to be a boon and not a curse, the ends to which those volitions are directed must grow commensurately with the growth of power to carry them out. Hitherto, although we have been told on Sundays to love our neighbor, we have been told on weekdays to hate him, and there are six times as many weekdays as Sundays. Hitherto, the harm that we could do to our neighbor by hating him was limited by our incompetence, but in the new world upon which we are entering there will be no such limit, and the indulgence of hatred can lead only to ultimate and complete disaster.

These considerations bring us to the sphere of feeling. It is feeling that determines the ends we shall pursue. It is feeling that decides what use we shall make of the enormous increases in human power. Feeling, like the rest of our mental capacities, has been gradually developed in the struggle for existence. From a very early time, human beings have been divided into groups which have gradually grown larger, passing, in the course of ages, from families to tribes, from tribes to nations, and from nations to federations. Throughout this process, biological needs have generated two opposite systems of morality: one for dealings with our own social group; the other for dealings with outsiders. The Decalogue tells us not to murder or steal, but outside our own group this prohibition is subject to many limitations. Many of the men who are most famous in history derive their fame from skill in helping their own group to kill people of other groups and steal from them. To this day, aristocratic families in England are proud if they can prove that their ancestors were Norman and were cleverer at killing Saxons than Saxons were at killing them.

Our emotional life is conditioned to a degree which has now become biologically disadvantageous by this opposition between one's own tribe and the alien tribes against which it collectively competes. In the new world created by modern technique, economic prosperity is to be secured by means quite different from those that were formerly advocated. A savage tribe, if it can exterminate a rival tribe, not only eats its enemies but appropriates their lands and lives more comfortably than it did before. To a continually diminishing degree these advantages of conquest survived until recent times.

But now the opposite is the case. Two nations which cooperate are more likely to achieve economic prosperity than either can achieve if they compete. Competition continues because our feelings are not yet adapted to our technique. It continues in ways quite obviously capable of producing ruin to all the competitors, but it continues none the less, because we cannot make our emotions grow at the same rate as our skills.

Increase of skill without a corresponding enlargement in feeling produces a technical integration which fails of success for lack of an integration of purpose. In a technically developed world, what is done in one region may have enormous effects in a quite different region. So long as, in our feeling, we take account only of our own region, the machine as a whole fails to work smoothly. The process is one which, in varying forms, has persisted throughout evolution. A sponge, while it is living in the sea, is like a block of flats, a common abode of a number of separate little animals each almost entirely independent of the others and in no way obliged to concern itself with their interests. In the body of a more developed animal, each cell remains in some degree a separate creature, but it cannot prosper except through the prosperity of the whole. In cancer, a group of cells engages in a career of imperialism, but, in bringing the rest of the body to death, it decrees also its own extinction. A human body is a unit from the point of view of self-interest. One cannot set the interest of the great toe in opposition to that of the little finger. If any part of the body is to prosper, there must be co-operation to the common ends of the body as a whole.

The same sort of unification is taking place, though as yet very imperfectly, in human society, which is gradually approximating to the kind of unity that belongs to a single human body. When you eat, if you are in health, the nourishment profits every part of your body, but you do not think how kind and unselfish your mouth is to take all this trouble for something else. It is this kind of unification and expansion of self-interest that will have to take place if a scientific society is to prove capable of survival. This enlargement in the sphere of feeling is being rendered necessary by the new interdependence of different parts of the world.

Let us take an illustration from a quite probable future. Suppose some country in the southern hemisphere sets to work to make the Antarctic continent habitable. The first step will be to melt the ice—a feat which future science is likely to find possible. The melting of the ice will raise the level of the sea everywhere and will submerge most of Holland and Louisiana as well as many other low-lying lands. Clearly the inhabitants of such countries will strenuously object to projects that would drown them. I have chosen a somewhat fantastic illustration as I am anxious to avoid those that might excite existing political passions. The point that I am concerned with is that close interdependence necessitates common purposes if disaster is to be avoided, and that common purposes will not prevail unless there is some community of feeling. The proverbial Kilkenny cats fought each other, until nothing was left but the tips of their tails: if they had felt kindly towards each other, both might have lived happily.

Religion has long taught that it is our duty to love our neighbor and to desire the happiness of others rather than their misery. Unfortunately, active men have paid little attention to this teaching. But in the new world which is coming into existence, the kindly feeling towards others which religion has advocated will be not only a moral duty but an indispensable condition of survival. A human body could not long continue to live if the hands were in conflict with the feet, and the stomach were at war with the liver. Human society as a whole is becoming, in this respect, more and more like a single human body; and if we are to continue to exist, we shall have to acquire feelings directed towards the welfare of the whole in the same sort of way in which our feelings of individual welfare concern the whole body and not only this or that portion of it. At any time such a way of feeling would have been admirable, but now, for the first time in human history, it is becoming necessary if any human being is to be able to achieve anything of what he would wish to enjoy.

Seers and poets have long had visions of the kind of expansion of the ego which I am trying to adumbrate. They have taught that men are capable of something which is called wisdom, something which does not consist of knowledge alone, or of will alone, or of feeling alone, but is a synthesis and intimate union of all three.

Some of the Greeks, and notably Socrates, thought that knowledge alone would suffice to produce the perfect man. According to Socrates, no one sins willingly, and, if we all had enough knowledge, we should all behave perfectly. I do not think that this is true. One could imagine a satanic being with immense knowledge and equally immense malevolence—and, alas, approximations to such a being have actually occurred in human history. It is not enough to seek knowledge rather than error. It is necessary, also, to feel benevolence rather than its opposite. But, although knowledge alone is not enough, it is a very essential ingredient of wisdom.

The world of a new-born infant is confined to his immediate environment. It is a tiny world bounded by what is immediately apparent to the senses. It is shut up within the walls of the here-and-now. Gradually, as knowledge grows, these walls recede. Memory and experience make what is past and what is distant gradually more vivid in the life of the growing child. If a child develops into a man of science, his world comes to embrace those very distant portions of space and time of which I spoke earlier. If he to achieve wisdom, his feelings must grow as his knowledge grows. Theologians tell us that God views the universe as one vast whole, without any here-and-now, without that partiality of sense and feeling to which we are, in a greater or less degree, inevitably condemned. We cannot achieve this complete impartiality, and we could not survive if we did, but we can, and should, move as far towards it as our human limitations permit.

We are beset in our daily lives by fret and worry and frustrations. We find ourselves too readily pinned down to thoughts of what seems obstructive in our immediate environment. But it is possible, and authentic wise men have proved that it is possible, to live in so large a world that the vexations of daily life come to feel trivial and that the purposes which stir our deeper emotions take on something of the immensity of our cosmic contemplations. Some can achieve this in a greater degree, some only in a lesser, but all who care to do so can achieve this in some degree and, in so far as they succeed in this, they will win a kind of peace which will leave activity unimpeded but not turbulent.

The state of mind which I have been trying to describe is what I mean by wisdom, and it is undoubtedly more precious than rubies. The world needs this kind of wisdom as it has never needed it before. If mankind can acquire it, our new powers over nature offer a prospect of happiness and well-being such as men have never experienced and could scarcely even imagine.

If mankind cannot, every increase in cleverness will bring us only nearer to irretrievable disaster. Men have done many good things and many bad ones. Some of the good things have been very good. All those who care for these good things must hope, with what confidence they can command, that in this moment of decision the wise choice will be made.

A NOTE ON THE TYPE

This book was set on the Linotype in ELECTRA, designed by W. A. Dwiggins. The Electra face is a simple and readable type suitable for printing books by present-day processes. It is not based on any historical model, and hence does not echo any particular time or fashion. It is without eccentricities to catch the eye and interfere with reading— in general, its aim is to perform the function of a good book printing-type: to be read, and not seen.

The book was composed, printed, and bound by Kingsport Press, Inc., Kingsport, Tennessee. The paper was manufactured by P. H. Glatfelter Co., Spring Grove, Pennsylvania. Typography by Vincent Torre.

CB
425
S357   The Saturday Evening
Post.

Adventures of the Mind.

24322

CB   24322
425
S357   The Saturday Evening Post.

Adventures of the Mind.